W9-AGR-690

NATURE/SCIENCE ANNUAL

LIFE WORLD LIBRARY

LIFE NATURE LIBRARY

TIME READING PROGRAM

THE LIFE HISTORY OF THE UNITED STATES

LIFE SCIENCE LIBRARY

GREAT AGES OF MAN

TIME-LIFE LIBRARY OF ART

TIME-LIFE LIBRARY OF AMERICA

FOODS OF THE WORLD

THIS FABULOUS CENTURY

LIFE LIBRARY OF PHOTOGRAPHY

THE TIME-LIFE ENCYCLOPEDIA OF GARDENING

THE AMERICAN WILDERNESS

THE EMERGENCE OF MAN

FAMILY LIBRARY:

- THE TIME-LIFE BOOK OF FAMILY FINANCE
- THE TIME-LIFE FAMILY LEGAL GUIDE

1973 NATURE/SCIENCE ANNUAL EDITION

TIME-LIFE BOOKS, NEW YORK

ON THE COVER

Acupuncture needles stud this Chinese bronze head, cast 400 years ago during the Ming Dynasty as an aid for students of the ancient art of needle therapy, which attracted wide attention among American doctors in 1972. On the surface of the statue, Chinese ideograms mark the 365 points that acupuncturists stimulate with needles to relieve pain and treat various maladies. Behind the figure a modern Chinese anatomical chart also shows acupuncture points in the head.

TIME-LIFE BOOKS

FOUNDER: Henry R. Luce 1898-1967

Editor-in-Chief: Hedley Donovan
Chairman of the Board: Andrew Heiskell
President: James R. Shepley
Chairman, Executive Committee: James A. Linen
Editorial Director: Louis Banks
Group Vice President: Rhett Austell

Vice Chairman: Roy E. Larsen

EDITOR: Jerry Korn
Executive Editor: A. B. C. Whipple
Planning Director: Oliver E. Allen
Text Director: Martin Mann
Art Director: Sheldon Cotler
Chief of Research: Beatrice T. Dobie
Director of Photography: Melvin L. Scott
Assistant Text Directors: Ogden Tanner, Diana Hirsh
Assistant Art Director: Arnold C. Holeywell

PUBLISHER: Joan D. Manley
General Manager: John D. McSweeney
Business Manager: John Steven Maxwell
Sales Director: Carl G. Jaeger
Promotion Director: Paul R. Stewart
Public Relations Director: Nicholas Benton

NATURE/SCIENCE ANNUAL

EDITOR: Jane D. Alexander
Text Editors: Betsy Frankel, David S. Thomson
Designer: Edward Frank
Staff Writers: Simone Daro Gossner, David Lawton, Suzanne Seixas, John von Hartz
Researchers: Malabar S. Brodeur, Catherine Ireys, Suad A. McCoy, Ann Morrison, Don Nelson, Gretchen Wessels

EDITORIAL PRODUCTION
Production Editor: Douglas B. Graham
Quality Director: Robert L. Young
Assistant: James J. Cox
Copy Staff: Rosalind Stubenberg, Charles Blackwell, Florence Keith
Picture Department: Dolores A. Littles, Barbara S. Simon

Portions of this book were written by Charles Elliott, Henry Moscow and Mae Rudolph. Valuable assistance in preparing the book was provided by the following individuals and departments of Time Inc.: Editorial Production, Norman Airey, Nicholas Costino Jr.; Library, Peter Draz; Picture Collection, Doris O'Neil; Photographic Laboratory, George Karas; TIME-LIFE News Service, Murray J. Gart; Correspondents Maria Vincenza Aloisi, Josephine du Brusle (Paris), S. Chang (Tokyo), Stanley W. Cloud (Saigon), Nancy Faber (San Francisco), Bob Gilmore (Auckland), Margot Hapgood (London), Mary Johnson (Stockholm), Elisabeth Kraemer (Bonn), Traudl Lessing (Vienna), Mario Modiano, Sheila Walsh (Athens), Ann Natanson (Rome), Ed Ogle (Sydney), Sue Wymelenberg (Boston).

Published simultaneously in Canada.
Library of Congress catalogue card number 70-99175.
School and library distribution by Silver Burdett Company, Morristown, New Jersey.

Contents

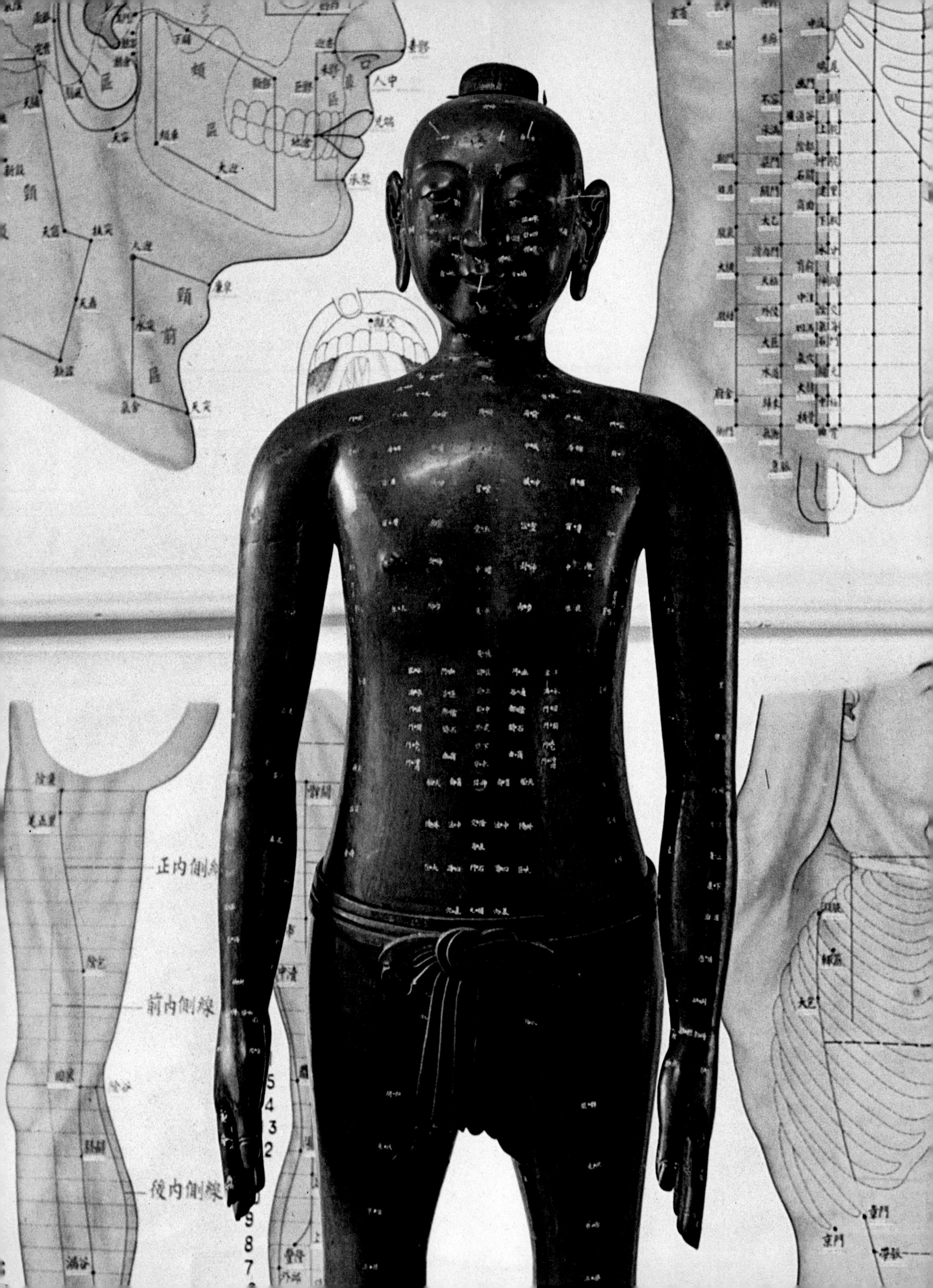
人中
前内側線
後内側線

The Year of the Needle

U.S. DOCTORS TRY OUT ANCIENT CHINESE ACUPUNCTURE

by Judith Randal

By the traditional Chinese method of reckoning, 1972 was the Year of the Rat. But for historians with an eye on medical science, 1972 was also the Year of the Needle—the year in which acupuncture, a traditional Chinese method of healing the sick, first attracted serious attention in the United States. Dozens of Americans returning from visits to China—including officials who accompanied President Richard M. Nixon to Peking—brought home tales of several near-miraculous treatments they had witnessed. Chinese-American acupuncturists, long ignored in out-of-the-way offices in city Chinatowns, suddenly became objects of attention. The government's National Institutes of Health initiated a major study of acupuncture. And in hospitals and offices across the country—sometimes in secret—U.S. physicians tried out needle pricking as a treatment for ailments and, tentatively at first, as a pain preventive during surgery.

One trial of acupuncture as an anesthetic was conducted in May at the Downstate Medical Center in Brooklyn: Dr. Abraham Lapidot performed a minor throat operation on a 23-year-old medical student named Fredric Newman. The patient received no drugs to kill the pain: the only anesthetic used in preparing him for surgery was acupuncture. Twenty minutes before the operation, Dr. John W. C. Fox, the anesthesiologist, took four stainless-steel needles about two inches long and inserted them a half inch deep into the patient's flesh—one needle in the back of each hand between thumb and index finger, and one in each foot between the second and third toes. Then Fox and his wife, Elisabeth (an anesthesiologist who was assisting him), began

The body's 365 needle insertion points for acupuncture are marked on this six-foot-high bronze figure from ancient China and on the modern anatomical charts behind it.

twirling the needles in place with the tips of their thumbs and index fingers. At specific intervals, Fox jabbed the patient with a long acupuncture needle to see if he was still sensitive to pain on the face, neck and various points inside the mouth. When Newman was no longer able to feel the pinpricks, he was pronounced ready for surgery—and although he remained wide awake throughout the procedure, he did not even flinch when the surgeon reached into his mouth with a sharp-edged forceps and snipped a piece of tissue growth from his left tonsil.

Three months prior to that, Newman had gone through a similar operation with a conventional anesthetic—a pain-killing drug sprayed on the back of his throat. In comparing the two experiences, Newman left no doubt about which he preferred. He said that he had suffered "excruciatingly sharp pain" during the first operation, and the excised area had been sore and tender for 24 hours. But with acupuncture for an anesthetic he felt "virtually no pain" in his throat, and only "a slight sense of discomfort" in his left hand five hours after the operation.

This operation was hardly an isolated incident. While doctors were experimenting with acupuncture for anesthesia in many different types of operations, other researchers were exploring the more traditional uses of the ancient Chinese technique—as a treatment for a wide variety of diseases ranging from degenerative spinal arthritis to migraine headaches. In fact, so much attention was focused in 1972 on the needle cure that it became difficult to separate reliable reports from the self-serving puffery of quacks and charlatans—U.S. doctors among them—eager to cash in on a new and profitable fad.

The sudden flowering of interest in acupuncture in this country has been due at least as much to political factors as to scientific curiosity. After two decades of mutual hostility, relations between the United States and China took a turn for the better in 1971. Americans could once again visit the Chinese mainland; and whether they were businessmen, doctors, journalists or diplomats, they all brought back stories about the therapeutic miracles that Chinese doctors had accomplished by the curious method of sticking needles into people. Capping such stories and giving them an undeniable air of authenticity was the eyewitness account of James Reston, the *New York Times* columnist, who came down with acute appendicitis while visiting Peking. Reston's appendix was removed with conventional anesthesia at the Anti-Imperialist Hospital, but when he developed an uncomfortable case of postoperative gas pains, he was treated by an acupuncturist. His next dispatch described in great detail the treatment and the almost immediate relief it brought him. For those Americans who were still skeptical, President Nixon's visit to China in February of 1972 provided the clincher. The two doctors in the Presidential party were invited to Peking's Friendship Hospital to watch three operations with acupuncture anesthesia—the removal of a cataract from a 67-year-old man who was almost completely blind, the excision of an ovarian cyst from a 37-year-old woman, and the removal of a tumor from the thyroid of a young girl. The old man and the young girl had needles inserted in their ears; the woman with the cyst was pierced on the sides of her nose and upper lip. In each case, the patient was wide awake and alert during the operation; when the surgeons had finished their work and sewn up the incisions, the patients got to their feet and walked away from the operating table. Similar scenes were also witnessed by other qualified scientific observers, including Dr. Paul Dudley White, the Boston heart specialist.

THOUSANDS OF YEARS OF NEEDLE THERAPY

Some Western visitors were surprised to learn from questioning their Chinese hosts that the employment of acupuncture to suppress pain during surgery was a recent development in China. The newness of this use of the needle sharply contrasts with the antiquity of its application to disease. The Chinese have been relying on needle therapy to treat their ailments for thousands of years. According to one legend, acupuncture was discovered by a warrior-emperor who noticed that a soldier pierced by an arrow in battle felt numb in parts of his body distant from the wound. One of the first written descriptions of acupuncture can be found in a book entitled *The*

Yellow Emperor's Classic of Internal Medicine written around 200 B.C. Archeologists have unearthed very early "needles" made of stone. European missionaries returning from the Far East brought the first reports of acupuncture to the Western world in the 17th Century. (The word itself comes from the Latin *acus,* for needle, and *pungere,* to sting or prick. The Chinese name *chen-chiu* means "needle and heat"—a reflection of the fact that needle therapy is often combined with moxibustion, the burning of herbs at or near appropriate sites on the body.)

With the growth of Western colonial influence in the 19th Century, all of the ancient healing arts fell into disrepute among China's educated classes. The Kuomintang, which came to power in 1928, considered acupuncture to be an outmoded superstition from a feudal past. They went so far as to formulate a law forbidding acupuncture and other forms of traditional medicine. In the late 1930s, however, the Chinese Communists reversed this trend, and gave their full support to the teaching and practice of acupuncture. They did so partly out of national pride and partly out of plain necessity: Mao Tse-tung's guerrillas were so short of Western-style drugs and doctors that they had little choice but to rely on traditional remedies. Mao himself stated: "Chinese medicine and pharmacology are a great treasure house and effort should be made to explore them and raise them to a higher level."

After the Communist takeover in 1949, acupuncture attained official status as a form of medical therapy. But it was not until the late 1950s that serious attempts were made to combine the pain-killing effects of acupuncture with modern surgical techniques. Chinese authorities now claim that more than 400,000 operations of almost every conceivable type have been performed with acupuncture anesthesia in the last six years, and that the method has been successful in nine out of 10 cases. Some of the patients were infants less than a week old and some were in their eighties, and a number of the operations lasted as long as six hours. The Chinese believe that acupuncture anesthesia greatly shortens the postoperative recovery period, reduces the need for expensive and complex equipment, makes surgery possible for seriously ill patients who could not survive ordinary anesthetic drugs and eliminates the risk of anesthetic death—a mishap that now claims one out of 3,000 patients a year in the United States.

In addition, there is no vomiting or nausea and considerably less pain after the operation. Moreover, the anesthesia produced by acupuncture is not the general, or total, anesthesia that Westerners undergo for a major operation. For while the patient feels no pain, his senses are otherwise intact. Lying on the operating table, he can see and hear what is going on, can sense the lightest touch or pressure. Thus a surgeon does not have to wait for anesthesia to wear off to evaluate the success of certain operations, such as one to correct squinting.

The Chinese readily acknowledge, however, that acupuncture anesthesia works on only about 90 per cent of the surgical patients, and under certain circumstances leaves something to be desired. Chest surgery in people with two weak lungs, for example, still requires drug anesthesia (if they are able to withstand it). In abdominal operations, patients often report unpleasant sensations of pressure when the surgeon must pull or push an organ aside, though evidently the sensations are not painful.

IN HARMONY WITH THE UNIVERSE

Chinese physicians with Western-style training are the first to admit that they do not know exactly how acupuncture works. The traditional explanation is deeply rooted in the philosophy of Taoism, which has been an important influence in Chinese life for more than 2,000 years. Tao means "the way." The Taoist seeks a way of living in harmony with the universe. This harmony is expressed metaphorically as a balance between the two universal principles of yin and yang—which, like shade and light, are fundamentally opposed and yet absolutely indispensable to each other.

Using the yin-yang balance as a guiding principle, Taoism insists on contemplating the broad picture—in contrast to Western science, which must take things apart to comprehend them. The Western physician examines a sick person to

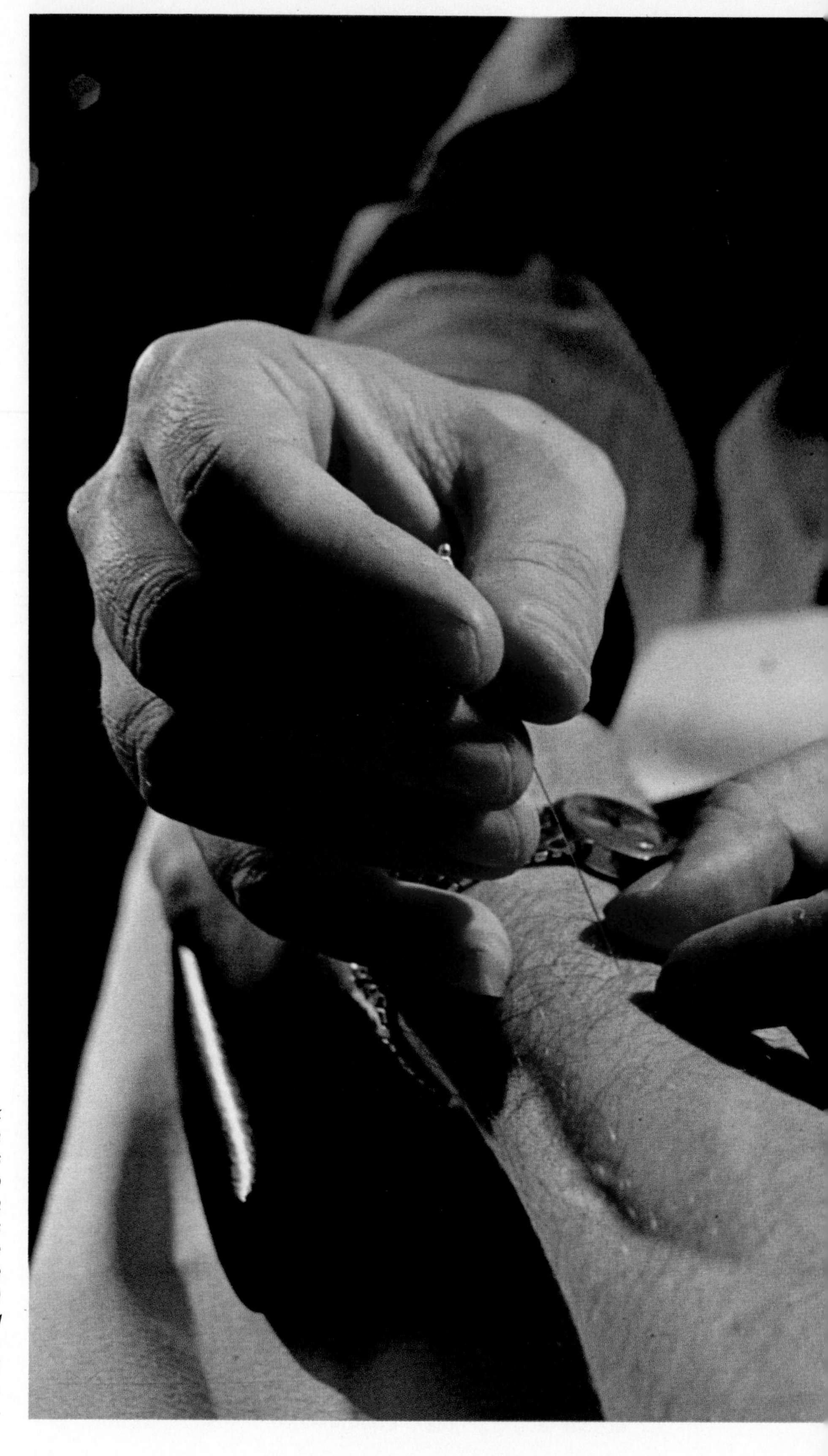

The steady hand of New York acupuncturist Ting Ching-yuen rotates a stainless-steel needle in the arm of his patient, Stephen Barr, who came to Ting's Chinatown clinic a year after a stroke left him semiparalyzed. Ting has put the needle into a point called the outer gate, which lies on the triple warmer meridian line (diagram, page 13) running from the head down along the shoulder and the outside of the arm. As Ting twirls the needle it causes no pain and draws no blood. Afterwards, Barr feels only a warm sensation.

"see where the trouble is"; once a diagnosis is made, the doctor tends to focus his attention on the diseased area. The traditional acupuncturist, on the other hand, views the human body as a microcosm of the universe—a repository of the basic life force, or energy, called *ch'i,* which is distributed through the body as the opposing forces of yin and yang. All bodily ills result from a temporary imbalance of this energy, which is constantly circulating through the various organs. Needle therapy is intended to restore this harmony by stimulating or reducing the flow of energy at certain key points in the system. What the needles are made of is apparently not crucial. Most practitioners agree that almost any metal is suitable if it can be worked into hair-thin, flexible instruments a half inch to six or seven inches long. While gold and silver needles are still in use in some parts of the world, the mainland Chinese have switched to stainless steel because it is inexpensive and sturdy.

NEEDLING AWAY STROKE DAMAGE

Ting Ching-yuen is a Chinese-born and Chinese-trained acupuncturist who has practiced for a year in a cubbyhole office behind a store on a narrow street in downtown Manhattan. He uses stainless-steel needles in applying the traditional methods of treatment to a variety of ills, and his procedures illustrate the practice of an enlightened modern specialist in this ancient art. The case of Stephen Barr is typical. Barr, whose entire right side had been paralyzed by a stroke in 1971, had undergone seven months of intensive physical therapy at a major medical center, but his condition had shown little improvement and he stopped therapy completely for about five months. Then his personal physician suggested that he try acupuncture. In April 1972 he went to see Ting Ching-yuen, who, unlike most of the estimated several hundred acupuncturists who practice in the Chinatowns of large American cities, requires a letter of referral from a licensed doctor of medicine before he will accept a patient. After examining Barr, he agreed to begin a course of weekly treatments.

The first stage in acupuncture therapy, as in most forms of medicine, is the diagnosis. The

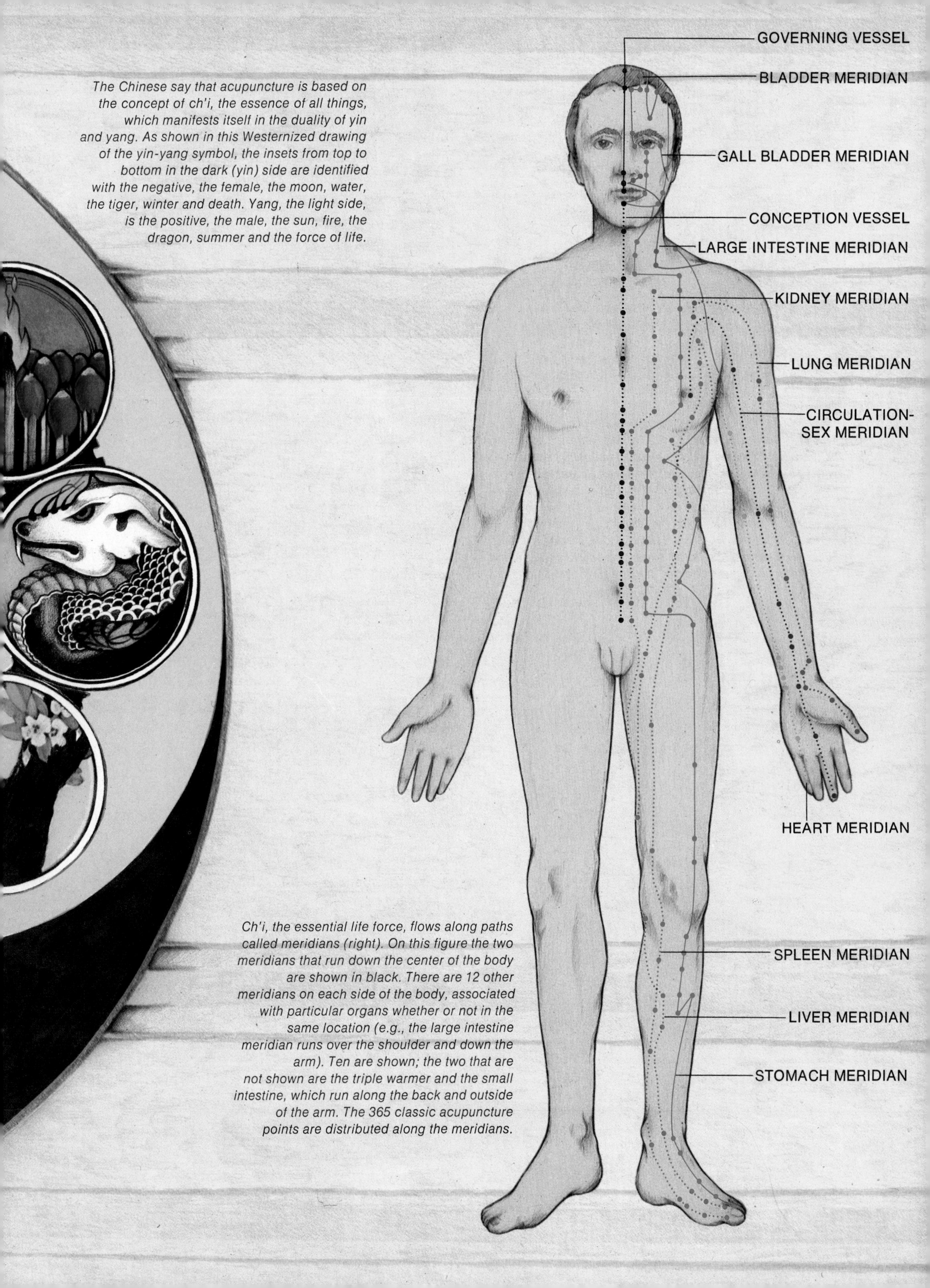

The Chinese say that acupuncture is based on the concept of ch'i, the essence of all things, which manifests itself in the duality of yin and yang. As shown in this Westernized drawing of the yin-yang symbol, the insets from top to bottom in the dark (yin) side are identified with the negative, the female, the moon, water, the tiger, winter and death. Yang, the light side, is the positive, the male, the sun, fire, the dragon, summer and the force of life.

Ch'i, the essential life force, flows along paths called meridians (right). On this figure the two meridians that run down the center of the body are shown in black. There are 12 other meridians on each side of the body, associated with particular organs whether or not in the same location (e.g., the large intestine meridian runs over the shoulder and down the arm). Ten are shown; the two that are not shown are the triple warmer and the small intestine, which run along the back and outside of the arm. The 365 classic acupuncture points are distributed along the meridians.

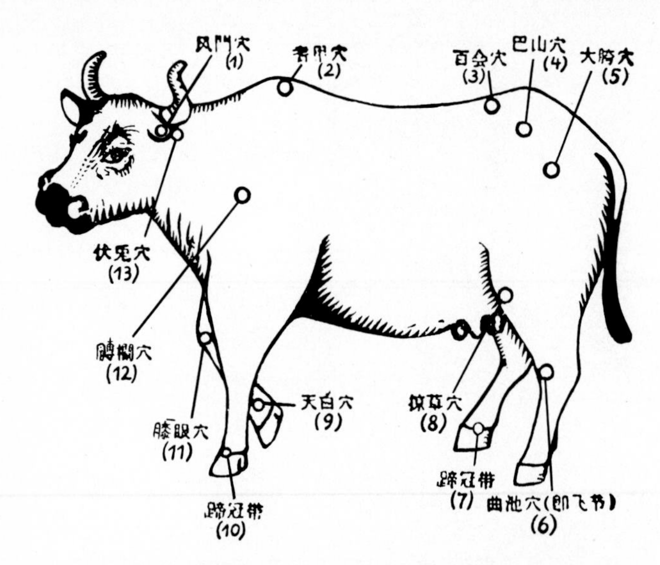

A Chinese veterinary journal contains this drawing of a cow with 13 acupuncture points indicated. Americans visiting China have observed operations upon animals anesthetized by acupuncture. The efficacy of needle treatment for animals is often cited as indicating that neither hypnotism nor the placebo effect that works on humans would affect animals; thus acupuncture must be a physical phenomenon. As one observer put it, "It's very difficult to hypnotize a mule." But skeptics note that animals must be bound or restrained for acupuncture, and this itself might mesmerize them.

acupuncturist keeps in mind at all times what might be called a wiring diagram of the patient's entire body. This diagram, which can be found in any classical acupuncture handbook *(drawing, page 13)*, shows the channels, or "meridians," through which the life energy is supposed to flow. There are 14 meridians running lengthwise through the body from head to toe and up and down each arm. Twelve of these run in pairs on both sides of the body and govern the internal organs. The other two run down the center of the body and regulate its overall well-being. Various horizontal linkages connect the meridians and the organs to one another and to the muscles and the surface of the skin. (This network is quite separate from the nervous system and from the miles and miles of arteries and veins that carry blood from the heart to the extremities and back again.) Because it is impossible to accurately "sense" imbalances in the meridians' flow of energy, the acupuncturist must base his diagnosis on other clues. For example, when Ting Ching-yuen faces Barr at the beginning of each 30-minute session, he studies his patient's outward appearance and asks detailed questions about his bodily functions, activities and feelings. Next, he feels the pulsation of blood in the radial artery of each wrist with the sensitive finger tips of his right hand. Whereas a Western physician learns only three things from a pulse reading—the rate, rhythm and strength of the heartbeat—the acupuncturist claims to get six distinct impressions from reading the pulse of each wrist. A complete reading, which generally takes from five to 10 minutes, enables him to infer the condition of the 12 organs in the body. Then he is ready to make the mental calculations that determine where and how he will insert the needles on that particular day.

TO TREAT THE LIVER, NEEDLE THE FOOT

There are hundreds of critical points along the meridians where the energy flow can be redirected to correct a variety of complaints. Student acupuncturists learn to keep the relationships straight by memorizing them in rhyme. The insertion points are not necessarily close to the diseased organ; to treat a liver ailment, for instance, the acupuncturist may stick a needle in the patient's foot. Nor is the treatment necessarily the same from session to session. On any given day Ting Ching-yuen may decide to use the needle on Barr's paralyzed side, or on his unaffected side. To make sure that he is inserting the needle in exactly the right place, the practitioner makes quick mental calculations concerning the measurements of the patient's body. All insertion points are defined in terms of the individual physique—for example, an acupuncturist measures the length of the middle phalanx of the second finger—a point may be so many phalanx lengths from the corner of his eye. For obvious anatomical reasons, acupuncturists are forbidden to place needles in certain areas of the body, such as the female nipple, the womb of a pregnant woman and the fontanel (the soft spot on a baby's head). There are other forbidden points that can cause injury or death.

How the practitioner inserts and manipulates a needle is every bit as important as where he places it. When Ting guides one of his instruments into Barr's flesh, he uses a motion more like that of a seamstress working with delicate fabric than that of a nurse giving a hypodermic injection. According to Barr, the needle causes little or no sensation when inserted. If Ting decides to rotate the needle in Barr's calf and forearm, Barr often feels a not-unpleasant response in his paralyzed side, a feeling he finds very difficult to describe. When the needle is withdrawn after a period of two to 15 minutes, there is no blood and no subsequent bruise. Sometimes a small red weal is temporarily visible, and a few minutes later Barr may feel a rush of warmth into his hand.

The improvement in Barr's condition is unmistakable. In less than two months he regained the ability to speak intelligibly, and he now walks with only a slight limp in his right leg. Whether he will ever be entirely free of his disability is uncertain. Ting, like any reputable practitioner, makes no extravagant promises. And there is no proof that Barr's recovery was caused by acupuncture—skeptics point out that the effects of stroke often disappear spontaneously, and many victims get well without (or despite) treatment. Still, when stroke victims go as long as Barr did without showing any improvement, there is little likelihood that they will experience a spontaneous recovery. Barr believes that the progress he has made so far could not have been achieved through any of the conventional rehabilitation therapies known to Western medicine.

A CATALOGUE OF CURES

A complete catalogue of the conditions that modern acupuncturists claim they can treat successfully would read much like a hypochondriac's nightmare. Included are: diarrhea and constipation, dizziness, tinnitus (ringing in the ears), problems related to the menstrual cycle and menopause, childhood allergies, disorders due to physical trauma such as tennis elbow, chronic diseases like arthritis and minor neurotic symptoms (such as the dependence on tranquilizers). There are also some diseases against which acupuncture is not considered effective; foremost among these is any form of cancer. In general, it is assumed that the needle cannot restore tissue that has been destroyed or seriously damaged. But in certain conditions, such as varicose veins and gallstones, acupuncture may be used to prevent symptoms from getting worse. To prevent gallstone attacks, for example, the acupuncturist first must determine from pulse diagnosis whether the gall bladder is "flabby"—indicating not enough energy—or "contracted"—indicating too much energy. He then inserts needles along the appropriate meridian and at the proper angle, and twirls them either to stimulate or to calm the organ. As for the diseases that are caused by viruses or bacteria, acupuncture is neither a specific cure, like an antibiotic, nor a specific preventive, like a vaccine. But practitioners claim that their methods can sometimes help a person fight off an infection by "reestablishing" —or as Western doctors would say, mobilizing— the body's resources.

With a government-sponsored research project underway, it is too early to predict which claims will stand up to rigorous scientific tests. Awaiting the outcome of the tests are a number of Western doctors who suspect that acupuncture, when used to eliminate pain during and after surgery, is little more than a very effective form of hypnosis. Hypnosis has indeed been used to anesthetize patients for surgery and to alleviate chronic pain since the 19th Century. But not all people respond to hypnosis. Neither, point out the skeptics, does everyone respond to acupuncture anesthesia. In China, they argue, the adult patients who choose acupuncture anesthesia over a conventional anesthetic receive days of training before being made insensitive by acupuncture; as one doubting scientist put it, they are "highly preconditioned." This same skeptic declares that when acupuncture is used on animals, the animals are very tightly bound so that they will hold perfectly still, since binding itself can produce a trancelike state known as "animal hypnotism."

Other scientists raise the question of the "placebo effect"—the relief often provided by an innocuous treatment, or placebo, such as a sugar pill. Pain and discomfort are so influenced by mental attitude that many patients respond to a remedy in which they have confidence whether or not it has any relationship to what ails them, much as a child will stop crying after getting a bump when his mother kisses it "to make it well." Similarly, a confirmed believer in acupuncture may well experience a seemingly magic relief, based solely on his conviction that acupuncture works. As a placebo, it would put the patient at ease while nature did the rest.

But the evidence of pain-free surgery with acupuncture cannot be lightly dismissed. George Wald, the Harvard biologist who won a Nobel Prize in 1967 for his work on the biochemistry of vision, observed an experiment at a veterinary hospital near Peking. He witnessed an abdominal operation on a mule in which anesthesia was induced by the stimulation of two needles, one in the animal's left shoulder and the other piercing two points in the left thigh. Less than an hour after the needles were first inserted, the mule was back in the barnyard, feeding contentedly from a bowl of mash.

Wald also observed the pain-killing effect of acupuncture in laboratory animals. In one series of experiments, a white rabbit whose nose had been shaved and painted black (to absorb heat more rapidly) was exposed to a very strong light. A stop watch was used to record the amount of time that passed before the animal began to show signs of discomfort. Without acupuncture the rabbit became obviously uncomfortable in about four seconds. With hand-twirled needles in its hind legs, the same animal endured the heat calmly for 16 seconds. In both cases, Wald was struck by the similarity of the acupuncture techniques used on animals and humans and by the fact that the effects were similar as well.

Before his trip to China, a skeptical American colleague had assured him that he would find acupuncture to be nothing more than hypnosis. On his return, Wald commented wryly, "It's very difficult to hypnotize a mule."

HOW THE NEEDLES PREVENT PAIN

Such direct personal observation has now impressed many Western scientists and has already prompted a search for a logical explanation in the context of modern medical knowledge. Most lines of inquiry lead back to the "gate control" theory of pain, which was first proposed in 1965 by psychologist Ronald Melzack of McGill University and physiologist Patrick Wall, then of M.I.T. and now of University College, London. Their theory is based on some well-established facts of neuroanatomy. To begin with, the fibers of the sensory nerves that link various parts of the body to the spinal cord come in two different diameters: large and small (usually designated A and C). Within the spinal cord there are other nerve cells that relay the incoming sensory information to the brain. And because of the way the nervous system is constructed, these relay stations act as data processors; they continually weigh information being carried by the large A fibers and the small C fibers. This function of the relay stations is important because the signals that the brain interprets as pain are carried mainly on the small C fibers, while nonpain impulses are carried by the large A fibers. According to the gate control theory, if the appropriate relay circuits are preempted by heavy traffic coming from the large A fibers, the pain signals cannot get through to the brain. The gate is shut—and it can be kept shut for several hours by continuous nonpainful stimulation of the right kind.

How much of a basis for acupuncture anesthesia lies in the gate control theory is apparently a question in the minds of the theory's originators themselves. When Melzack and Wall first proposed the gate control theory, they did not have acupuncture in mind. But Melzack believes that acupuncture's ability to block pain must be linked to some sort of gate scheme. Wall, however, does not. In July 1972 he published a paper arguing that acupuncture is probably just some form of hypnosis.

Still, the gate control theory does provide a rational mechanism for acupuncture anesthesia. Presumably, when an acupuncture anesthesiologist twirls his needles he is stimulating only the large A fibers, closing the gate so that pain sensations transmitted on the small C fibers cannot get through to the brain. The effect may be similar—though more pronounced—to that provided by the "white noise" some dentists use to alleviate the pain of drilling.

To account for the blocking of pain signals that do not pass through the spinal cord gates—such as pain in the face and scalp—some scientists postulate one or more pain gates inside the brain itself. One adherent of the multigate theory is Dr. Chang Hsiang-tung, a senior neurophysiologist at the Institute of Physiology of the Academy of Sciences in Shanghai, who has found evidence to support this idea. George Wald, who visited Chang early in 1972, reported that Chang and his associates have used electrodes to record brain activity in animals when a painful stimulus is applied to the body. They have found that the response of individual brain cells varies significantly, depending on whether or not the painful stimulus is accompanied by electrical stimulation of a large nerve.

Some variation or refinement of the gate control theory may eventually provide a satisfactory explanation of acupuncture anesthesia. The gate control theory, however, cannot explain the apparent healing power of the needles—and it cannot begin to account for the complex distribution of insertion points that the acupuncturist must memorize. Why should a needle inserted into the foot help to alleviate a liver ailment? Ac-

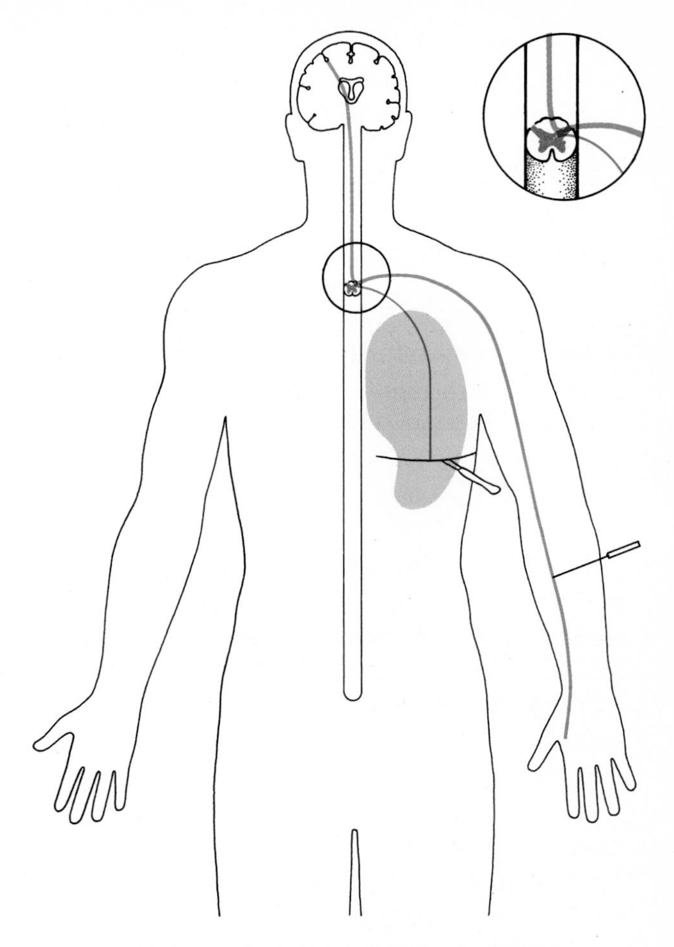

An extremely simplified schematic drawing illustrates how the "gate control" theory, propounded in 1965 by Ronald Melzack and Patrick Wall, may possibly explain acupuncture. The sketch represents a patient undergoing lung surgery. He is anesthetized by insertion of a needle in his arm. The needle stimulates a large sensory nerve fiber, which transmits a nonpain impulse to the part of his spinal cord called the dorsal horn (inset). When the surgeon cuts through the skin with the scalpel, the pain signal travels along a small nerve fiber to the dorsal horn, but the acupuncture stimulation of the thicker fiber drowns it out —the "gate" is "flooded" and the pain is stopped. Only nonpain signals are carried up the spinal cord to the brain.

cording to Western science, the nervous system simply does not work that way. As for the network of meridians that is supposed to lie behind the insertion points, it remains a complete mystery. No one has ever been able to find a meridian by dissecting a cadaver; and the network does not show up on X-rays.

A further enigma is presented by Chinese reports that acupuncture can bring back at least partial movement to limbs paralyzed by poliomyelitis. These reports seem incredible because polio destroys the cells in the spinal cord, which are believed to be essential to muscle function. How does acupuncture bring about such seemingly miraculous cures? Scientists do not have satisfactory explanations, although there does seem to be general agreement that the electrical activity of the nerves is in some way related to the acupuncture points on the skin.

If they are right, electrical instruments of various kinds may someday supplement—or even replace—the traditional paraphernalia of acupuncture. In many Chinese hospitals, acupuncturists have already begun using needles wired to electrodes that send weak electrical impulses into the skin. Moreover, operations have been successfully performed with electrical plates applied directly to the skin, thereby doing away with needles entirely. There is also talk of diagnosing ailments with electrical recording devices instead of pulse readings; such devices might resemble the electrocardiograph, which helps physicians diagnose heart disease.

In the United States, meanwhile, doctors are successfully employing a different kind of electronic device to alleviate the suffering of terminal cancer and disabling chronic back pain. The electronic painkiller called a Dorsal Column Stimulator "tunes out" suffering by sending weak doses of electricity to the spinal cord. The DCS works essentially like acupuncture: it evidently closes gates in the spinal cord to incoming pain signals and prevents them from going to the brain. Developed primarily by Dr. Norman Shealy of the Pain Rehabilitation Center in La Crosse, Wisconsin, and Dr. William Sweet of Massachusetts General Hospital, DCS is currently being tested at 15 medical centers across the country.

The Chinese report that their own examination of acupuncture has already yielded a number of practical benefits. Anesthesiologists, for example, have learned that pain is not blocked until the patient reaches and maintains a state called *te-ch'i,* which is best translated as "sore, numb, swollen and heavy feelings." Once this state is reached—after about 20 minutes of needle twirling—the patient can no longer feel the prick of a pin. According to the Chinese, the acupuncturist can sense when *te-ch'i* has been induced because he then feels the needle being "sucked" into the skin—much as water is absorbed by parched soil around a plant. And *te-ch'i* must be maintained throughout the operation, or the anesthetic effect will wear off.

EIGHTY NEEDLES REDUCED TO ONE

Research in Chinese hospitals has also shown that the needles can regulate blood pressure and respiration during surgery and that operations formerly thought to require many needles can be performed with only a few—if the acupuncturist knows exactly where to place them and how to manipulate them. Several years ago, as many as 80 needles were used to anesthetize a patient for a lung operation; gradually the number was reduced to 40, to 16, to 12 and then to two. Today, a competent acupuncturist inserts only one needle into a spot on the forearm where two meridians supposedly lie close together. By reducing the number of needles, the Chinese have also eliminated what threatened to become a severe problem of overcrowding in the operating room. The 40-needle stage, for instance, kept four needle twirlers busy throughout the operation.

Whatever the results of intensified research into acupuncture, in the United States as well as in China, Americans stand to learn a useful lesson from the Year of the Needle: the methods and beliefs of the nonscientific past need to be evaluated very carefully, not ignored simply because they are old. By keeping an open mind about their "great treasure house" of traditional medicine, Chinese medical scientists have made a considerable contribution to their countrymen's well-being—and, conceivably, to the development of medical science.

On the operating table of a state hospital in Michigan, a 56-year-old woman, anesthetized by acupuncture, is awake but feels no pain as surgeons excise a tumor from her neck.

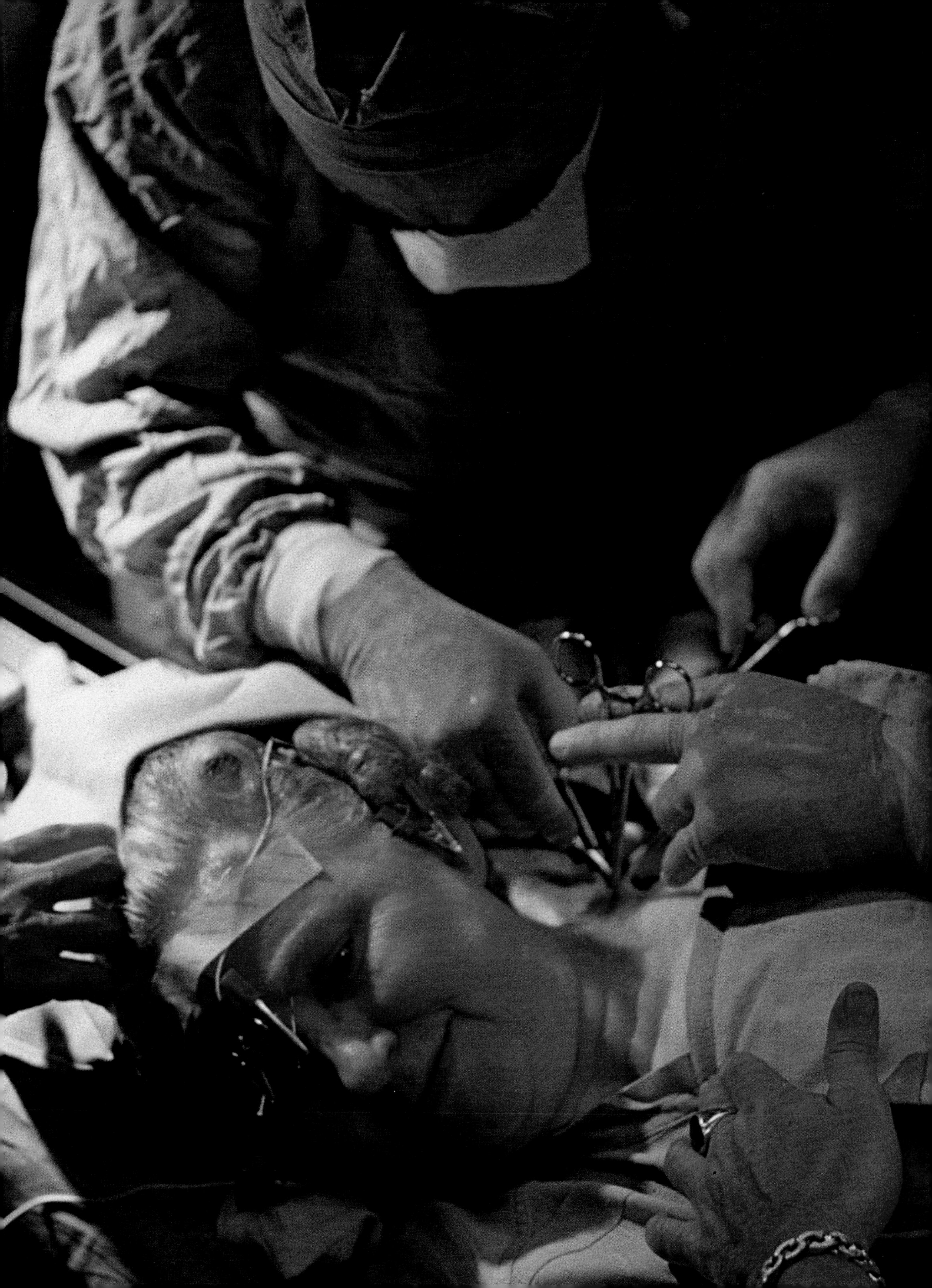

The Useful Liquid-Solids

They are mysterious substances that change color with temperature variations, turn from clear to opaque when electrified and give off iridescent displays under a variety of influences. They have a contradictory name—liquid crystals—indicating their borderline existence: partly liquid, partly solid. They were discovered in 1888 when chemists wondered what was interrupting the orderly change of some substances from solid to liquid under heat. But not until 1972 did they graduate from their role as laboratory test subjects to widespread employment in industry and medicine: in wrist watches, pocket calculators and in devices to indicate everything from a baby's temperature to the onset of cancer.

Liquid crystals are liquids—like liquids, they flow. But they also possess a quality that is characteristic of solids: their molecules are stacked in regular patterns to form orderly structures called crystals. This borderline existence is precarious; external influences easily disrupt their combination of qualities so that they turn all liquid or all solid.

The instability of liquid crystals has been both a blessing and a curse. Subjected to heat, vapors, pressure, light or electricity, they change their molecular structure and their external appearance. Thus they can be used as detectors and gauges. But while instability makes them useful, some stability is necessary to keep their qualities within a usable range. And maintaining liquid crystals in their tenuous state has been a problem until recently. Now they can be held sufficiently stable to be useful over a wide range of temperatures. This understanding promises new advances, for some scientists feel that much of the human body is composed of liquid crystals—and knowledge of their action may help explain the functioning and failures of all living systems.

One of the commonest examples of a liquid crystal is a soap bubble. It holds its shape because molecules on the surface interlock, forming a patterned arrangement.

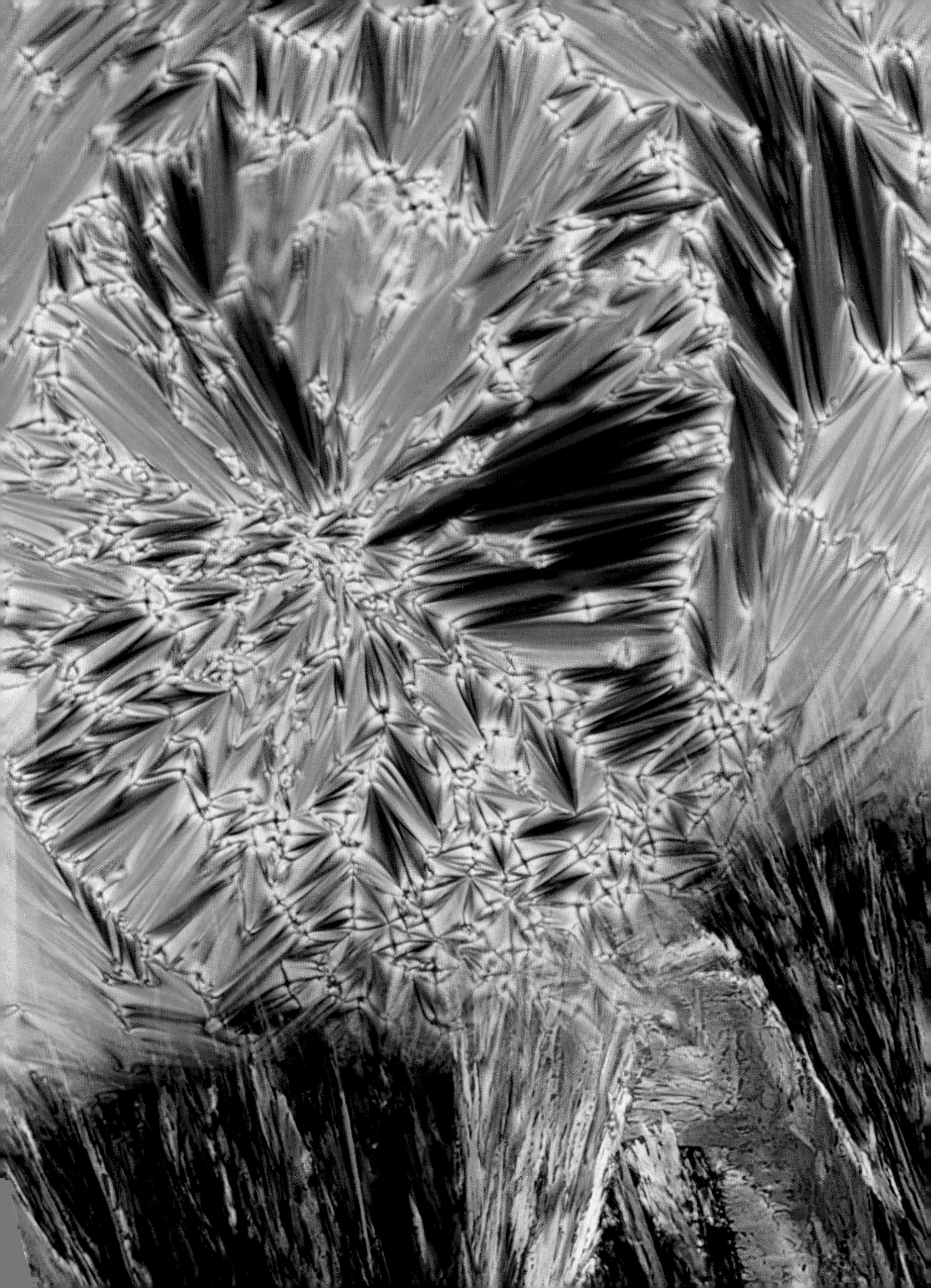

A Matter of Molecular Line-up

◀ *A photomicrograph of a substance called cholesteryl nonanoate (left) shows it to be part liquid crystal, part solid. The blue-and-white facets in the upper part of the picture are liquid crystals, able to flow, while the multicolored needles at the bottom are rigidly solid.*

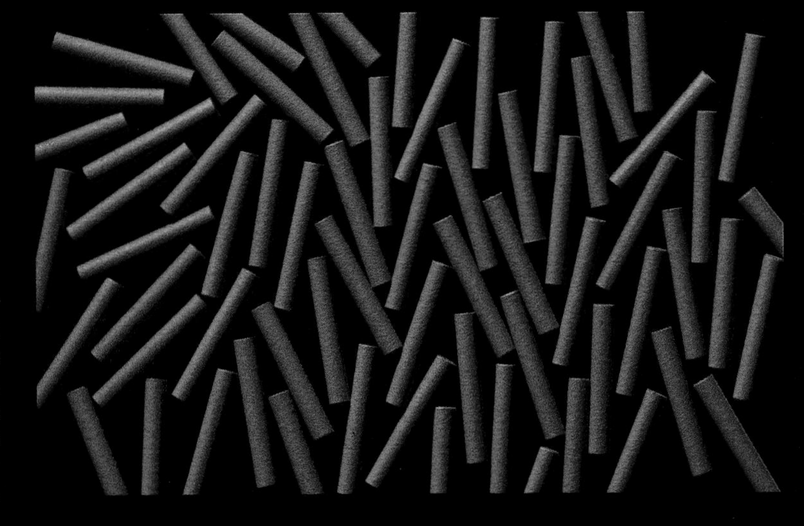

The models at right show how the molecular structure of a compound, such as the one opposite, alters as the compound changes (top to bottom) from liquid to liquid crystal to solid. When the compound is liquid, its molecules are randomly grouped (right). Because of this disorderly molecular structure, the compound has no shape of its own and can flow.

When the compound becomes a liquid crystal, its molecules align themselves parallel to one another in two dimensions and may lie in layers. The layers give firmness to the substance, yet because they do not interlock they can slide over one another. Thus, liquid crystals have form, yet retain fluidity.

When the molecules arrange themselves in a three-dimensional pattern the compound becomes a solid crystal. Locked into a rigid "lattice" structure, the molecules are held together both as individuals and as layers. There is no sliding between layers, and the firm molecular order prohibits flowing.

Workaday Jobs for a Lab Oddity

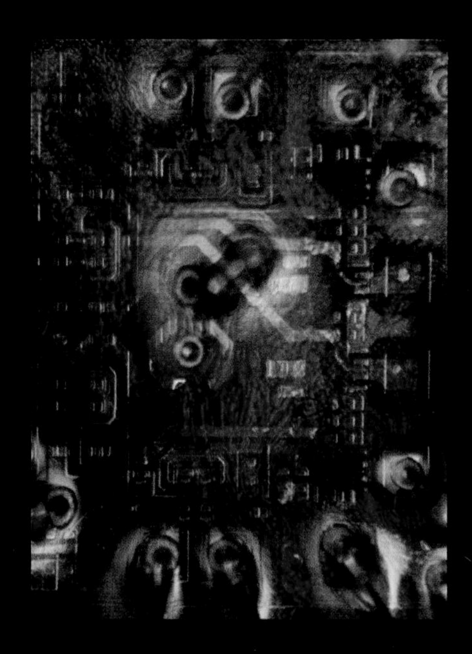

The blue area circled by a red ring is the trouble spot in this enlarged view of an electronic circuit just one sixteenth inch square. The heat-sensitive liquid crystals sprayed on the circuit as a test have turned from red to blue at hot spots caused by the leakage of current.

The deep-blue bands on this metal bar are liquid crystals that have changed color at the hottest—and weakest—points. When metal is strained, weak points get hot before breaking.

ndustry has long been at work examining ways
o profit from the ability of liquid crystals to alter
heir appearance under differing influences, and
n 1972 it finally placed its first two commercial
products on the market.

Some liquid crystals change color when they
are exposed to heat—the heat makes their molecules rearrange themselves, thus altering the
portions of the spectrum they reflect *(left and fol-
owing pages).* Other liquid crystals can shift
rom transparent to opaque when electrified—instead of letting light pass through them, they
scatter the light back to make possible the new
numeral faces of watches and calculators *(right
and below),* providing very bright number displays that can change rapidly. The change, like
hat in liquid-crystal heat detectors, is produced
by slight rearrangements of the molecules in the
iquid-crystal structure; but in this case the al-
eration is not triggered by temperature fluctuations, but by a minute electric charge from the
electronic circuitry in the watch or calculator.

Each of the numbers on a new wrist watch (above) and pocket calculator (below) is made up of seven bars treated with transparent liquid crystals. To make the desired numbers visible, a tiny electric charge goes to the bars to form any number from 0 to 9, turning the liquid crystals opaque.

An Aid to Medical Analysis

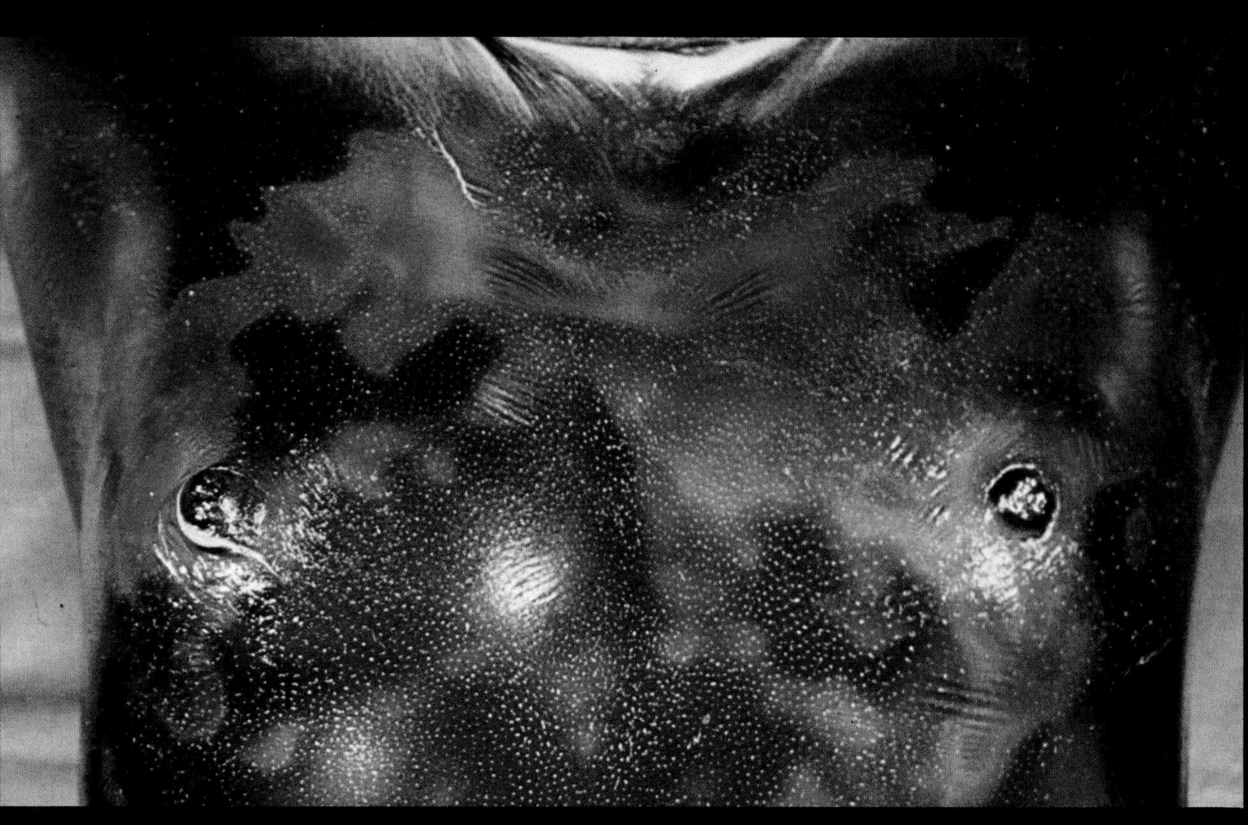

Liquid crystals on this woman's breasts turn blue from warmth caused by the concentration of blood around a malignancy below the center of the breast at the right. If there were no tumor, blood flow would be the same in both breasts. Above both breasts are normal warm spots.

Liquid crystals on the forearm of a cyclist aid research on exercise and blood flow. At first the arms were cool, and the liquid crystals were largely reddish (top). But as the exercise continued, more blood flowed to the arm, bringing greater warmth that turned the crystals bluer.

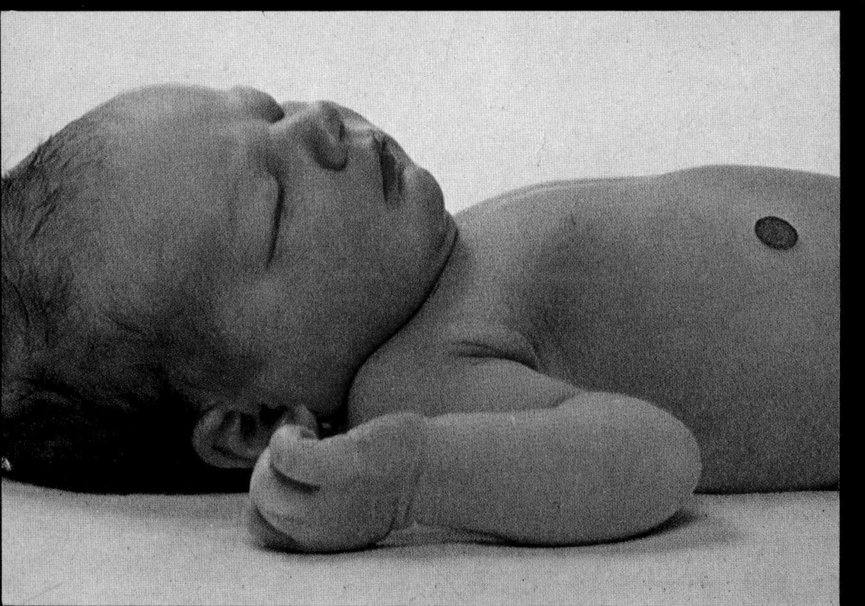

Placed over the liver area of a new-born baby, a small liquid-crystal monitor changes colors if the baby's temperature shifts. The monitor only works on infants less than a few weeks old, for skin temperatures in older children are not close to actual body temperatures. In this case, it eliminates the time-consuming, and sometimes dangerous, practice of inserting thermometers into the bodies of squirming babies.

Medicine has found a valuable diagnostic and research tool in liquid crystals because they turn color when exposed to the smallest changes of temperature. These liquid crystals have spiral molecular structures, and their spirals wind tighter as temperature increases, but unwind as temperature decreases. If the spirals unwind, the longer, or red, light waves become visible.

Thus the liquid crystals can be used to indicate temperature variations in a baby. They can also be sprayed onto the body to chart blood flow, the warmth of which makes the liquid crystals change colors. With this new technique the hot spots caused by the excessive blood flow around tumors can be seen; the success of a recent skin graft can be judged by seeing if blood is flowing through it; and during childbirth the blood-rich placenta can be located to help determine if it is out of place, a condition calling for a Caesarean section to deliver the baby.

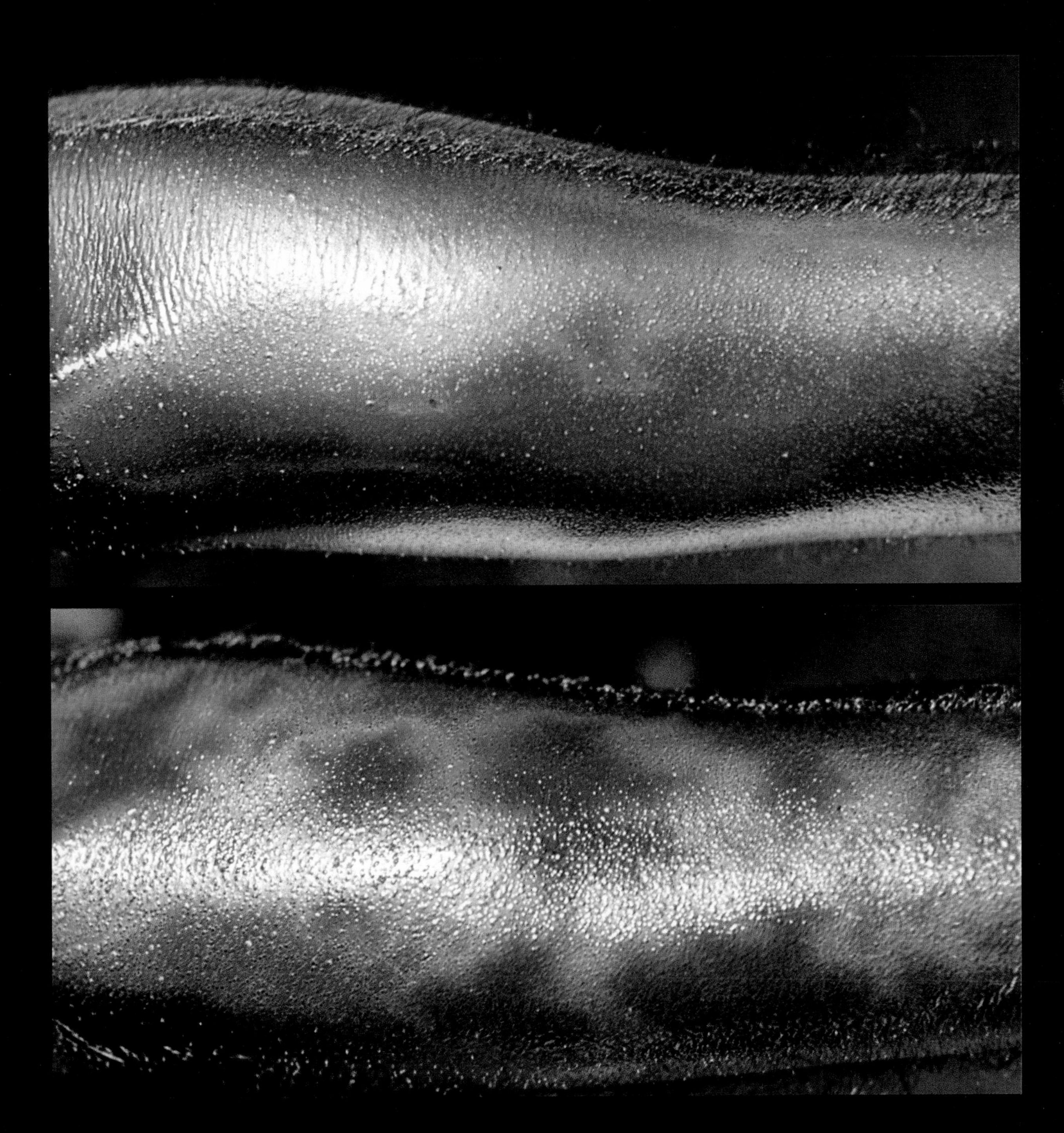

The Body's Own Liquid Crystals

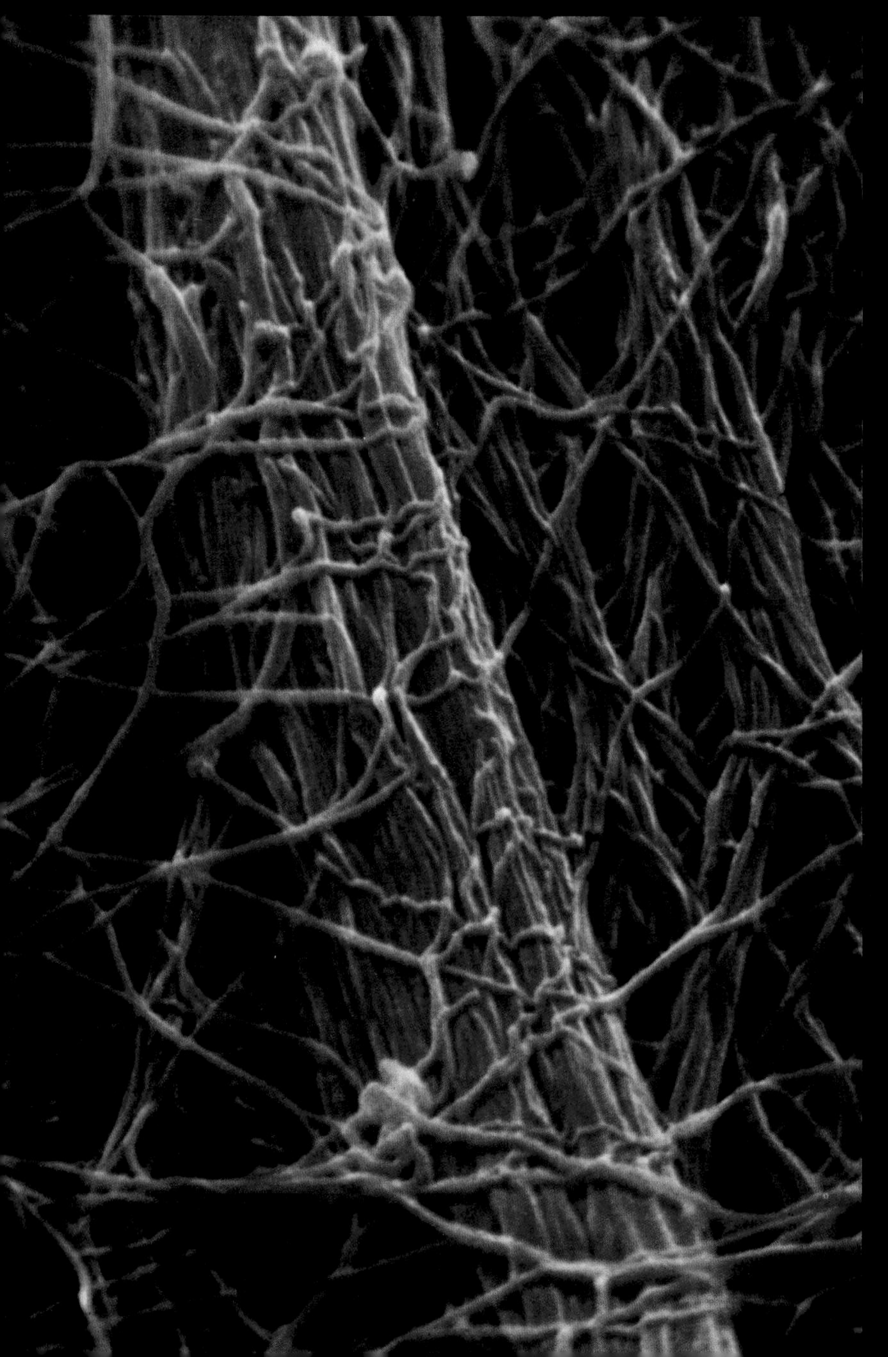

In sickle-cell anemia, red blood cells assume a sickle shape (above), apparently because molecules gum together into liquid crystals instead of floating freely; as a result, blood flow is impaired and the body's oxygen-distribution system is disrupted.

Layers of liquid crystals sheathe nerves of the thigh (left), which are shown here partially unraveled. The liquid-crystal sheath serves as an insulator to prevent signals from leaking or short-circuiting.

The rods and cones of the human eye, magnified ▶ 4,500 times at right, are liquid crystals that are sensitive to light. The slender rods are able to respond to black and white, while the thicker cones,

Recent discoveries have indicated that much of the human body is made up of liquid crystals —the rods and cones of the eye *(below),* the insulating sheaths of certain nerves and many cell membranes. Indeed, the brain itself may be constructed of liquid crystals.

Liquid crystals play complex roles. Extremely sensitive to their environment, they pass along, or store, sensory information gathered from the stimuli that assail the body—light, vapors, pressure, heat. With the combination of fluidity and structure, liquid crystals provide a flexibility that other components of the body cannot.

Studies of liquid crystals in the body have only begun. But as the properties of these unusual substances are better understood, the knowledge may lead to a cure for such diseases as sickle-cell anemia, which affects 50,000 Americans. At the least, it will help give man a much clearer understanding of his physical nature.

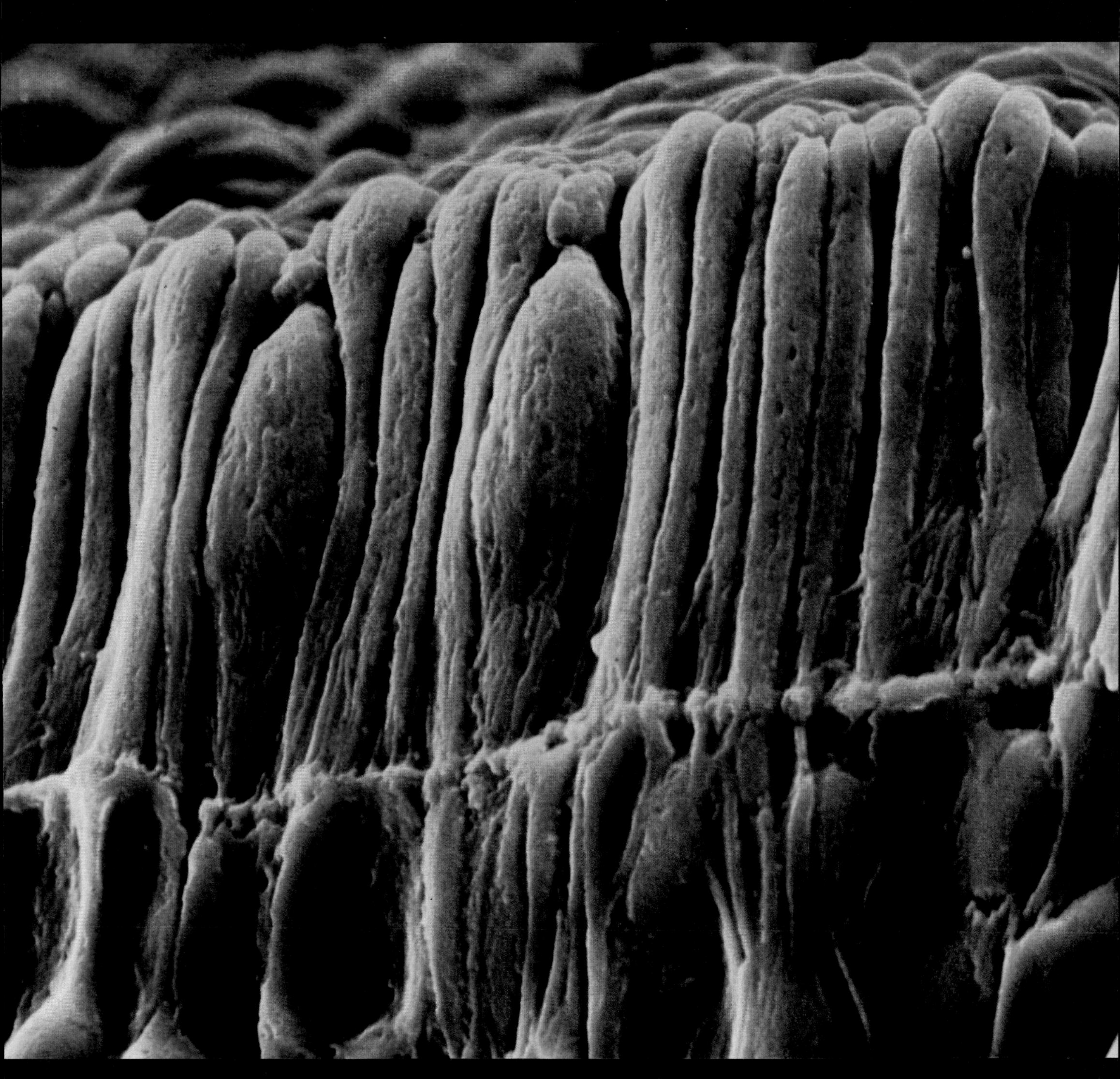

Building Laboratories

in the Sky
USA

In the painting overleaf (reduced at left), a space shuttle opens to disgorge a unit for a space station as two floating astronauts supervise. The astronauts will then nudge the weightless structure across the void to join it to the other units of the station that are being assembled at far left—a variable number of units can be added to enlarge the station. The station's windmill-like vanes convert energy from the sun (right) to electricity to power its activities, while another space shuttle nearby, having delivered its space-station unit, prepares to fly back for a landing on earth.

SPACE SHUTTLE WILL LAUNCH A NEW AGE OF DISCOVERY

by Thaddeus Graves

One of the lesser-noticed milestones in the history of space exploration came in May 1972 when Congress appropriated $200 million for the development of a program called Space Shuttle. The move signaled a wholly new stage in man's conquest of space: the first step, space exploration, was ending, and space exploitation was about to begin. Past missions have sent men and machinery for brief forays into space to reconnoiter and report to scientists on earth; Space Shuttle will send the laboratory itself into space—to stay there. Scientists will rocket back and forth, new equipment will be lifted as needed, space industries may even be set up to produce rare vaccines, semiconductors and other exotic products that can be made more efficiently in the weightlessness of orbital flight.

The concept has been dreamed of at least since the early 1930s: the first detailed plans were worked out by Eugen Sänger, one of Europe's foremost space scientists, 12 years before men landed on the moon. But the first actual test came only in June 1971 when Russia launched a flying laboratory and sent three cosmonauts to dock with, and enter, the orbiting lab; after 21 days of successful operation, all three died when a pressure hatch failed in the returning capsule. In 1975—by the terms of an agreement signed by the U.S. and the U.S.S.R. in 1972—three American astronauts will dock their Apollo module with a Russian spacecraft.

The Space Shuttle program looks far beyond these rudimentary laboratories to the days of sophisticated machines *(above and on previous pages)* that can carry into orbit the components to build, in space, even larger space-station research facilities. It will be five years before these hybrid space planes begin to rise from their pads —and another decade before they will assemble huge stations in space. But the first U.S. space laboratory is scheduled to be sent into orbit in the spring of 1973. A modified Saturn V rocket will carry this station, to be called Skylab, 270 miles into the sky and release it into a circular orbit around the earth. The next day another assembly will be readied for lift-off; it will consist of a two-stage Saturn 1B rocket, mounted on a 127-foot-high pedestal designed to make it tall enough to fit into the launch tower originally manufactured for the 363-foot Saturn V of the

Apollo program. The Saturn 1B will lift a command and service module containing Skylab's three-man crew into orbit to dock with Skylab. What the astronauts will encounter as they enter this prototype space station, and what they will do once they are inside, is already planned in detail. Scenes that until now have been imaginary will become real. As the Apollo docks with Skylab, science will take over from science fiction for these three adventurers:

> As they drew closer it looked like a great black-and-white aluminum canister with wings. Almost 86 feet from nose to tail, Skylab appeared wider than its 22-foot breadth. Perhaps this was because of the "wings," each 34 feet across, extending from the sides of the flying laboratory.
>
> At their orbital speed of 17,000 miles an hour, they felt as if they were flying in slow motion. They carefully maneuvered toward the forward end of Skylab where, like the neck of a giant whiskey bottle, the 17-foot-long docking module awaited their docking maneuver.
>
> In little spurts of movement, as if approaching a stationary object, the Apollo module moved alongside and up to the docking port of Skylab. Looming over them now were the windmill vanes with Skylab's solar-cell panels, unfolded to provide power for the hundreds of machines, motors, cameras, pumps, oxygenators, oscilloscopes and other pieces of scientific equipment aboard this laboratory floating through space. A final push and they were docked.
>
> It had been an eventful 12 hours since they had awakened that morning at Cape Kennedy. Securing the Apollo capsule for its long storage period, the astronauts now ate their dinner and got a night's sleep so as to be alert for the busy day ahead of them aboard Skylab.
>
> The entrance to Skylab was like a short tunnel, lined with storage cabinets, control panels, circuit breakers and handrails to assist them in moving through the tunnel toward the working area of the space station. The three men floated out of their Apollo capsule and, pulling themselves from one handhold to the next, swam like fish into the tunnel. There they began the process of switching on and testing the life-support and other systems on which the mission would depend. This done, the trio moved into the airlock module of Skylab—a short passage through which all entrances and exits were to be made. The three men then swam on through this little room to the porthole hatch at the other side. They checked a gauge to make sure the pressures were equal. A swing of the hatch handle; the door opened; and the men emerged into the big work chamber.
>
> After their confinement in the Apollo module, this chamber seemed to them almost cavernous. The room was decorated in pastel colors, but it was a laboratory nonetheless, with water storage tanks, freezers filled with food, rows of dials, film storage units and a dazzling variety of experimental equipment. At the other end of the workroom was a grilled partition. Like a family opening a summer cabin for the season the astronauts went on through the circular opening to inspect the rest of the living quarters that would be their home for 28 days.
>
> Beyond the partition were the wardroom with its refrigerator and tiny pantry, the sleeping quarters and the bathroom. (Only NASA would call the latter a "waste management compartment.") Everything was as it had been on inspection back on the Cape. The powerful 7.5-million-pound thrust of the Saturn V rocket had not dislodged any of the essential equipment: hot water was on tap in the miniature sink; the toilet was in place; the food lockers still contained their 1,500 pounds of frozen, canned, dehydrated and ready-to-eat foods; the clothing lockers were brimming with 60 jackets, 60 pairs of trousers and 210 sets of underwear.

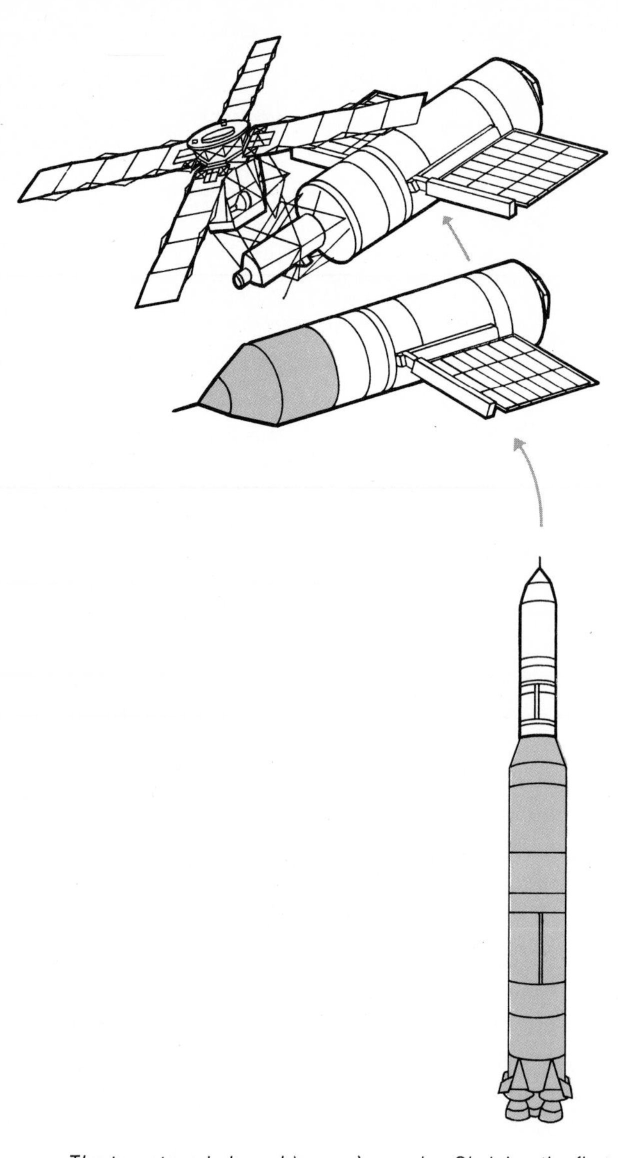

The two steps in launching and manning Skylab—the first U.S. space station, scheduled to go into operation early in 1973—are shown on these pages. Above, the unmanned laboratory vehicle, a modified third stage of a Saturn V rocket, is lifted off the pad by the Saturn's first two stages (shaded, lower right), which are then jettisoned. Once Skylab is in orbit, the shroud around its lab gear (shaded, center) will be cast off. On command from the ground, the "wings" and "windmill vanes" will swing into position to draw energy from the sun for Skylab's electricity.

They still had the day ahead of them to settle in, examine their equipment and ready it for use. After starting the circulation fans, the three voyagers double-checked all the electrical connections from the solar panels to make sure everything was functioning properly. They pulled off their boots and stowed them in giant shoe holders, and "hung" their perspiration-drenched spacesuits up to dry. They removed the metal restraining clamps from the fire extinguishers, and readied their photographic equipment.

Then, with their chores behind them, they dug into the larder for their first dinner: dehydrated shrimp cocktail, frozen steak and potatoes, peaches and canned brownies. The food was packed in pop-top cans, which they fitted into the food trays on the wardroom table; a push of a button and a heating element in the table defrosted and cooked the meat and potatoes. Carefully placing the empty cans in the bottom of the waste bin, they pulled themselves along the handholds into the sleeping area. Each man took his turn in the bathroom, washing with premoistened towels and relieving himself in the toilet, which would store his excrement for later analysis (a fact that occasioned some scatological humor). Then, in their weightless but tired state, they floated themselves to lie flat against the padded wall in the bedless bedroom, zipped their sleeping-bag restraining gear around their bodies and fell into deep sleep. . . .

A page out of science fiction, yet an actual scientific scheme—and a quantum jump in the development of space hardware from the tiny, cramped LEMs that squatted down on the moon in the late '60s and early '70s. For Skylab, initiating a new era in the domestication of space, is only the first step leading to the more ambitious Space Shuttle program, which envisions spaceships commuting from earth to numerous orbiting space stations, on schedules as regular as those of airlines today. The stations' size will permit experiments that have been impossible until now. Despite the sophistication of the U.S. and Russian programs, the Mariners and the Soyuzes and two men driving around on the moon could only report back to earth, or bring back the few samples their relatively tiny craft could carry. With laboratories aboard orbiting space stations, however, the universe lies open to be explored, sampled, tested, compared and recorded in a manner and to an extent it never could have been with the first generation of space vehicles.

If size and versatility are the secret of the practical space station, the key to these attributes is a reusable space vehicle, one that can make repeated round trips. No such vehicle is available for Skylab, and this lack limits the usefulness and lifetime of the first U.S. space station. It is designed for an eight-month mission; then it will be abandoned, a $540 million empty in the space garbage. Space Shuttle changes the situation dramatically. Each of its craft will be capable of flying a hundred missions or more; each will take off on its rocket engines (two of which will parachute back for reuse), then return from space to land like an airplane *(pages 36-37)*. Such an operation is expected to turn around the economics of working in space. The major part of the cost is simply transportation. Instruments, astronauts, life-support gear, materials for space stations, all must be lifted free of the earth, and the cost is high—$1,000 a pound on the average. Space Shuttle orbiters, their planners claim, can bring that rate down to $150 a pound, primarily because they will be reusable.

It is this promised economy that makes possible the big craft of Space Shuttle—their total cost can be spread over a hundred missions. Even more important, their relatively low freight-hauling rates transform into reality the dream of carrying up, piece by piece, units for huge permanent space stations—in this way building stations far larger than any single vehicle could lift.

But the total costs of the project—$7.5 billion spread over six years—raised serious objections to it. A number of influential Congressmen, including Representative Les Aspin of Wisconsin, Senator Walter F. Mondale of Minnesota and Senate Majority Leader Mike Mansfield of Mon-

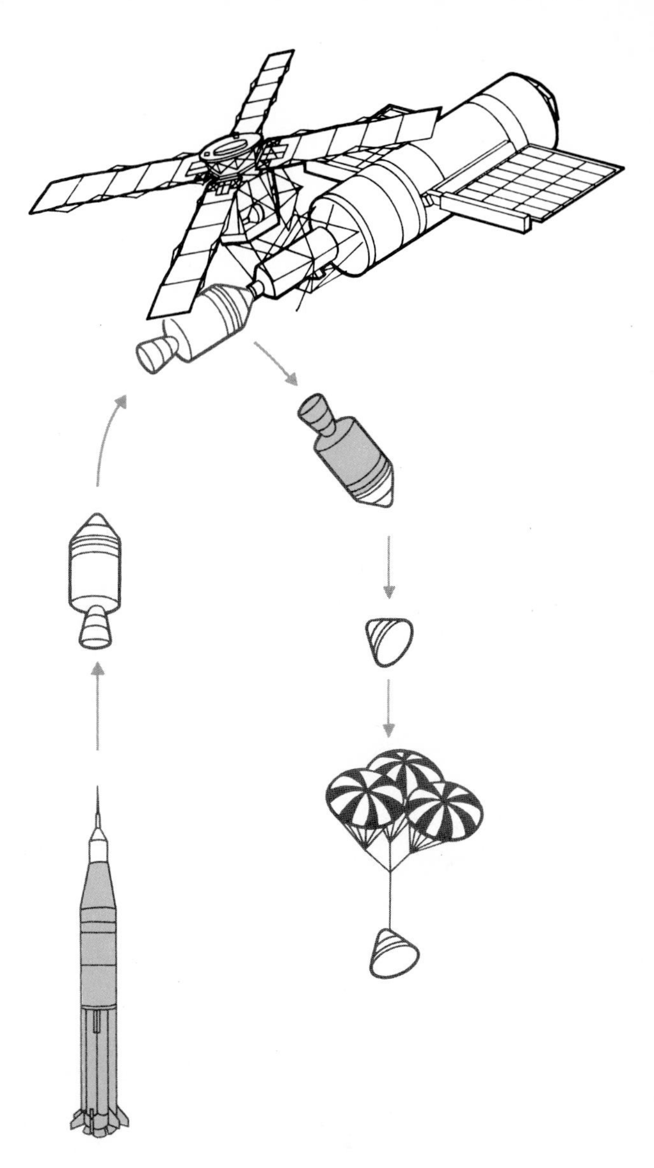

The day after Skylab is orbited, a command and service module, with a three-man crew, will be launched into space by a Saturn 1B rocket, and the first two stages (shaded, lower left) will be jettisoned. In orbit the command module will dock with Skylab (top center), and the crew will enter Skylab for a 28-day tour of duty. To return home, they will climb back into the command module, detach from Skylab, drop back toward earth and, after jettisoning the burnt-out service module (shaded, top right), parachute to a landing in the command module (bottom right).

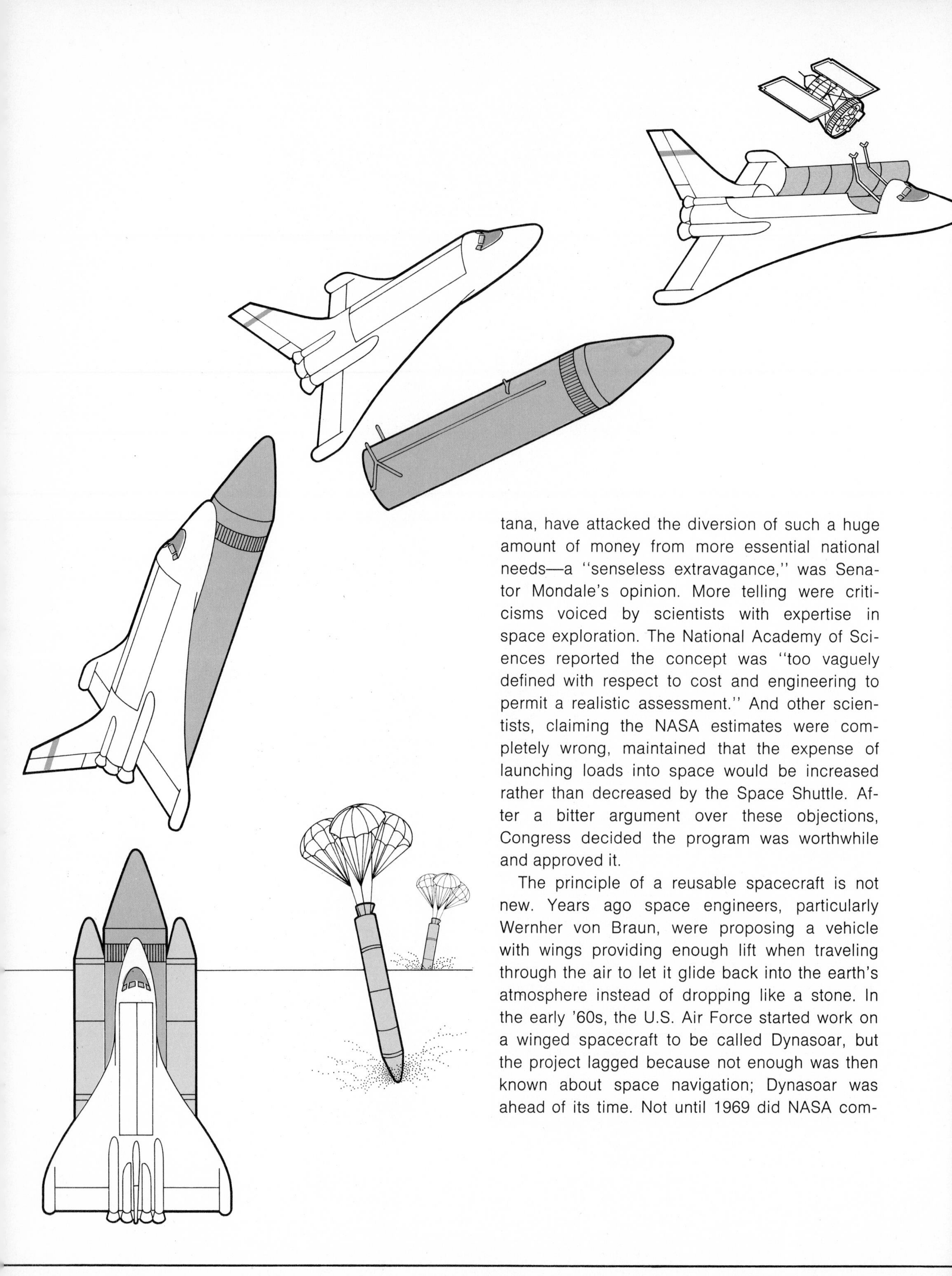

tana, have attacked the diversion of such a huge amount of money from more essential national needs—a "senseless extravagance," was Senator Mondale's opinion. More telling were criticisms voiced by scientists with expertise in space exploration. The National Academy of Sciences reported the concept was "too vaguely defined with respect to cost and engineering to permit a realistic assessment." And other scientists, claiming the NASA estimates were completely wrong, maintained that the expense of launching loads into space would be increased rather than decreased by the Space Shuttle. After a bitter argument over these objections, Congress decided the program was worthwhile and approved it.

The principle of a reusable spacecraft is not new. Years ago space engineers, particularly Wernher von Braun, were proposing a vehicle with wings providing enough lift when traveling through the air to let it glide back into the earth's atmosphere instead of dropping like a stone. In the early '60s, the U.S. Air Force started work on a winged spacecraft to be called Dynasoar, but the project lagged because not enough was then known about space navigation; Dynasoar was ahead of its time. Not until 1969 did NASA com-

The heart of the Space Shuttle program of the late 1970s will be this Space Shuttle orbiter, which can be used for as many as a hundred round trips, taking off and landing as shown in the sequence of drawings beginning at the bottom of the opposite page. It will be launched by reusable solid-fuel boosters (darkly shaded) and a liquid-fuel engine. The solid boosters will be returned by parachute for reuse, but the liquid tank (lightly shaded) is jettisoned at orbital speed (top left). The shuttle crew will perform tasks such as retrieving a satellite or hauling up a component for a large space station (top center) before returning to earth and landing like a standard airplane (below).

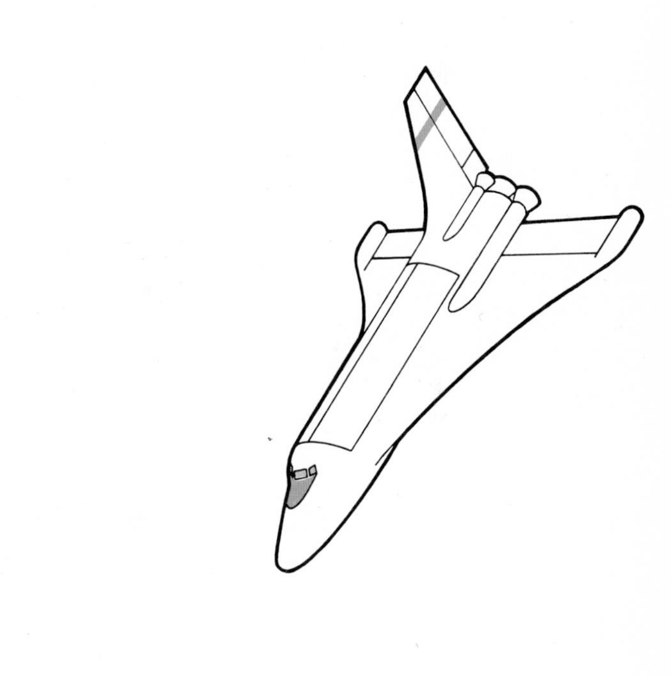

mence serious planning on the Space Shuttle program. Then in 1970 it authorized a preliminary design competition between three large aerospace industry corporations; it was won in the summer of 1972 by North American Rockwell, a California-based company that spent $40 million on planning alone to win the competition. North American Rockwell is now the prime contractor of the program.

Originally Space Shuttle was to consist of a spacecraft and a booster vehicle for launching. Each would be independently powered by liquid-hydrogen and liquid-oxygen engines, the type of engine that has dominated recent space propulsion because it employs the highest-energy fuels available in the most controllable way. In these earlier plans the booster vehicle, as well as the spacecraft, would be reusable, the booster vehicle being piloted by a two-man crew who would bring it back to its base when its fuel was gone. But the development cost of two liquid-fueled, manned and fully returnable orbiter and booster vehicles seemed prohibitive. And further study indicated that an unmanned, partially reusable booster would reduce the overall cost enough for the project to continue.

The need for further economy led the design-

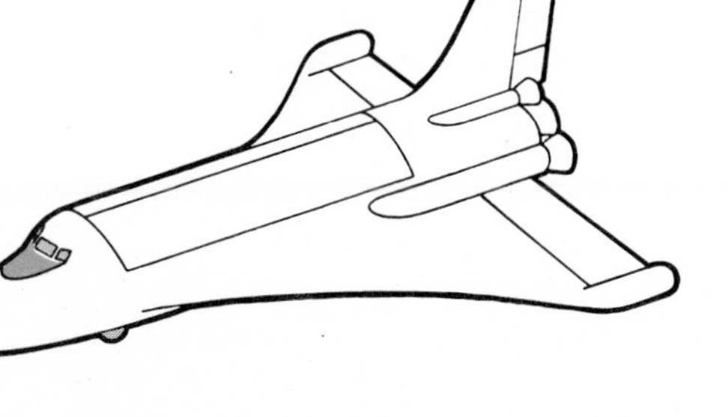

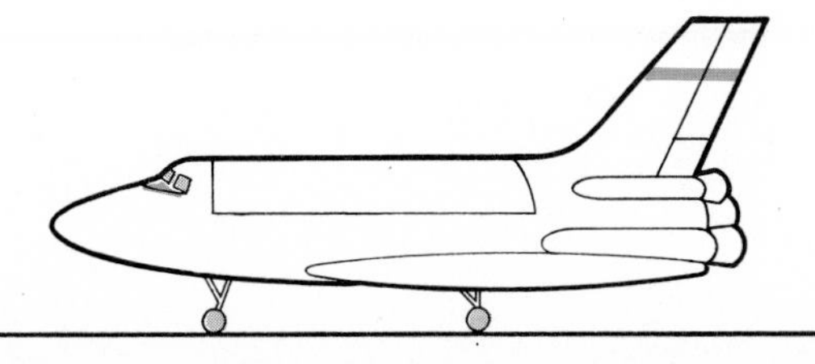

A Satellite for Almost Everybody

Besides such functions as testing man's biological reactions in space and providing gravity-free launch platforms, the Space Shuttle will advance the practicality of the communications satellites that make possible such technological feats as television coverage of the Olympic Games. At the end of the first decade of the satellites' operation, they have proved so enormously profitable that there is a current satellite boom, with the giants of the telecommunications business scrambling for a piece of the action. In June 1972 the Federal Communications Commission ended the monopoly held for 10 years by the semigovernmental Communications Satellite Corporation (COMSAT) and opened up the orbits to competition. COMSAT will continue to operate satellites for international communications but not those for domestic use. Western Union wants to put up two, RCA another pair, and Hughes Aircraft a couple more for use by General Telephone.

The plan is for NASA to launch satellites for the private corporations—at a fee—into orbits assigned by the FCC, much as radio and television channels are currently assigned. The upshot will undoubtedly be an increased capacity to transmit telephone information, computer data and television traffic.

During the next 10 years, communications satellites will come to be associated less with transmitting international extravaganzas such as the Olympics and more with social uses. For example, in 1973 or 1974 NASA will launch a satellite that will broadcast educational and public health programs to remote communities in the Rocky Mountains. This satellite, thanks to recent technological innovations, will have transmitting power so strong that no earth-bound receiving-and-relay station will be necessary. Mountain folk will be able to tune in directly to the satellite with home antennas of little more than glorified chicken wire.

The Space Shuttle will make these satellites even more practical by providing a repairman in space. As of now the communications satellite business has been somewhat like stuffing notes in $30-million bottles and casting them into the ocean. When a launch goes awry, or its innards go on the blink, all the engineers can do is gulp, accept the loss, and shoot up another one. Moreover, all space satellites have to be engineered like Rolls Royces for desert sheiks—on the assumption that they will never receive any maintenance or service. In the last 10 years, 20 per cent of the satellites sent into space have failed to perform. But the Space Shuttle program will correct this situation by providing "space tugs," which can repair malfunctioning satellites in orbit or pick them up and bring them back to earth.

ers away from Apollo's liquid-fuel rockets to the solid-fuel type that is today used primarily for missiles. Solid fuel produces less energy per pound than the best liquids; but solid rockets are much lower in cost than liquids, since they use far less complicated engines. More for budgetary than design reasons, then, NASA decided to compromise and proceed with a pair of partially reusable solid-fuel boosters in combination with a liquid-hydrogen, liquid-oxygen rocket for launching the Space Shuttle orbiter; for maneuvering in space and for the return flight to earth, the craft would carry small liquid-fuel engines.

So if present designs become reality, this is how the Space Shuttle craft will take off on its round-trip flight. At lift-off the two solid-fuel booster rockets and the orbiter's liquid-fuel engine will fire simultaneously. Such simultaneous starting of all engines is a new procedure for manned flight; in the Apollo launches, each stage fired in sequence after the earlier stages had been jettisoned. The combined firing is necessary for Space Shuttle because of the solid fuel's lower energy per pound, but it will undoubtedly cause control problems for the first few critical minutes after lift-off. At a height of some 20 miles, the spent solid-fuel booster rockets will drop away, to be parachuted and recovered at sea; after the liquid fuel is used up, the emptied external fuel tank will be jettisoned into the ocean.

The Space Shuttle orbiter, at least as currently planned, will carry a crew of four and up to six passengers, or as much as 65,000 pounds of cargo. It will be equipped to stay in orbit for missions of a week or more. At journey's end, it will fire a pair of small inboard rocket engines and skim back aerodynamically into the atmosphere, to make an airport landing on earth. Ideally, it will land at the launch site, so it can more promptly be checked out and prepared for its next trip.

During its week or so in space, a Shuttle orbiter, with the help of a lighter space tug, can dispose of all kinds of chores now impossible. It can carry technicians up to repair or replace ailing instruments in scientific or communications satellites already orbiting. It can pick up defunct vehicles for repair or for return to earth. It can place new satellites into orbit, making certain that the communications types *(box, page 38)* are boosted precisely to the 22,300-mile altitude where their orbital speed keeps them fixed over a selected spot on earth. And it provides the first rescue vessel for saving men marooned in space. But its most exciting potential lies in its ability to haul materials into space for the building of large space stations.

Such huge islands in the sky are not likely to be in use until 1990. But the multitude of missions they can accomplish is suggested by some of the experiments and observations that will take place aboard Skylab in 1973. While it is not large compared to future stations, it is so much bigger than anything previously available that it offers a whole new way of examining the mysteries of space and the still unanswered questions about man's ability to endure in the void.

East meets West in space in an artist's conception showing the beginning of the U.S.-U.S.S.R. link-up planned for July 1975, as the American Apollo craft (lower right), its 10-foot-long docking module preceding it like a long nose, approaches the Russian Soyuz ship in earth orbit. Once docked, the two ships will remain joined for about two days while the crewmen visit each other's craft.

The most impressive part of Skylab will be its solar observatory—the United States' first man-operated telescopes in space. There will be eight solar telescopes that can be used to make the most complete record of the sun yet obtained. From their vantage point in space, these telescopes can study such manifestations of the sun as its sunspots and solar flares, examining components of the flares' light that are screened out by the atmosphere and thus invisible from earth. Besides the telescopes, Skylab will carry recording instruments and cameras to photograph solar activity. Periodically, two crew members will get into their spacesuits and climb out through the airlock chamber into space, inching along Skylab's side to retrieve exposed film and reload the cameras, in a delicate task that should take about four hours.

At another Skylab control console, scientists will use a battery of devices—cameras, infrared sensors, electronic scanners that can distinguish wavelengths of light to which human vision is blind—to make a comprehensive study of earth that will complement the new Earth Resources Technology Satellite, which was launched in July 1972. ERTS is taking a look at many of earth's features and environmental problems that Skylab will also scrutinize. Skylab should detect fishing shoals, changing patterns of offshore water pollution, geologically active areas that may reveal the locations of new oil and mineral deposits and alternation in ocean currents. By monitoring amounts of snowmelt and rainfall, Skylab technicians should be able to predict incipient floods. By using special film to photograph changes in the color of vegetation, they may be able to spot the onset of crop or forest diseases. Skylab's cameras may also locate hitherto unnoticed geological fault lines, thereby helping forecast possible earthquakes. These observations should lead to new discoveries that can perform the reverse function of finding out from the heavens more about earth than man has found out with his telescopes aimed at the sky.

But the major subject of Skylab and the entire Space Shuttle program is space itself. And the essential information Skylab must collect, if man is to spend months at a time in space stations made possible by the Space Shuttle program, concerns how the human animal can adapt to the altered conditions of space. There are 18 experiments of this nature on Skylab's agenda and hundreds of biological measurements will be made. The importance of this study is indicated by the fact that one member of the first group of three astronauts to board Skylab will be a doctor —U.S. Navy Commander Joseph P. Kerwin; the group's leader will be Navy Captain Charles "Pete" Conrad Jr. and the pilot will be Navy Commander Paul J. Weitz.

HOW WILL LIFE IN SPACE AFFECT THE BODY?

During their planned 28-day visit to Skylab, Dr. Kerwin will put his fellow space travelers—and himself—through a rigorous routine of experiments to test the effects upon their bodies of life in a space station. He will make them ride a machine like a bicycle, so that he can compare their metabolic reactions in space to similar reactions on earth. He will have them encase their legs and lower bodies in a pressurized tank, seal it at the waist and lower the pressure, to measure each man's blood pressure and circulation in the weightless conditions of space. Such measurements can be of great help to medical researchers on earth: for example, does the lack of gravity slow the circulation of blood, just as prolonged bed rest does in the gravity of the globe? And is lessened gravity easier on the human heart? If so, future flying space laboratories might also serve as intensive-care units for patients whose hearts need a rest (if, of course, the excitement of lift-off doesn't kill the patient).

So the Skylab occupants can expect to find themselves plugged into sensors and recording devices much of the time. Even when they sleep at night, their bodily functions will be monitored to gauge the long-term effects of a zero-gravity existence. And when he is not testing his fellow astronauts, Dr. Kerwin will be experimenting with other forms of life brought into space for the purpose. One such test, for example, will determine the effect of weightlessness on the emergence of a vinegar gnat from its pupal state.

Since the weightlessness of space provides an ideal environment for testing new industrial methods, Skylab scientists plan a battery of experiments to determine the advantages of such an environment. A particularly intriguing experiment will require taking a small oven (for heating crystals) into orbit. When crystals are heated for transistors on earth, it is difficult to get their chemical components to form a perfect mix because gravity tends to make the heavier ones settle to the bottom. In a gravity-free environment, however, it might be possible to form nearly perfect crystals because all the components should be uniformly distributed in the mix. But perhaps the most ingenious industrial application of weightlessness is a proposed experiment to suspend drops of molten metal in space as they cool—in zero gravity they should form perfect spheres.

Economical factories in the sky are still a distant dream. But such notions are no farther out than some of the other conjectured uses for the large space stations that Space Shuttle craft can assemble in the future. One of the most spectacular proposals is for a solar plant in orbit. The scheme, as advanced by Peter Glaser of Arthur D. Little Inc., would tap electric power directly from the sun, using a huge version of the solar-cell panels that already provide power for instruments aboard space satellites. A satellite plant would orbit in a fixed position above one spot on earth. The plant would be attached by cable to a huge panel of solar cells, which would be oriented toward the sun. The sun's rays could then be converted by the panel's solar cells into electricity; current would flow through the cable to the satellite's conversion apparatus. There the electric current would be converted to microwave energy and sent in a narrow beam to earth. A large antenna on earth would receive the microwaves and reconvert them to electric energy for the power lines. Glaser calculates that one such electric plant in orbit, using a five-mile-square panel of solar cells, could supply enough electric power for all the needs of a city the size of New York by the year 2000.

And the wildest dreamers of all visualize, as the next step after our missions to the moon, the use of a large space station for launching a manned mission to one of the asteroids, the small bodies revolving in space between Mars and Jupiter. Scientists conjecture that even more might be learned from them than from the moon about the earliest coalescence of the type of matter that formed the planets. Reaching an asteroid would be practical if the vehicle were fired from a space station instead of from earth, since far greater distance and far larger payloads are made possible by launching a satellite outside the pull of earth's gravity.

In a sense, however, one of the more pragmatic results of the Space Shuttle program could be the most revolutionary. Arthur Kantrowitz, director of Avco Everett Research Laboratory, a pioneer in space physics, argues that nothing has demonstrated that space cannot be made habitable, even attractive, for colonization. Three centuries ago not many Europeans were willing to consider the possible advantages of the New World wilderness over the amenities of Old World civilization, he points out. Perhaps, like the sailing vessels of that time, the Space Shuttle may become the first major transport toward new worlds yet unknown.

The Puzzle of the Pandas

Ling-Ling, the female panda sent from China to the U.S. National Zoo in Washington, stretches in front of the fence separating her from the male.

The animal of the year, to most Americans at least, was a rotund creature that resembled a black-eyed teddy bear come to life. In an exchange that marked the renewal of diplomatic relations between Communist China and the United States, two giant pandas were flown to Washington's National Zoo in return for two musk oxen that were sent to the Peking Zoo. There was little doubt in anyone's mind that the United States got the best of the bargain.

The pandas at the National Zoo—the first in captivity in the United States in 19 years—attracted long lines of tourists—more than 1,000 an hour—from the moment they arrived. Photographers recorded the pandas from every angle. As National Zoo Director Theodore Reed explained, "You *like* musk oxen; but pandas can steal your heart away."

Not the least of the panda's attraction is the air of mystery that surrounds it. Naturalists have studied the few that have been captured, only to realize how little information they really have about the animals. Although the pandas' natural habitat is the wilderness of China's mountainous Szechwan province, they seem to adapt to zoo life and appear to enjoy posing for crowds; yet they are evidently too unsocial to breed in captivity. The panda is unrelated to the creature it most resembles, the bear. It sits up like a human to eat stalks of bamboo, has a "pseudo thumb" on its paw, a powerful, dangerous swipe and an apparent preference for humans over other pandas. But the animal's behavior in its natural habitat, its evolution, even its relationship to any other living creature, all are enigmas, or at least subjects of continuing controversy, and presumably will continue to be until the naturalist can one day stalk the giant panda through the remote forests of China's interior.

The male, Hsing-Hsing, perches atop a log in his play area at the zoo. More reserved than Ling-Ling on arrival, he has become increasingly playful in front of his audience.

Mysterious Creatures from the East

When the famous French priest and naturalist Père Armand David sent the skin and bones of a giant panda to Paris in 1869, a scientific curiosity was aroused that to this day has not diminished. Père David, who was in China as a missionary at the time, believed the creature was a "black and white bear." But the director of the Paris Museum of Natural History, Alphonse Milne-Edwards, who examined the remains in preparation for making a lifelike drawing *(right),* guessed that it was not a bear but a large member of the raccoon family. He created a new genus for it, *Ailuropoda.* The debate continues over which animals are the panda's closest relatives. It is possible that the creature exists in its own family without any close relations at all.

The first scientific portrait of a giant panda was made by Alphonse Milne-Edwards in Paris in 1869. Considering that he drew it without ever having seen a live panda, the portrait is a reasonably accurate representation.

◀ *The approach to panda country, the rugged mountainous region of Szechwan province (left) where the Chialing River winds through forests of fir and bamboo, has sheer slopes and plunging valleys that almost defy human passage.*

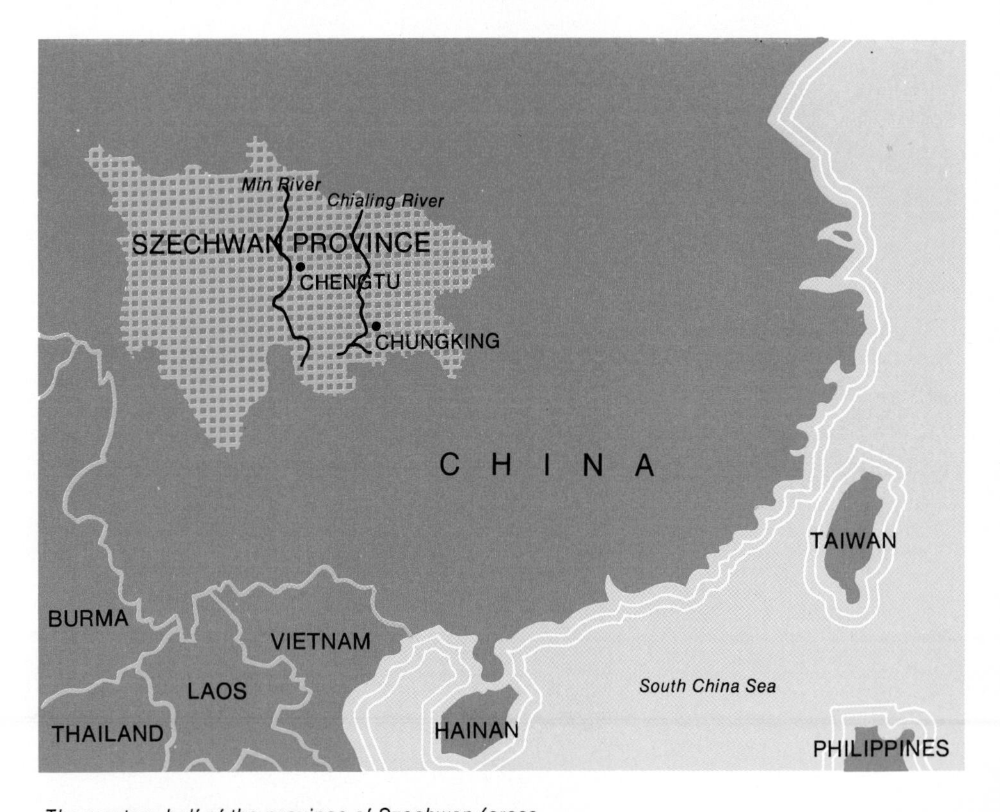

The western half of the province of Szechwan (cross-hatched in the map above) is the panda's natural habitat. A few live west of the Chialing River, but most inhabit the high bamboo forests that grow abundantly west of the Min.

A Powerful Paw with a "Thumb"

The cuddly-appearing panda is in fact a potentially dangerous animal. When mature it can reach six feet in length, may weigh about 300 pounds, and can send a man sprawling with one swat from its powerful paw. The panda paw is more than a weapon, however. It is equipped with a unique appendage, resembling a thumb, that allows the animal to grasp its food while eating.

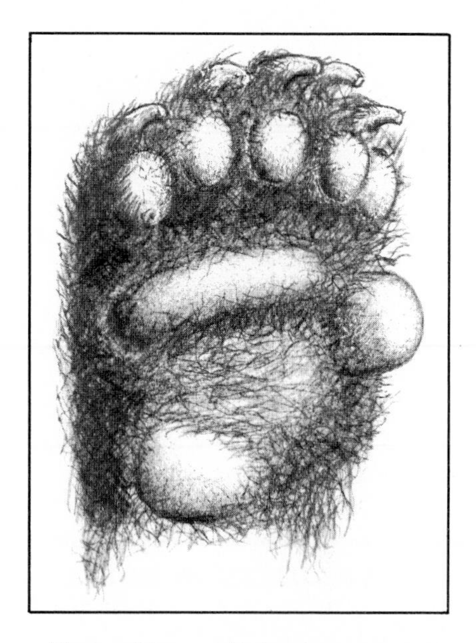

The panda's pseudo thumb is actually an elongated wristbone covered with a tough pad (above). The first two claws close on it, enabling the panda to grasp its food and even a tin feeding dish.

◄ The panda walks with a lumbering gait, climbs trees and plays with such abandon that it has been known to destroy a basketball in a few minutes.

By rubbing itself against objects, the panda deposits a pattern of scent markings, either to attract its mate or to denote the boundaries of its territory.

The Bashful and Reluctant Lovers

One of the unfortunate characteristics of pandas in captivity is their reluctance to mate. Most attempts to breed them in zoos have ended as ignominiously as the affair between London's female Chi-Chi and Moscow's male An-An. First in 1966 and then in 1968 the zookeepers of the two nations attempted to bring their pandas together—both times in vain.

The 1966 attempt in Moscow was hardly aided by the presence of movie cameras and a riot squad with shields and tranquilizer guns in case the animals should begin serious fighting; not surprisingly, Chi-Chi and An-An shied off. More discreet sessions in Moscow and London were also fruitless. Raised in solitude, Chi-Chi was more drawn to her keeper—or almost any human—than to another panda. In 1972 both these pandas died—still virginal.

The first panda ever born in captivity, male cub Ming-Ming is cuddled by his mother at China's Peking Zoo in 1963. China is the only country to breed pandas in captivity.

London's female Chi-Chi wistfully greets her keeper (right) ▶ on her return after an ill-fated attempt at courtship in Moscow in 1966. A second try two years later also failed.

A Row over Food Additives

AN EXPERT APPRAISAL WEIGHS RISKS VERSUS BENEFITS

by Michael F. Jacobson and Jean Mayer

The subject of food additives is charged with emotion. At one extreme are those who consider the mere existence of additives—of any nature and in any amount—to be a plot by food processors to make money at the expense of their fellow citizens' health. At the other extreme are those who deride the critics as antiprogress and antiscience.

Both camps were stirred to fresh rhetoric in 1972 when the U.S. Food and Drug Administration (FDA) banned two compounds and added that it was suspicious of at least four others. One banned compound was an artificial hormone, diethylstilbestrol, called DES, used in cattle feed. Supplied in tiny amounts to cattle, it had favorable effects on their growth rate. But there were indications that, at least in much larger amounts, it also might stimulate cancerous growths in test animals and humans *(box, page 59).* The other newly prohibited substance, diethyl pyrocarbonate, called DEPC, had been used in human food to halt fermentation in wines and soft drinks. The food-processing additives under suspicion included nitrite, which seems to be essential to the keeping qualities of bacon, sausages, and other cured meat and fish; a food dye named Red No. 2, which had been in use since about 1900, and another called Violet No. 1; and saccharin, the single remaining sugar substitute since the controversial 1969 ban on cyclamates. Red No. 2 was under suspicion because it may interfere with reproductive processes. The others on this list of suspects—nitrite, Violet No. 1 and saccharin—were accused of being possibly carcinogenic—that is, causes of cancer.

The red maraschino cherry decorating a grapefruit owes its color to seven food dyes, including Red No. 2—one of many long-used food additives now undergoing scrutiny.

These announcements by the FDA, which followed each other with rapidity throughout 1972, heightened the debate over additives—and increased the necessity for a reasonable, calm and informative study of the entire subject.

The first principle to understand is that additives are not new. Many additives have been in use for a long time. Salt, sugar, vinegar, pepper and other spices have been used for centuries. Nor are all of the familiar ones safe for everybody—many people, for instance, have to curtail the sugar or salt in their diets. Nevertheless, most of us have been consuming a great many additives in our food without observable harm. It is sometimes argued that the well-known additives are all right because they are "natural," whereas "chemical" or "artificial" additives are the villains. This argument makes little scientific sense if the only consideration is the source of the additive. The flavoring agents in such common additives as vanilla, pepper or cloves are extremely complex organic molecules, as sophisticated as any synthetic molecule produced in a test tube. And some of the most potent poisons known to man, such as strychnine and curare, are natural compounds. Moreover, several natural compounds, such as the flavoring agents safrole and coumarin, were banned as additives after laboratory tests proved them to be toxic.

A second point is that in many cases food additives do provide clear-cut economic benefits. Calcium propionate and sorbic acid, for example, prevent the growth of mold in bread and cheese. These chemicals are not only safe, but provide nutrients as well. The calcium in calcium propionate can aid the growth of teeth and bones; sorbic acid is digested and absorbed like fat. Allowing bread or cheese to grow moldy is ridiculous when the addition of a safe chemical can prevent spoilage.

Other additives have positive benefit to health. Rickets, a debilitating bone disease caused by a deficiency of vitamin D, used to cripple thousands of Americans, but since dairies began adding amounts of vitamin D to milk, rickets has become virtually unknown in the United States. The addition of niacin to cornmeal and bread was instrumental in eliminating pellagra, the vitamin-deficiency disease that used to afflict people dependent on a cereal diet. In the same way, adding iodine to salt has greatly reduced the incidence of goiter. Clearly, the carefully controlled use of some additives can be beneficial without introducing a significant risk.

Further, many products would not exist or would be priced beyond the reach of most people, if artificial coloring and flavoring were not used in place of the natural food. Expensive brands of ice cream, candy and yogurt may contain real fruit or fruit extract, but cheaper brands have to rely on color and flavor additives to provide the desired taste and appearance. As long as we know that the additives being used are safe, imitation fruit flavoring permits the marketing of useful, tasty products at prices the majority of people can afford.

WEIGHING BENEFITS AND DANGERS

And even in the case of additives that pose some possible dangers, the benefit may outweigh the drawback. One such case concerned the use of sodium nitrite and sodium nitrate in hot dogs, ham, bacon and sausage. These chemicals both add flavor and maintain a pink color in the meat—but more important, they appear to be necessary to prevent the growth of the bacteria that cause the deadly food poisoning called botulism. Nitrite, however, can combine with other chemicals, called amines, to form nitrosamines, which can cause cancer. Government scientists have found small amounts of nitrosamines in bacon, sausage and other products. Should we remove nitrite and permit the deadly bacteria to grow, or should we use the additive and take a chance, however small, with cancer? Certain foods like smoked fish and some sausages, for example, can be preserved by alternative means such as freezing, but other foods cannot. Each individual, of course, has another option: he can decide not to eat foods containing nitrite.

What it all comes down to is that putting additives in foods—introducing new molecules into human digestive systems—always involves risks that should not be taken lightly. That is the main reason why Congress passed a law in 1958 to force chemical manufacturing firms or food processors to test all new additives. Still, an enormous problem remained. When the law went into effect, hundreds of additives were already in use, including flavorings, preservatives, artificial colorings and texturizing agents. And these were only the *intentional* additives: hundreds of other compounds may migrate into food from packaging materials or from agricultural chemicals such as pesticides. To go back and examine only the intentional additives would be a herculean task —and an extremely expensive one. Testing a single compound can cost $100,000 or more.

This great explosion of additives has occurred only in the years since World War II—and it has transformed our food supply. Until the 1940s we had progressed from the subsistence economy of the pioneer to a market economy; but our foods still came from what was essentially an agricultural supply. The food went from the farm through the distribution system to the consumer. The only highly processed foods most people ate were bread and macaroni.

Since World War II, and more and more rapidly during the last several years, we have largely converted from an agricultural to what can be called an industrial food supply—from the farm to the factory before proceeding to the distribution system and to the consumer. The industrial processing may be relatively limited, as it is in canning and in freezing; or it may be extremely elaborate, with foodstuffs being broken down into useful components that are then incorporated into still other foods.

The post-World War II period has seen an equally explosive development of convenience foods. These have been an instrument of liberation for women, freeing them from hours of kitchen work; but the trend has brought its own technological and economic difficulties. First, many of these packaged, often precooked and easy-to-serve foods had to resemble traditional home-cooked dishes in both color and taste. But the manufacturing processes often removed just those constituents in the original foodstuffs that gave them flavor and made them look appetizing. The only answer was to substitute artificial colors and flavors. Second, many of the ingredients in these foods were "purified" to the point of removing many of their vitamins and minerals. This led to "enrichment" programs that replaced at least some of the vitamins and minerals that had been eliminated. Third, the only way to provide a food that in a few minutes of cooking or defrosting would resemble one that took hours of preparation was to add texturizing, moistening and emulsifying agents. And finally, a great many of these new foods were distributed nationwide; they had to last weeks, even months, on the shelves of grocery stores. This required preservatives.

The intentional additives that perform any of these functions are at least recognized. The accidental additives, on the other hand, are, in a way, more sinister. These include the pesticide residues, the packaging contaminants, and even some of the chemicals that are employed in food processing. These additives, of course, are not supposed to be in our food in the first place. Contamination by herbicides, fungicides and insecticides constitutes a major worry. After all, these compounds were developed specifically to be toxic to some biological species.

Both kinds of additives, then, whether intentional or accidental, result from some attempt to aid the farmer, the processor or the consumer. But many, if not most, of these aids can exact a price. The problem is to calculate whether the aid is worth the price.

MEASURING FOUR KINDS OF RISK

As a rough rule of thumb, food additives can be placed in one of four "risk" categories. The safest chemicals are those that occur in nature and that are easily metabolized by the body. Proteins, vitamins, starches and minerals are in this category. Proteins can tenderize meat and speed the brewing of beer. Vitamins and minerals can increase the nutritional value of foods. Cornstarch serves as a wholesome thickening agent in soups and sauces. Any of these compounds— and, in fact, anything at all—could be dangerous if taken in excess. An excessive caloric intake leads to obesity, which shortens life. A high sugar intake, besides introducing a large amount of nonnutritious or "empty"—but nonetheless fattening—calories, helps cause dental cavities and perhaps helps precipitate diabetes in susceptible individuals. But the amounts of these lowest-risk additives commonly consumed in foods are safe in the usual sense of the word.

The second major category, which introduces slightly more risk than the first, consists of compounds that are not absorbed at all by the body. Because they do not enter the bloodstream, they never have a chance to damage the liver, kidneys, heart and other sensitive internal organs directly. Cellulose, a major component of broccoli, lettuce and other vegetables, is typical of these chemicals. It, and such similar complex carbohydrates as the pectin used in making preserves, cannot be digested by enzymes in the stomach or by the bacteria in our intestines. These compounds are harmlessly excreted. Not only are they generally safe—whether found naturally in farm produce or used as additives—but they also may have beneficial side effects. By adding bulk, they act as natural laxatives; some scientists believe that the laxative effect may help to prevent intestinal cancer. However, these compounds cannot be considered totally harmless since theoretically they could affect any portion of the digestive system from the tip of the tongue to the inside of the intestine.

The third category of compounds—and the first really worrisome one—includes chemicals that occur in nature and are known to affect the human body's normal operation. Caffeine, which exists naturally in coffee, tea and chocolate, is added to cola soft drinks. It is a powerful stimulant of the central nervous system, and has caused birth defects in laboratory animals. Quinine, a soft-drink flavoring, also falls into this third category. Large doses can have the beneficial effect of killing the parasite that causes malaria. But, again in large doses, it can also bring on blindness and severe heart damage. Hormones and antibiotics are other powerful natural substances that can upset the delicately balanced functioning of a human body. DES, banned as a cattle-feed additive in 1972, is a synthetic version of such a hormone. All of these physiologically active compounds, by their very nature, are highly questionable food additives. Even if their short-term effects are known, sci-

Food additives are everywhere, as shown in this chart indicating which major additives appear in widely consumed food products. The acidity-controlling agents, for example, show up in a wide range of foods from butter to canned fruits and vegetables. Processors use rancidity preventives to keep many fatty products from smelling or tasting bad. Preservatives include not only the sugars that keep jams and jellies from spoiling, but also the calcium propionate that retards mold in bread. The color and flavor stabilizers include sodium citrate, which prevents trace metallic compounds from spoiling the flavor and color of soft drinks. Emulsifiers keep substances in food from separating, while thickeners and stabilizers—mostly plant extracts such as gum arabic—add thickness to the consistency of ice cream, cake mixes and cooking oils.

FOODS	ADDITIVES Preservatives	Rancidity preventives	Color and flavor stabilizers	Emulsifiers and lubricants	Thickeners, stabilizers	Bleaching and maturing agents	Acidity-controlling compounds	Dyes	Non nutritive sweeteners	Nutrient supplements	Flavorings
BREAKFAST CEREALS		✓			✓	✓		✓		✓	✓
BREAD	✓	✓		✓		✓	✓			✓	
PROCESSED CHEESE	✓			✓	✓		✓	✓			
BUTTER	✓	✓					✓	✓			
MARGARINE	✓		✓	✓				✓		✓	✓
SALAD AND COOKING OIL, SHORTENING	✓	✓	✓	✓	✓						
PEANUT BUTTER		✓		✓							
JAMS, JELLIES	✓				✓		✓	✓	✓		
PROCESSED MEATS	✓		✓					✓			
CANNED FRUITS AND VEGETABLES	✓	✓			✓		✓		✓		
SOFT DRINKS	✓	✓	✓		✓		✓	✓	✓		✓
BEER	✓				✓						
CRACKERS, COOKIES	✓	✓		✓		✓	✓	✓	✓		✓
CAKES AND CAKE MIXES	✓	✓	✓	✓	✓	✓	✓	✓	✓		✓
GELATIN DESSERTS				✓	✓		✓	✓	✓		✓
ICE CREAM			✓	✓	✓			✓			✓

Two scientists at a Swift & Company laboratory examine the efficacy of nitrite additives in combating the botulinal bacteria that cause botulism, the deadly food poisoning. The swollen cans of ham in the foreground, which were prepared with insufficient amounts of nitrite, proved to contain botulinal bacteria and the poison they produce.

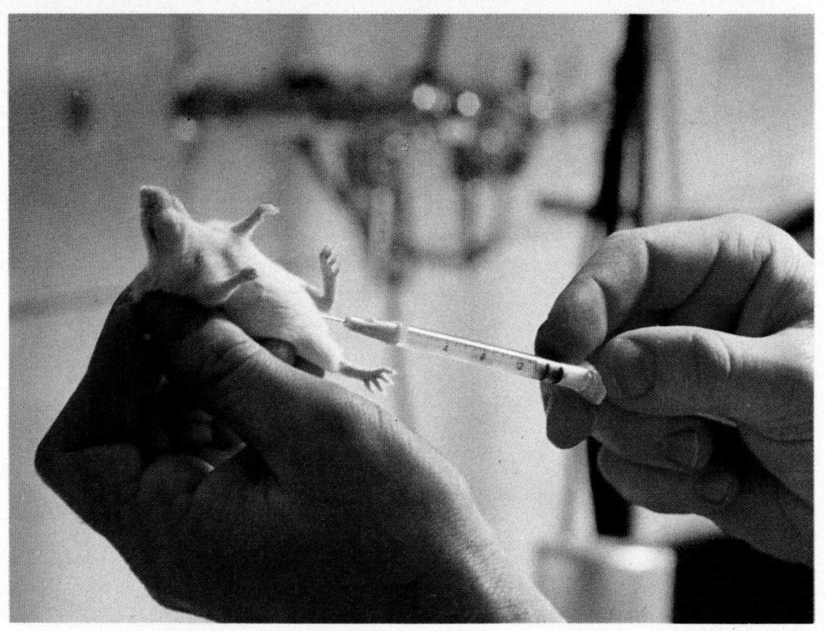

A mouse gets an injection of an extract from nitrite-free canned hams. It died of botulism, while mice injected with an extract from hams cured with proper levels of nitrite were not affected. But in recent tests on laboratory animals, the nitrites themselves were found to produce cancer-causing substances.

entists still cannot be sure that they do not have subtle long-term impact on the body.

The last—and the most worrisome—group of compounds includes the synthetics—chemicals that do *not* occur in nature and *are* absorbed into the body. These are the most questionable of all additives. Many artificial colors and several preservatives fall in this group. The human body deals with many of these unnatural chemicals by transporting them to the liver, where they are "detoxified" before being excreted. But this process does not always work satisfactorily. Many of the chemicals that the government has banned as harmful in recent years belong to this category. Cyclamates do, and so does one of the compounds—the artificial coloring agent called Red No. 2—that the Food and Drug Administration was testing intensively in 1972.

Simply because these synthetic compounds form the most questionable group of additives does not mean that they are the only ones needing examination. Not all natural chemicals are safe—witness strychnine. Nor are chemicals that go through the digestive tract without being absorbed by the bloodstream—they could harm the stomach or intestines. Ideally, every additive should be tested to determine its exact chemical makeup, how the body metabolizes it and whether long-term ingestion of it can have harmful effects. But as we have noted before, this is an immense, time-consuming and expensive task. Until Congress passed the 1958 law requiring additive or food manufacturers to examine all new products, there were no such laws—at least none with any teeth in them. And meanwhile hundreds of additives were being put on the market.

The federal government first attempted to deal with the problem at the beginning of this century. In 1906, after "muckraking" authors such as Upton Sinclair had exposed the foul conditions in Chicago's slaughterhouses, Congress banned the presence of "poisonous" substances in food. But this law required the government to prove that a chemical was dangerous, rather than requiring the food manufacturer to demonstrate that it was safe. Three decades passed before Congress reconsidered the question of chemical additives; but the law of 1938 contained the same flaw—it still allowed the chemicals to remain in the food until the government could prove in court that they were dangerous.

A LAW WITH TEETH IN IT

The public's concern about food additives rose again in the 1950s, when it became clear that the 1938 law was insufficient to police the safety of the many new chemical additives introduced after World War II. Years of Congressional hearings led to the passage, in 1958, of the first effective food-additive law. Finally, the law required food or additive producers to establish that a chemical was safe *before* adding it to the food. This transferred the burden of proof from the government to the processors.

The second key feature of the 1958 law, which became known as the "Delaney Clause" after its chief advocate, Representative James Delaney of New York, required the government to ban an additive if *any* amount of it caused cancer—either in people or in laboratory animals. Food colors did not come under the 1958 ban, but an amendment passed in 1960 included them as well. The Delaney Clause was prominent in the much-publicized battle involving cyclamates in 1969 and 1970. Scientists who had fed large amounts of cyclamates to laboratory animals discovered that some of the animals developed tumors. Instead of banning the sweetener immediately, as the law stipulated, government officials vacillated. Consumer groups and a number of scientists demanded that the law be enforced. The food industry, which stood to lose tens of millions of dollars should the additive be banned, brought up a crucial objection to the Delaney Clause: the amount of cyclamates fed to the animals in the tests was many times larger than any human being would ever consume, even if he guzzled cyclamate-sweetened "diet" soft drinks for years. In the end, after much vituperation, cyclamates were banned. But the controversy they generated is still simmering.

The problem raised is inescapable, and perhaps insoluble. Because of the seriousness, even finality, of cancer, it is crucial that food additives be extensively tested on animals for their tendency to cause the disease. But cost consider-ations, and the availability of pure strains, dictate that only a few hundred animals be used in most experiments; larger numbers of test animals are simply too expensive. To be sure that the results of such small-scale, short-term animal experiments provide a reasonable safeguard for the hundreds of millions of persons who will eat these chemicals during a lifetime, it becomes essential to feed abnormally large quantities of the additive to the animals. Feeding them the small amounts that occur in a normal human diet would not reveal the dangers of any but the most powerful and quick-acting carcinogens. And thus a very important question arises: if an enormous amount of an additive will cause cancer, will a small amount have the same result? It is clear that lowering the dosage of a carcinogen reduces the frequency with which it causes cancer. Is there, however, a concentration below which the chemical poses no threat at all? This question is the subject of intense scientific investigation; and so far the evidence is not decisive one way or the other. Lacking conclusive proof, leading cancer specialists and toxicologists understandably recommend erring on the side of safety. There is no sense, they feel, in playing Russian roulette with a questionable additive, perhaps exposing millions of people to the risk of cancer —especially in those instances when safe substitutes are readily available.

The Delaney Clause is strongly favored by consumer groups because the law's rigid wording is a safeguard against the tendency of administrators to procrastinate in their decision making when subjected to pressures from special interest groups. Since the cyclamates episode, many people have been suggesting that the clause be extended to ban additives that cause birth defects and mutations. However, it is very difficult to test the tendency of additives to cause birth defects. If a large amount of almost any chemical is fed to a pregnant animal, it will cause birth defects or death in the next litter. Therefore, the massive doses used in cancer tests cannot be used in birth-defect tests. Small amounts of the additive must be fed to the animals involved, and the tests must be continued over several generations. Either that or the additive must be fed to a huge number of animals so that even a small incidence of birth defects or mutations will show up in the first generation.

Screening out additives that might cause cancer or birth defects raises special difficulties. But any testing of food additives is a complex problem that calls for judgment and skill as well as scientific knowledge. If a chemical compound harms an animal, does it follow that it will harm a human being? There is always the possibility that the species of animal used in the test may be basically different from humans in some crucial metabolic reaction. The difference may make the animal more (or less) sensitive to an additive, thus giving a false result. This hazard can be decreased by feeding the compound to more than one species, but even then the question of similarity to humans remains unanswered.

CLOSING THE KNOWLEDGE GAP

The difficulties of interpreting animal tests apply not only to proposed new additives but also to the many additives that were already in use when the 1958 law was passed. Nobody knew, since most of these compounds had never been tested, which ones were safe and which ones were harmful. To try to close this knowledge gap, the FDA in 1958 drew up a roster of the additives then in use, and submitted it to doctors, nutrition experts and other scientists across the country. They were asked to indicate any that they felt needed testing. Those that were not singled out became the basis of a list of compounds Generally Recognized As Safe—which was quickly shortened to GRAS. The GRAS list included such old standbys as salt, pepper and starch—approximately 500 additives in all—that, although for the most part untested, were assumed to be innocuous or even healthful.

But the GRAS list has proved to be less than perfect. Some chemicals originally on the GRAS list were later revealed to be hazardous. Cyclamates, for example, were on the GRAS list when their cancer-producing effects were discovered. Saccharin was on the list until 1972, when its safety was also questioned. Brominated vegetable oil (BVO), an emulsifier that keeps flavor oils dispersed in citrus drinks, was removed from the

DES: A Controversial Cattle Fattener

DES is as potent a compound as its full name, diethylstilbestrol, is difficult to pronounce. Fed to beef cattle and sheep in minute amounts—as little as a gram during an animal's lifetime—the synthetic hormone speeds their growth. A steer given DES reaches a market weight of 1,000 pounds 35 days sooner than a steer with no DES in its diet. The cattle raiser saves not only time but also some 500 pounds of feed.

Despite these advantages, the Food and Drug Administration, on December 31, banned the use of DES in cattle feed. The FDA's action understandably prompted a hot debate.

The FDA was forced to act by the terms of the Delaney Clause, which is part of the 1958 law governing food additives. This clause was named after its advocate, Congressman James Delaney of New York, and states that any food additive that induces cancers in either men or animals must immediately be banned. DES stimulates the growth of tumors in test animals such as mice. And DES was also under indictment for causing cancers in humans. A team of Boston doctors led by Arthur L. Herbst had traced an outbreak of a rare vaginal cancer in eight young women to DES: years before, the women's mothers had all been given DES to prevent miscarriages.

The crux of the argument, however, concerned not whether DES had caused tumors, but how much DES it had taken to do the damage. The mothers-to-be whose daughters later developed cancer had been given a great deal of the hormone many years earlier. The test mice had also been given substantial doses, considering their small size. Some doctors, biologists, and not a few cattle raisers, argued that the Delaney Clause is too sweeping. Feeding excessive amounts of any compound to an animal may cause an adverse reaction; in some instances cancers will result. Scientists point out that tiny amounts of the same compound consumed by humans might do no damage whatever. A further argument was this: a normal human body naturally produces such large amounts of hormones as to overshadow any threat from minute traces of DES.

A rebuttal was promptly offered by the anti-DES faction, led in the Senate by Wisconsin's William Proxmire. Why take a chance by introducing *any* potential carcinogen into the nation's diet? Furthermore, they pointed out, it had been proved that minute amounts of DES were in fact being consumed. In the spring of 1972 FDA investigators found DES in 2 to 10 per cent of the beef livers tested.

This seemed to indicate that cattle raisers were not scrupulously obeying an FDA edict of 1971. This ruling was prompted by the fact that cattle appear to get rid of DES quickly: tests showed that no trace of the chemical remained in the meat of a steer slaughtered only 48 hours after its last ingestion of the hormone. On the basis of these tests, the FDA had ruled that cattlemen must withdraw DES from cattle feed a full seven days before slaughtering.

The presence of DES in some of the tested beef livers (the liver is the last organ in the animal to discharge DES) seemed to indicate either that some farmers were slaughtering cattle without waiting the required seven days, or that they were not successfully isolating them in separate DES-free feed lots. The third possibility was that sensitive new testing techniques were able to detect minute traces of DES that had previously slipped through unnoticed.

Whatever the cause, DES was creeping into the nation's meat supply and the FDA had to act. According to the Delaney Clause, any cancer-causing additive, no matter how much is used in the tests, must be banned. For the time being, at least, cattle raisers had to do without DES in cattle feed. And while the antiadditive partisans were somewhat reassured, the meat industry leaders predicted that meat prices would climb even more steeply. Fierce as the debate sounded, it was only one of the many battles in the war over all food additives.

list only after Canadian scientists demonstrated that it might damage the heart, liver, kidneys and other organs (small amounts are still permitted in soft drinks).

Since the well-publicized battles concerning the safety of cyclamates, BVO and saccharin, the FDA has been examining the entire list of GRAS compounds and sponsoring toxicity studies on the ones whose safety is most questionable. Special attention is being paid to artificial colorings, spurred by the news that Red No. 2 may cause infertility. The number of dyes used in foods and in drugs is considerable: recent compilations found no less than seven dyes being used in gelatin desserts, seven in maraschino cherries, six in sausages, eight in ice cream and sherbets, eight in carbonated beverages, eight in candy, eight in bakery products, six in breakfast cereals and seven in dessert-making powders. Because the advantages afforded by dyes are the most tenuous (does anyone deeply care how red his maraschino cherries are?), the dyes were a logical target for both an early and a comprehensive review. At any rate, it seemed probable that several compounds would be removed from the GRAS list—because they pose a danger, because their advantage is outweighed by the risk or because they are so little used that it would not be worth the expense of testing them.

Furthermore, not all food additives are always necessary. Sometimes chemicals are added just for variety's sake, like the artificial colorings and flavorings in breakfast cereals, the colors found in pharmaceuticals and many candies. Some companies add preservatives to their products to increase the shelf life by a marginal amount. For instance, many brands of oily foods contain synthetic rancidity preventives, whereas competing brands do not. In some areas of the country, meat packers coat their hot dogs with an artificial coloring to make them bright red. In all these cases the benefits that the consumer derives from the additives are trivial, and the additives may be introducing small risks into our food.

In the past few years, with one controversy after another focusing critical attention on the FDA, consumer confidence in an agency whose principal mission is to safeguard our food supply was impaired. In part, this lack of confidence has been based on misunderstandings of testing procedures. But to some extent the lack of public confidence stemmed from what appeared to be arbitrary rulings. A number of additives, for example, were eventually removed from the GRAS list only after protracted pressure from scientists and consumer organizations, even though the results of the tests raised serious doubts about the additives' safety. Such demonstrations of reluctance to ban additives of doubtful benefit to the consumer—as well as some which might indeed be unsafe—could only result in widespread anxiety over all FDA rulings. These doubts were exacerbated by the extremists who contended that every food additive was dangerous and that Americans were systematically being poisoned by food producers.

FRESH ACTION BY THE FDA

The FDA's increased activities in 1972 were helping to restore the public's confidence and clear up some of these confusions. But more than firm and rational policing by the FDA is needed to assure a plentiful supply of healthy foods. Food additives are similar in one important respect to computers, rockets and the other technological achievements of our day: they offer great benefits if used wisely, but can cause harm if used improperly. Additives can save time, money and protect everyone's health when used judiciously. Used unwisely they entail unnecessary health risks. Thoughtful buying habits on the part of shoppers, plus vigorous citizen contribution to the government's decision-making processes, will help ensure that additives serve the public's needs in the safest and most beneficial manner.

Worthless mountains of cyclamate-sweetened canned fruit fill a Stockton, California, warehouse. Canners and growers, their products made unsalable by a ban on cyclamates, may be reimbursed under a law proposed in 1971.

HALVES Y.C. PEACHES
24-303
0274-24
LOW CALORIE
Diet Delight
CALIFORNIA CANNERS and GROWERS • SAN FRANCISCO, CALIFORNIA
HALVES Y.C. PEACHES
24-303
0274-24
LOW CALORIE
Diet Delight
HALVES Y.C. PEACHES
LOW CALORIE
Diet Delight
CALIFORNIA CANNERS and GROWERS • SAN FRANCISCO, CALIFORNIA
HALVES Y.C. PEACHES
0274-24
24-303

Remaking the Map of Mars

In the first eight months of 1972 astronomers learned more about the planet Mars than they had discovered in the whole previous history of their science. The source of this revelation was Mariner 9, the first space satellite to circumnavigate Mars and the first to go within 1,200 miles of the mysterious planet.

What little the astronomers had surmised of Mars previously had led them to expect a dry, moribund, moonlike wasteland pockmarked by meteor craters. Much of Mars is indeed like that. But as Mariner's photographs were pieced together into composite photomaps *(pages 64-65)*, they revealed such spectacular features as a volcano that dwarfs Mount Everest, a gorge with 10 times the expanse of the Grand Canyon, a number of what appear to be dried riverbeds and massive polar ice caps—altogether a lot of dramatic scenery for a planet half the size of Earth.

The riverlike shapes astonished astronomers because the present Martian atmosphere could not support water: there is not enough pressure to keep it from vaporizing. But Mariner's evidence indicates that water did once flow through the canyons and gullies of Mars. And in that case, some kind of life may have developed.

Mars has always been the most intriguing of the planets. A century ago the Italian astronomer Giovanni Schiaparelli declared that Mars was seamed by *canali.* The Italian word means channels or fissures, but English speakers assumed that he meant "canals," and drew fanciful maps of man-made Martian waterworks all over the planet *(right).* The new satellite pictures vindicate Schiaparelli: there are indeed *canali* etched into the Martian surface. And, taken with the volcanoes, they imply another surprise from Mariner's camera eye: far from being a dead planet, Mars may still be undergoing geological activity.

The "canals" of Mars were laid out in this map in 1903 by Percival Lowell, a Bostonian diplomat-turned-astronomer. Mistranslating Giovanni Schiaparelli's canali as "canals," Lowell laid down a crosshatch of waterways. In 1972 Mariner 9 confirmed that there are lines on Mars, but that they are fault cracks on the planet's surface.

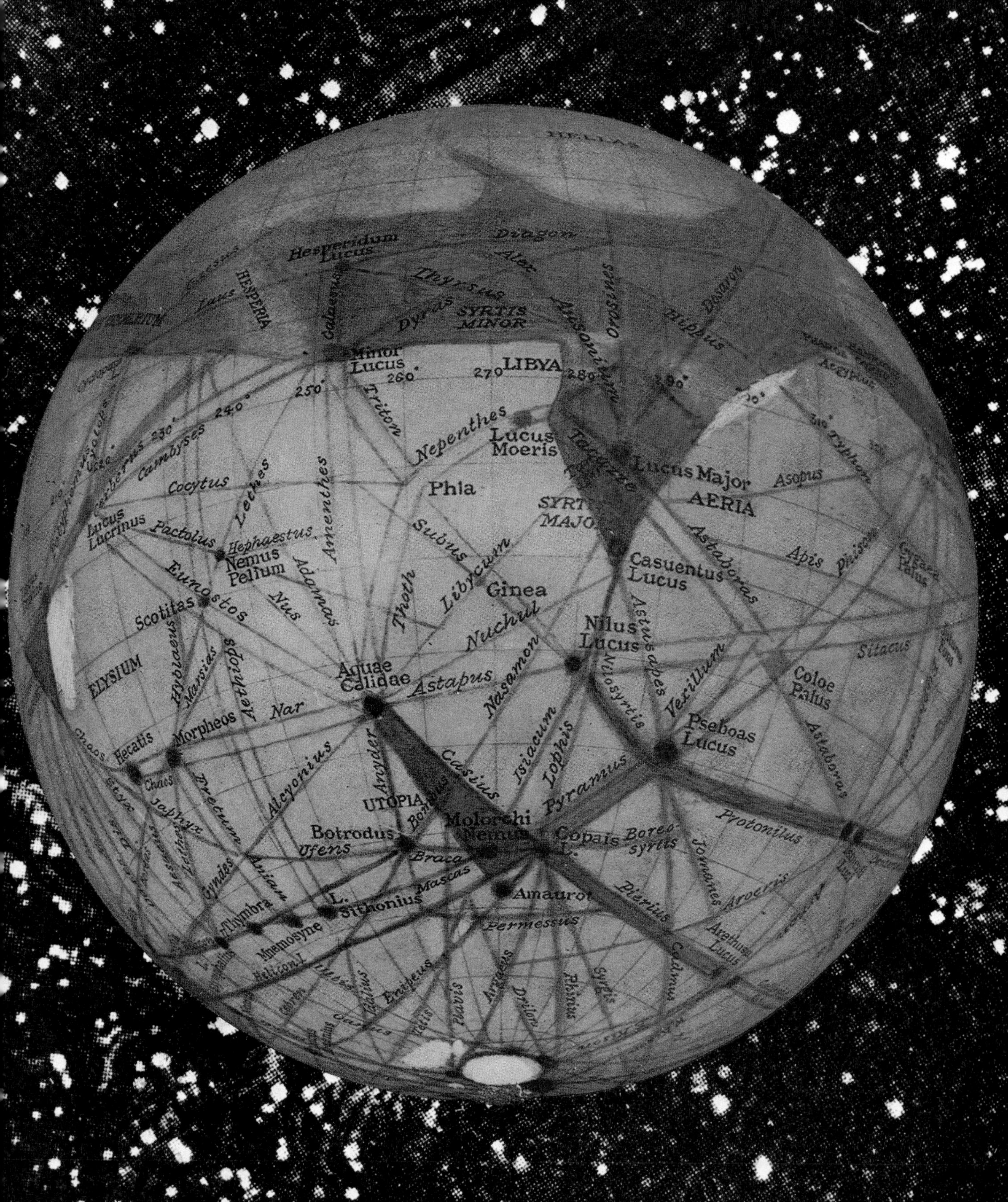
HELLAS
Hesperidum Lucus
HESPERIA
Dragon
Alex
Thyrsus
Dyras
SYRTIS MINOR
Ausonia
Hippus
Minor Lucus
LIBYA
260°
270
250°
240°
Triton
Nepenthes
Lucus Moeris
Cambyses
Cocytus
Lethes
Amenthes
Phla
Lucus Major
AERIA
Asopus
Lucus Lucrinus
Pactolus
Hephaestus
Nemus Pelium
Subus
Eunostos
Adamas
Thoth
Libycum
Ginea
Casuentus Lucus
Apis
Phison
Scotitas
Nus
Nuchul
Nilus Lucus
Astusapes
ELYSIUM
Hyblaeus
Aethiops
Aquae Calidae
Astapus
Nasamon
Nilosyrtis
Vexillum
Sitacus
Coloe Palus
Morpheos
Nar
Hecatis
Chaos
Alcyonius
Anyder
Casius
Isiacum
Lophis
Pseboas Lucus
Astaboras
UTOPIA
Pyramus
Protonilus
Botrodus
Molorchi Nemus
Copais L.
Boreosyrtis
Ufens
Braca
Mascas
Amaurot
Pierius
Sithonius
Mnemosyne
Permessus
Arethusa Lucus
Enipeus
Argaeus
Drilon
Rhenus
Cadmus

A Surface Charted by Camera

Covering every awesome kilometer of the surface of Mars, Mariner 9's cameras took enough photographs for scientists to make the first mosaic photomap of Mars *(below).* The map shows three distinct types of terrain. At left is a group of four huge volcanoes. The largest *(square)* is Nix Olympica; it is shown close-up on page 67. Toward the center of the map is a chain of canyons 2,500 miles long. One segment *(rectangle)* sprouts tributaries like earthly rivers, which are shown close-up on pages 68-69. The rest consists of meteor-cratered, moonlike wasteland.

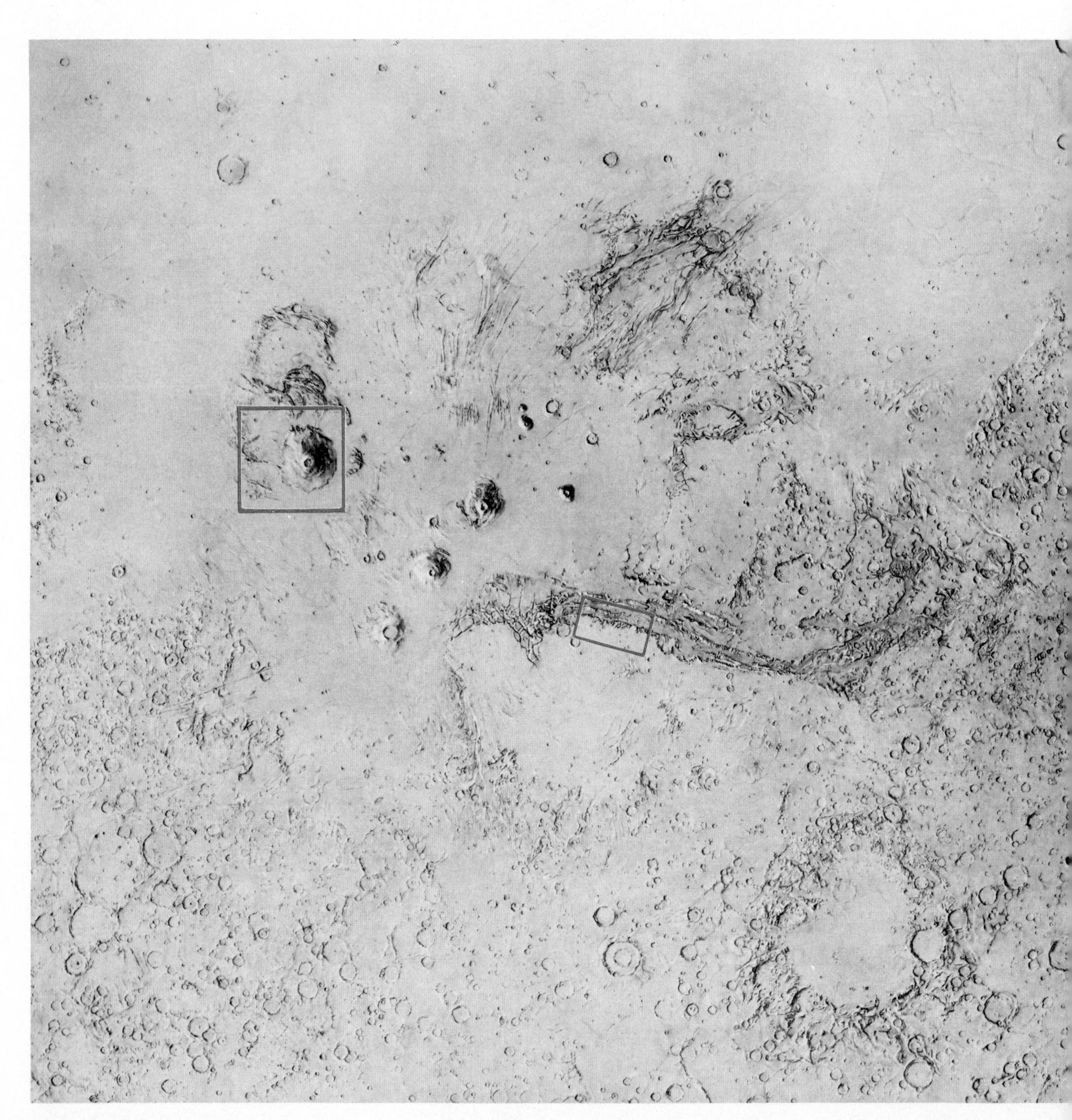

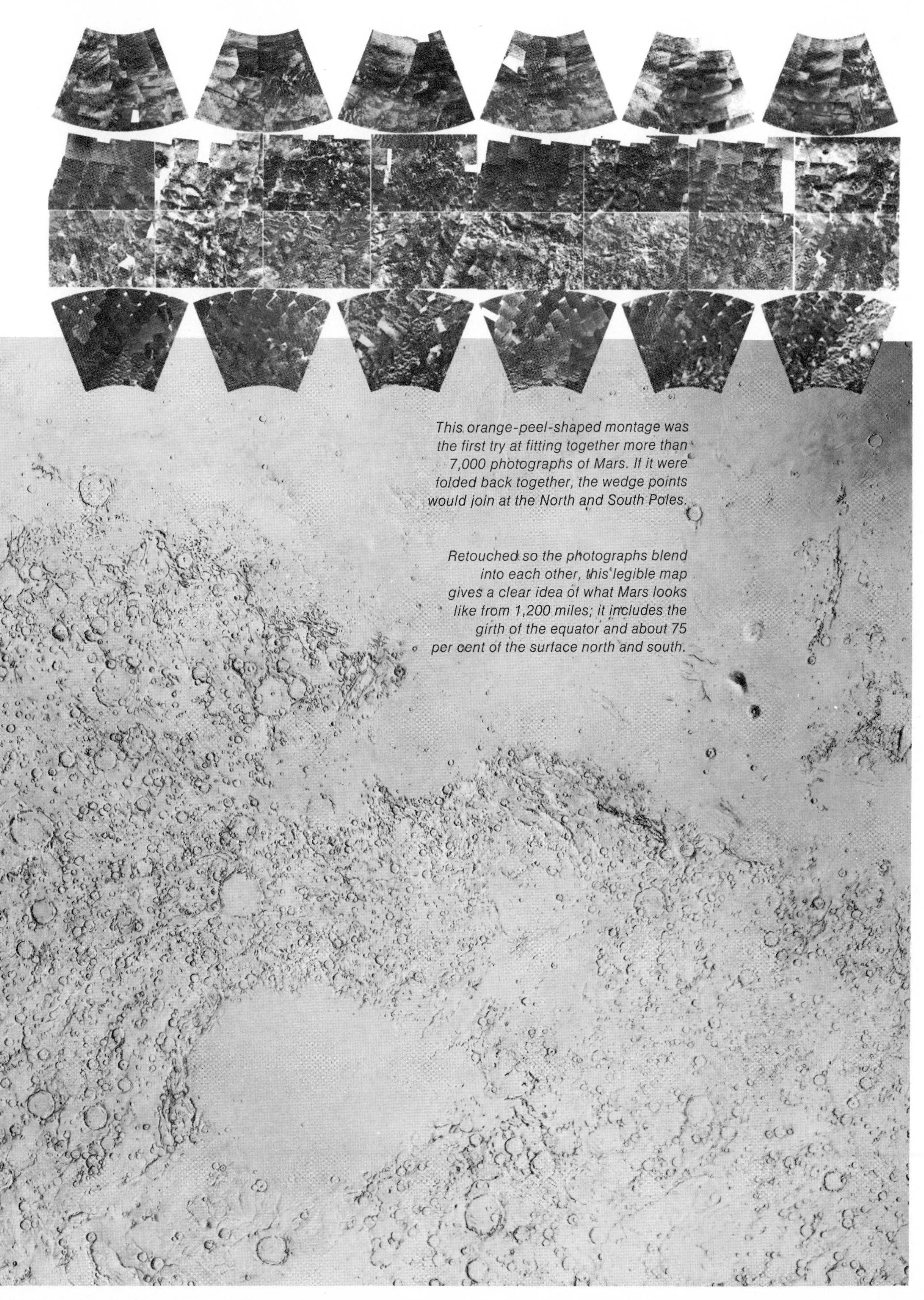

This orange-peel-shaped montage was the first try at fitting together more than 7,000 photographs of Mars. If it were folded back together, the wedge points would join at the North and South Poles.

Retouched so the photographs blend into each other, this legible map gives a clear idea of what Mars looks like from 1,200 miles; it includes the girth of the equator and about 75 per cent of the surface north and south.

A Martian Volcano Resembling Ours

So close and revealing have Mariner's photographs been that they have opened up a further field in investigating Mars. For the first time, scientists could study the resemblance of Martian characteristics to those of Earth, and thereby perhaps learn something about Mars from what we already know about similar aspects of our own globe. Nix Olympica (Olympian Snows), as Mars's main volcano *(opposite)* is called, bears remarkable similarity to volcanoes on Earth, except that it is much taller and wider. At 40,000 feet, it stands higher than Everest, our tallest mountain. Its 310-mile base is twice as broad as the 140-mile base of the volcano that formed the Hawaiian Islands, and its 40-mile crater is six and a half times as large as Crater Lake in Oregon.

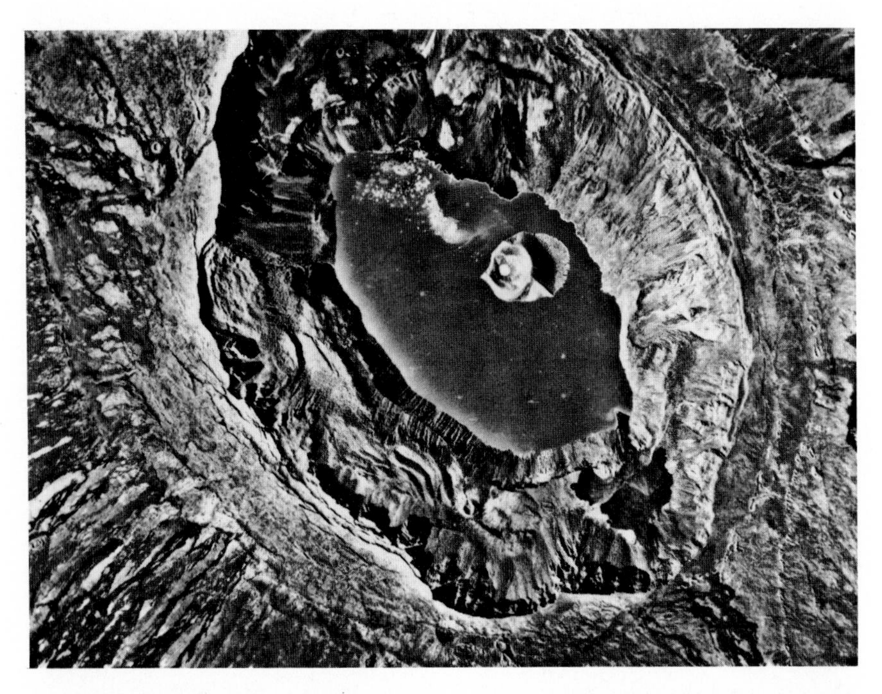

On Earth, the Fernandina volcano in the Galápagos Islands looks like a miniature Nix Olympica; but its crater is only one tenth as wide. Earth's atmosphere and oceans may have been created by primordial volcanoes that belched carbon dioxide and water vapor from the globe's hot center.

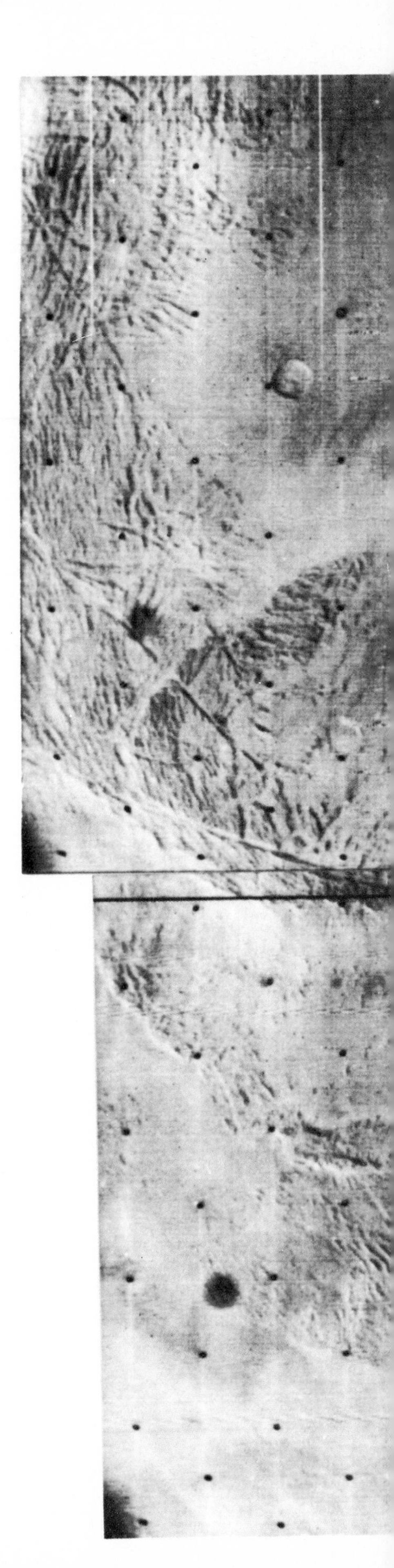

The crater at the summit of Mars's Nix Olympica (right), 40 miles across, is apparently no longer active; but unmarred lava flow on the slopes below the crater's lip suggests that Nix Olympica may have erupted not too long ago. If so, Mars could be at the early stages of primordial life.

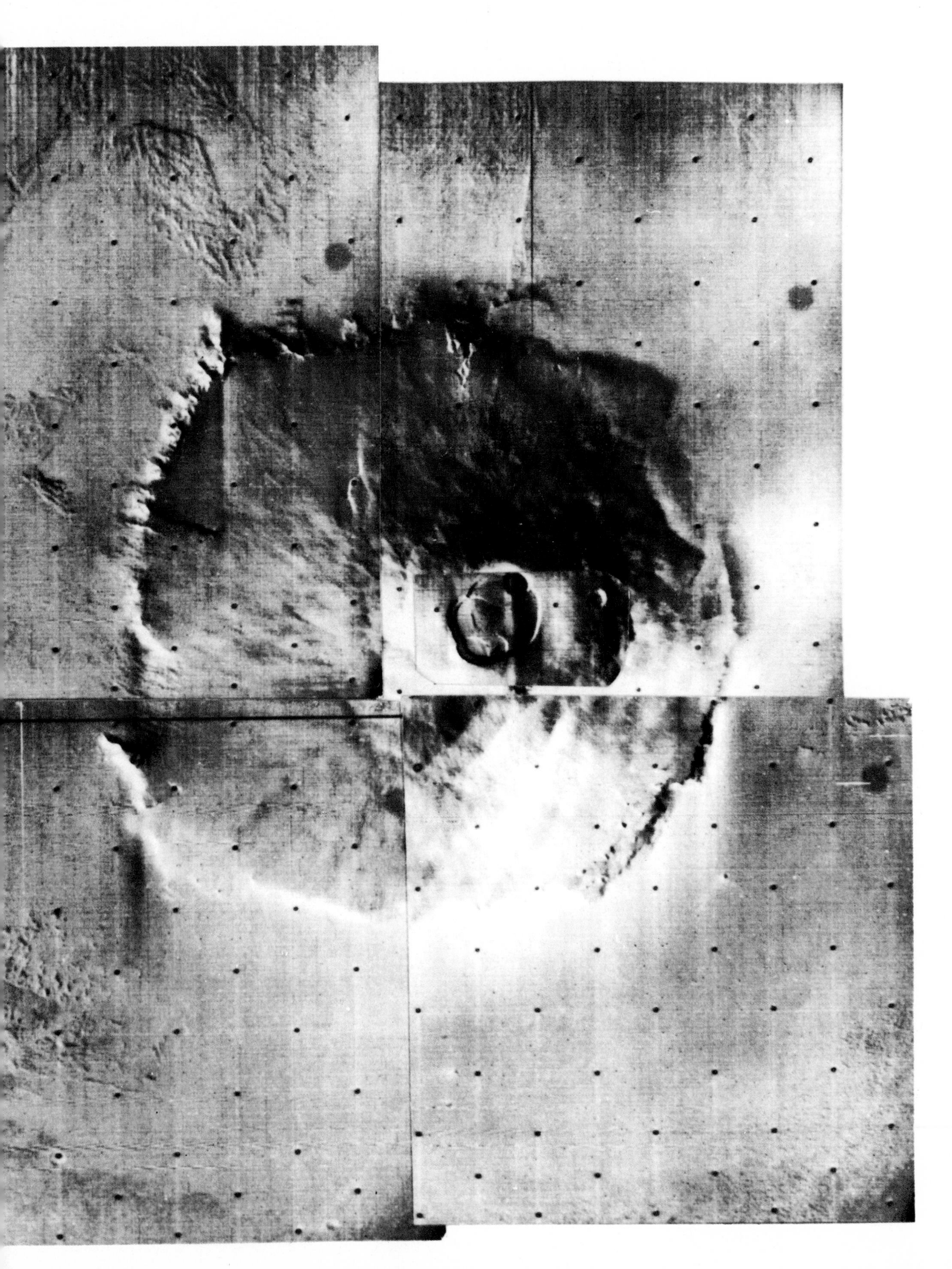

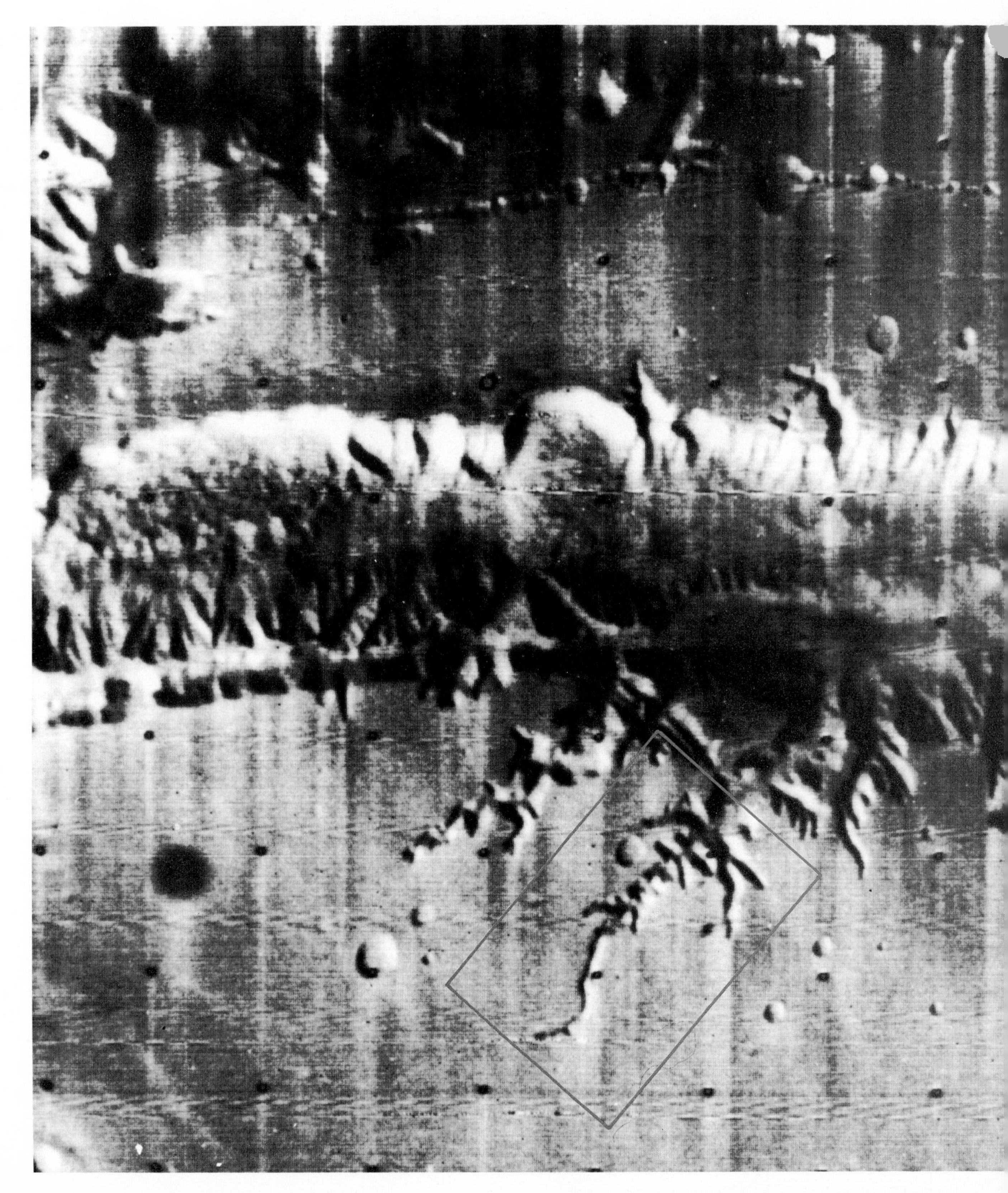

A Gorge with Earthlike Riverbeds

Vast chasms with branching canyons slash the Martian plateau from the slopes of Nix Olympica eastward for 2,500 miles. This Martian rift system was undoubtedly formed by geological shifting and straining. But were its canyon tributaries formed by water like the canyons and deep rivers on Earth? Their form suggests as much, for the tributaries resemble earthly rivers: one of the branches *(rectangle, left)* bears a remarkable resemblance to the salamander-shaped River Volta that meanders across West Africa to the Gold Coast *(below).* Water is not the only possible explanation for how the tributaries were formed; geological activity could have opened up faults that split the plateau. In either case, the 9,500-foot-deep canyon is proof that Mars is by no means a long-dead planet.

◀ *Fingering out from the edges of the Martian rift (left) is an intricate network of tributaries that look precisely like the water-cut arroyos of the U.S. Southwest. One offshoot (rectangle) is a near look-alike of the River Volta in West Africa (above).*

The waters of the River Volta (above) flow for some 800 miles across West Africa toward the Gold Coast. The Volta's resemblance to the Martian tributaries may be of help to scientists in solving some of the mysteries of those intriguing canyons.

Next: A Search for Life

That age-old question has arisen again because of Mariner's discoveries: there may be—or there may have been—life on Mars. Mariner 9's photographs have convinced astronomers of the possibility that some sort of life could have existed, and may still be hibernating, on the planet. It would almost certainly be bacteria, but it would be different from anything on Earth. The mere possibility that Mars is not another barren planet excites the scientists. As one astronomer put it: "Anyone who says he isn't astonished is a liar."

The task of confirming this conjecture by searching for some trace of life will fall to Project Viking, whose initial launch is scheduled for 1976—a soft landing of two robots, equipped with life-detecting sensors. Two space vehicles will carry them to Mars and they will circle the planet for as long as a month until promising landing zones are found.

The greatest unknown in speculation about life on Mars has always been the question of whether there is water there, water being a prerequisite for the formation of life. Astronomers know now that water did exist on Mars, possibly in large quantities. But it cannot exist there now in liquid form because of the thin Martian atmosphere in which water would evaporate. But it must have been there once: Mariner 9 photographs show clouds and polar ice masses *(right),* which could not form without water.

Many of the scientists studying the photographs taken by Mariner are now convinced that a lot of water may be trapped underground, as in Alaska's permafrost. Some of Mars's surface features appear to be the result of water erosion. Perhaps there was a time when there was surface water, and when life flourished on Mars. This theory has posed a fascinating question for the Viking probes to answer. If life existed in some distant past, one must of course look for fossils, and the near consensus is that the fossils will be those of very tiny organisms. But there is at least one member of the Viking team who has made the point that the forms of life most likely to survive in a drying environment are those most capable of storing water, and he has, only half facetiously, admonished his colleagues to look for cacti and truffles.

But has life run its course on Mars, or is it only at its beginnings? Another intriguing Mariner discovery is the existence of the planet's volcanoes. Recent studies on the origin of life on Earth indicate that warm pools of water near volcanoes provided ideal conditions for the first stirrings of life some four billion years ago. Scientists believe that the volcanoes on Mars are recent, relatively speaking. They appear only on one side of the planet, suggesting that it has just recently begun to heat up and is still exuding its heat in a haphazard fashion. Thus it may be possible that Mars is just approaching the conditions that are favorable to the birth of life.

Meanwhile, the planning for the Viking program is beginning to read like a story by Jules Verne. The program calls for two spacecraft to circumnavigate Mars and to send down two 2,200-pound robot landing craft carrying at least four experiments specifically designed to hunt for life. One experiment will consist of trying to determine if a pinch of Martian dust can absorb carbon dioxide, as only the plants on Earth do. In a second experiment, some radioactive "food" will be sprinkled on a soil sample, to see if any radioactive excrement is passed—indicating a "feeding" process of some microscopic organism. In a third test, half a teaspoon of Martian soil will be put in distilled water, on the chance that the water will cloud up as organisms multiply, just as happens in spoiled soup. Finally, a fourth experiment will employ a small amount of what is considered a basic "diet"—vitamins, minerals and some 40 to 50 organic nutrients. A soil sample from Mars will be put into this mixture and watched for any discharge of gases that could result from the ingestion of this banquet by any animal forms present in the soil.

The Viking launch and these experiments are still at least three years away, and the plans are continually being revised in light of the latest discoveries from the Mariner pictures. But what understandably excites the astronomers is the realization that however dramatic the reports from Mariner, those from Viking may be still more astonishing: we may then be witnessing on Mars, if only vicariously and by example, the beginnings—or the end—of life on Earth.

Evidence that there must at some time have been life-sustaining water on Mars is indicated by this Mariner photograph of the Martian South Pole covered with ice —frozen water and frozen carbon dioxide. At present Martian summers (with noontime equatorial temperatures as high as 80° F.) melt some of the ice, which promptly evaporates. But the planet may have sustained free-flowing water in the past—or might in the future.

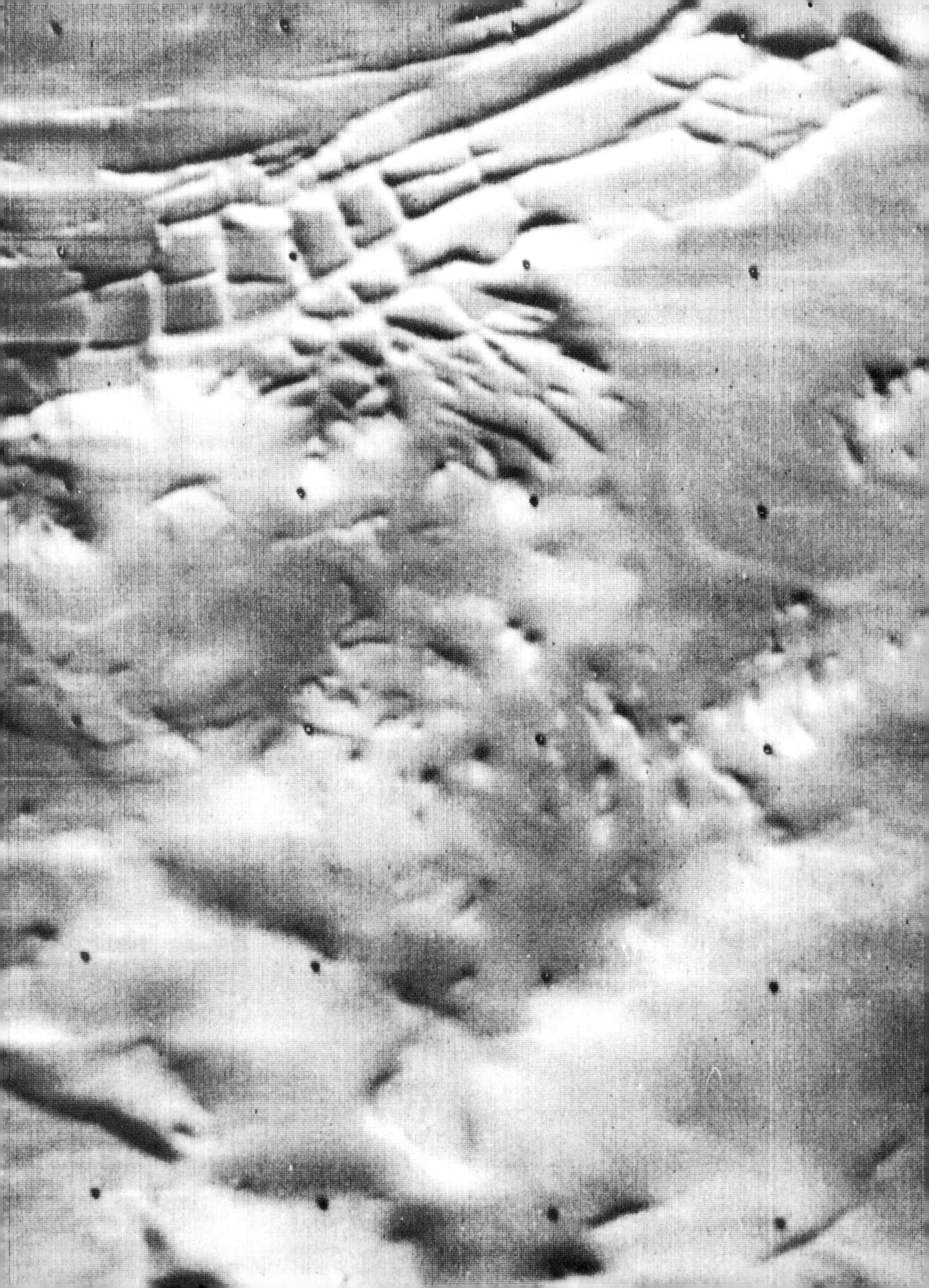

A Tree That Rewrote History

PINE RINGS REVEAL WHERE A DATING METHOD WENT WRONG

by Edward Kern

In October of 1972 about 100 scientists and scholars gathered in Lower Hutt, New Zealand, to ponder a most bizarre turn of events in the field of archeology. One subject for discussion was as important as any could be to that branch of science: how to put an accurate date on an archeological find. And what made the problem bizarre was that when a highly sophisticated method of dating had been cast into doubt it was later reaffirmed not by an even more sophisticated method of measurement, but by one more usually associated with campers and Boy Scouts: counting tree rings.

The scientific method under question is the carbon-14 process of dating; and the newer, evidently more accurate, clock is an ungainly species of tree called the bristlecone pine. This tree appears not only to have helped in solving a decades-old archeological mystery, but in the process it has also upset one of the major hypotheses of Western history.

The hypothesis is known as the diffusionist theory, which has argued for nearly a century that the course of ancient civilization traveled from east to west from Egypt and Mesopotamia to Western Europe. The theory, which depends on surface resemblances between major Eastern and Western monuments, seemed to be supported by carbon-14 dating, which indicated that the Western examples had indeed been built later than their supposed Eastern prototypes. But now the evidence derived from the bristlecone pine's tree rings is that the majority of the Western monuments were built before the Eastern examples they presumably were imitating; thus the diffusionist theory appears to be disproved,

With massive roots, ravaged trunks and scraggly foliage, bristlecone pines of California's White Mountains look their age—as old as 4,600 years. Their annual growth rings provide a method of counting years back to check against other techniques for dating the human past.

and the history books will have to be rewritten.

The story starts in 1949 with Professor Willard F. Libby, then at the University of Chicago and now at the University of California at Los Angeles, and his discovery of the radioactive carbon method of dating long-dead matter. The method became known as carbon-14 dating because it is based on certain constants in the actions of carbon 14 that help make it a measuring tool.

Carbon 14 is formed as cosmic rays from outer space bombard the upper atmosphere, producing neutrons that are absorbed by atoms of nitrogen. The resulting carbon-14 atoms combine with oxygen to form carbon dioxide, which mixes with greater quantities of ordinary carbon dioxide dispersed throughout the earth's atmosphere and oceans. Carbon dioxide is taken up by all living things—by plants through the process of photosynthesis, and in turn by animals through the food chain. There is thus a metabolic exchange in which each organism maintains a steady level of carbon 14 about equal to that of the surrounding atmosphere. This exchange continues throughout the organism's life. But what makes carbon 14 a measuring device for archeology is that this exchange ceases at death. Thereafter the amount of carbon 14 in the organism begins to decrease, and it does so at a predictable, measurable rate.

The half-life of carbon 14 is about 5,730 years. This means that in 5,730 years 50 per cent of the carbon 14 that exists in an organism at its death will disintegrate. And half of the 50 per cent that remains after 5,730 years will disappear in the next 5,730 years—or 25 per cent of the original. It will take another 5,730 years for half of that remaining quarter to disintegrate, and so on. Theoretically, half of some infinitesimal amount of carbon 14 will remain forever; but for practical purposes, what is left is immeasurable after about 40,000 years.

The radiocarbon measurement process for any specimen, such as a piece of wood or bone, is a complicated one. First the specimen must be burned in order to convert its carbon content to carbon dioxide. The resulting gas is then run through an intricate measuring device in which the carbon-14 disintegration is counted and recorded over a period of time. From the amount of carbon 14 still present, scientists can determine how long ago the organism died: the less carbon 14, the older the specimen; that is, the longer ago it had died. Conversely, the more radiocarbon, the younger the specimen.

The carbon-14 method can best be applied only to things that once were alive (though some nonliving objects like certain kinds of rock contain carbon, and therefore can be dated). Most inorganic objects like tools or other artifacts do not contain carbon and have to be dated by other methods *(box, pages 80-81),* or indirectly through whatever organic remains are archeologically related to them. However, excavations normally yield quantities of such organic debris as bones, charcoal, grain seeds, rushes, twigs, and fibers of cloth and twine. These do reveal traces of carbon 14, thereby helping date whatever inorganic objects were associated with them in the archeological discovery.

SUPPORT FOR DIFFUSIONISM FROM CARBON 14

Carbon-14 dating helped establish the age of many relics from prehistoric times. It also appeared to support the diffusionist theory. Heretofore the evidence had mainly been superficial: the walls at the Iberian site of Los Millares closely resemble fortifications on the Aegean Islands; spiral decorations on the temples of Malta look remarkably like the motifs of the graves of Mycenae; the oldest recorded historical chronology was in Egypt rather than, say, Britain, so it was assumed that the Egyptians had a sophisticated civilization long before the Britons did; and so on. Now there were scientifically measured dates to indicate that yes, indeed, Spain's Los Millares was built after its Aegean counterpart, and the temples on Malta were about the same age as the Mycenaean graves.

There were, however, a few puzzling exceptions. Among the scores of megalithic tombs, for example, the carbon-14 dates appeared to be generally in order. There were a few tombs in Brittany that yielded dates in the neighborhood of 3400 B.C.; their supposed models in Crete could not possibly have been built before 2500 B.C. Similarly in Vinca, a center of the ancient

Balkan copper culture, carbon-14 dates came out at about 4000 B.C.—again at least a thousand years before Early Bronze Age Troy in the Near East, from which the Balkan culture was supposed to have been derived.

And there were some exceptions even more puzzling when radiocarbon dating was tested on Egyptian samples whose ages were already known. Carbon-14 dates seemed roughly correct for objects dated since 1000 B.C. But for objects older than 2000 B.C., carbon-14 dates turned out to be several centuries too recent. The chronology of ancient Egypt, unlike that of prehistoric Europe, is historically documented back to 3000 B.C. Its records include astronomical events recorded by the Egyptians themselves; lists of kings and dynasties preserved since ancient times; and a host of inscriptions. Together they appear to form a chronological backbone for early Egypt—and for Crete as well, whose contacts with Egypt were close and continuous. In disagreeing with the early Egyptian dates, the carbon-14 method seemed to be at odds with recorded history itself.

All these discrepancies refused to disappear even after the techniques of employing carbon-14 dating were refined and improved. If anything, the errors became more numerous and irreconcilable. In one frustrating experiment in 1960, Paul Damon of the University of Arizona used the latest equipment to examine some wood that came from the foundations of a very early Egyptian fortress, and produced a date that, according to all of the historical evidence, was 600 years too young.

It was now quite apparent that there was something fundamentally amiss with the carbon-14 dating method. Many archeologists stopped using radiocarbon dating altogether. Others continued to have samples tested but tended to use the results only when it suited them. "If a carbon-14 date supports our theories," said one archeologist, only half in jest, "we put it in the main text. If it does not entirely contradict them, we put it in a footnote. If it is completely 'out-of-date,' we just drop it."

Unlike the archeologists, the chemists and physicists were not so ready to give up, for the

The interior of a Mycenaean tomb (top) built about 1500 B.C. is a fine example of the distinctive igloolike masonry construction called corbeling. More than a thousand miles to the west, a grave (bottom) in Brittany, France, was built by men who used the same technique. Such similarities strongly suggested that cultural influences flowed from east to west—until a new dating method showed that the French site is actually older, by about 3,000 years.

carbon-14 method depends on some of the fundamental laws of physics. If there was a basic flaw, something was wrong with much of modern understanding of the universe. Such a catastrophe seemed unlikely. The faulty dates must have been caused by some unknown factor. To determine what it might be, the first step was to find out exactly where and how great the errors were. This would require a complete double-check on carbon-14 dates against any known dates or dating process, matching dates at regular intervals backward along the time scale. Thus it would be possible to see if there were any general pattern in carbon 14's erratic behavior, and from there perhaps go on to suggest a reason and a remedy. One of the approaches suggested was tree-ring dating.

HOW TO CHECK CARBON-14 DATES

Tree-ring dating, scientifically known as dendrochronology, depends on the familiar fact that some trees—especially conifers in the temperate zone—add a new growth layer around their trunks every year. What makes the dating of these layers, or rings, useful as a check against carbon 14 is the fact that only the outermost ring of a living tree is biologically alive and in possession of its full living quota of carbon 14. The rest of the rings are biologically dead; so their reservoirs of carbon 14 are decaying radioactively like those of any other dead organism. Thus any sample of wood from the interior of a living tree can be dated by two different methods: the carbon-14 method, and simply by counting the number of rings inward from the bark. Both techniques should produce the same age. If there is any discrepancy, presumably the fault is with the carbon-14 method, since so far there has not been a dispute over the fact that a tree adds a fresh growth ring every year.

The problem with using tree rings to check carbon 14, however, has been that few trees live long enough. The most useful tree, of course, had been the giant sequoia, which lives to be at least 3,200 years old. So, in the late '50s, the section of an old California sequoia was put to the test in getting the survey of carbon 14 underway. Samples of wood were extracted from a number of

C. W. Ferguson of the Laboratory of Tree-Ring Research at the University of Arizona twists a borer into a bristlecone to obtain a sample core. The core, more slender than a soda straw to avoid harm to the tree, reveals the pattern of annual rings when studied under magnification.

points along the radius of the stump and were tested simultaneously at three separate university radiocarbon laboratories in Europe—Cambridge, Copenhagen and Heidelberg.

The dates were published by the three laboratories in 1960. They were in close agreement, and they all showed a great many discrepancies between the carbon-14 dates and the dates that had been determined by counting the sequoia's rings. The carbon-14 dates were sometimes too young, sometimes too old. But with few exceptions the discrepancies, though numerous, were small. These new results fortified the suspicion, based on the previous experience with Egyptian samples, that the really large differences would be found in much earlier periods.

The sequoia carried the survey back to 650 A.D.—a good beginning but far short of the eras that were of primary concern to archeologists. How, then, could the chemists and physicists check the accuracy of carbon 14 back into prehistoric times? Enter the bristlecone pine.

It is a rare and strange-looking tree. Bristlecone pines are found mostly high in the remote White Mountains of east-central California. Their struggle to survive 10,000 feet up at the timber line has left them spavined and stunted. Winter gales have wasted their squat trunks and flayed their gaunt limbs into grotesque snags clawing at the sky. Certainly these trees look ancient; but it took the late Edmund Schulman of the University of Arizona's Laboratory of Tree-Ring Research to discover how ancient they really are. During a 1957 field trip in California, Schulman used a borer to extract several long, slender cores from the flank of one particularly gnarled bristlecone pine. He discovered on examining the rings that the tree was 4,600 years old—about a century older than the pyramids of Egypt.

THE BRISTLECONE PINE: A NEW YARDSTICK

The bristlecone pine thus became the world's oldest known living thing, and supposedly the perfect yardstick to use in checking carbon 14's earlier dates. But it was not to be quite that easy. The main reason was that the bristlecone pine tree grows very slowly; its rings are closely packed together in the slow-growing wood (in some cores more than 100 to an inch). A few, in fact, have been described by C. W. Ferguson, who was Schulman's field and laboratory assistant, as "small to the point of being absent."

There was, however, a way around this obstacle. Dendrochronologists can determine from the general patterns of tree rings what they cannot from rings that are "missing." Trees growing in the same region and under the same climatic conditions display nearly identical chronological, ever-varying patterns of wide and narrow rings, signifying wet and dry years. Details in this shared pattern may differ from tree to tree. But when a number of cores from different trees are

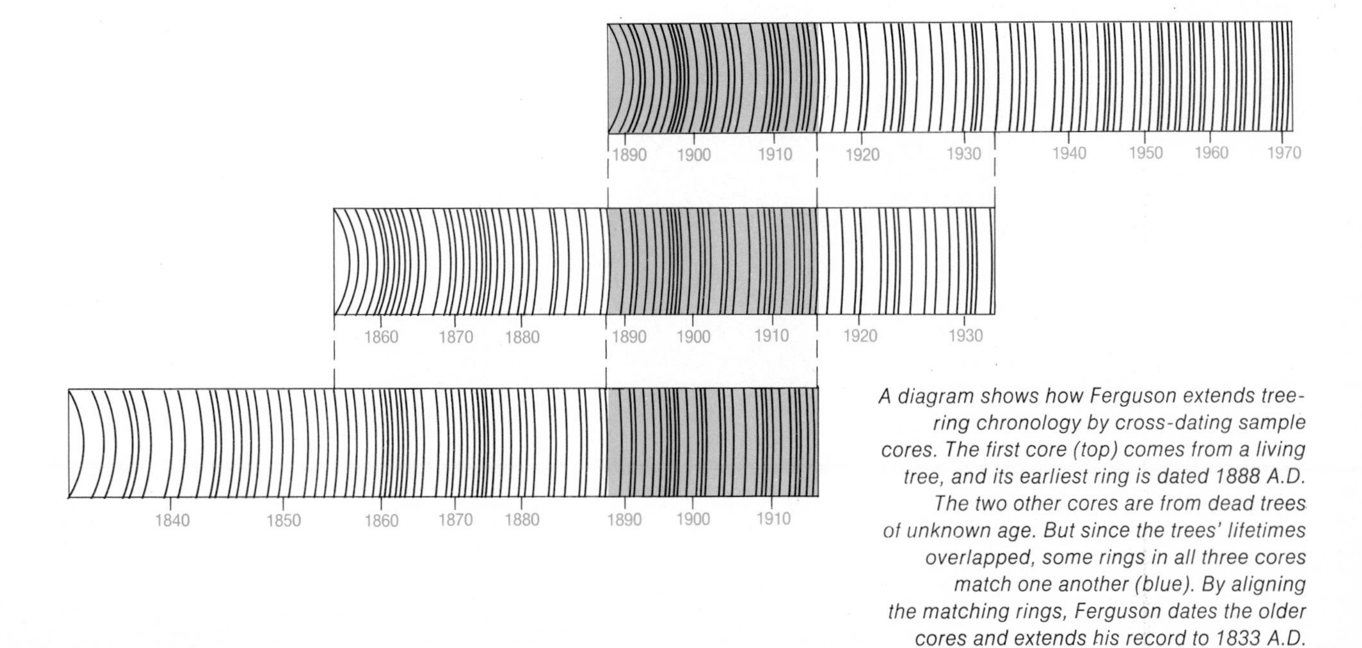

A diagram shows how Ferguson extends tree-ring chronology by cross-dating sample cores. The first core (top) comes from a living tree, and its earliest ring is dated 1888 A.D. The two other cores are from dead trees of unknown age. But since the trees' lifetimes overlapped, some rings in all three cores match one another (blue). By aligning the matching rings, Ferguson dates the older cores and extends his record to 1833 A.D.

laid side by side, the general pattern is immediately recognizable. And where patterns match, the more readable core can supply the information missing from the unreadable one.

So the bristlecone pine tree could be used to check carbon 14's earlier dates after all. But first the scientists had to assemble an accurate time chart of the bristlecone pine's rings. At the Arizona tree-ring laboratory this task has become a major undertaking that is still going on after nearly 20 years. It involves the compilation of a master chronology that is based on hundreds of cores taken from scores of bristlecones. As designed by C. W. Ferguson, the calendar is actually a computer print-out in the form of a continuous chart that represents the ring sequence in a theoretically perfect tree—a kind of Platonic ideal of a bristlecone pine. Every new specimen of bristlecone-pine wood that comes into the laboratory is matched against this master chart, both as a double-check on the accuracy of the chart itself and to correct errors and ambiguities in dating the rings of the new specimen.

At the same time that Ferguson was extending the master chronology back into the past with living trees, he was pushing his chart still further into prehistory by means of dead ones. Here again it was the telltale ring patterns that made it possible. To the extent that the life-spans of dead trees and living trees overlap, the ring patterns they share during that period can be correlated to show the time-span during which the long-dead trees once were alive. This technique of cross-dating has enabled Ferguson to extend his master calendar back beyond 6000 B.C. *(diagram, page 77).*

Ferguson's project has never suffered for lack of dead wood. Bristlecone-pine wood is highly resistant to rot, pests and even fire. It has survived for centuries in its arid environment, and the White Mountains of California are littered with stumps and fallen logs from trees that perished when many veterans now living were still in their remote infancy.

A MYSTERY SPECIMEN

One piece that Ferguson found is so ancient that its tree-ring patterns tally with no other specimen he has ever seen. So he has no way yet of verifying its age. But he has subjected the bristlecone specimen to radiocarbon analysis and the tests indicate that this venerable specimen must be approximately 9,000 years old. Ferguson believes that if he continues scouring the White Mountains, he may some day find additional pieces of dead bristlecone-pine wood whose rings will bridge the gap between the master chronology and the mystery specimen. If he succeeds, Ferguson thinks he has a good chance to carry the record back as far as 10,000 years.

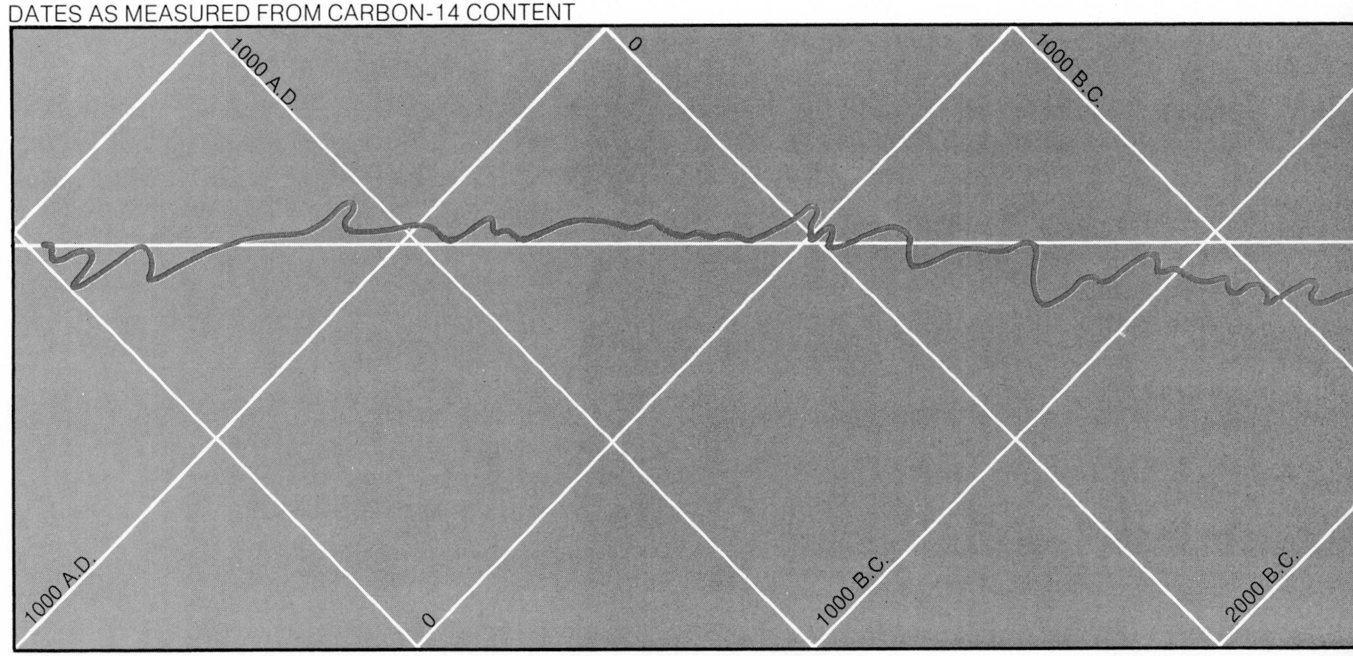

While the bristlecone pine's calendar was being compiled, the testing of carbon 14 continued uninterrupted. To provide a double-check on the method, Ferguson began sending out tree-ring samples for radiocarbon testing. Once again three different laboratories participated in the tests. This time it was the University of California in San Diego, the University of Pennsylvania and the University of Arizona.

The samples arrived in the form of chips, each ten rings wide, which were then splintered up, soaked in solvents to remove the thick resin, washed in distilled water and dried before the testing process. Hundreds of samples were measured in each laboratory: their carbon-14 dates and their true dates were systematically compared and recorded, decade by decade, starting with recent times and working back into the past.

It was a time-consuming and tedious process and—at a cost of $100 to $200 for each radiocarbon date supplied—enormously expensive. By 1962, Hans Suess, at the University of California in San Diego, had reached the start of the Christian era. By 1967 he had reached 3000 B.C. By 1969 he had worked his way back almost as far as Ferguson had got with his calendar: 5300 B.C. And in that year he was finally ready to produce a graph, or "calibration curve," at a radiocarbon conference in Uppsala, Sweden.

Suess's graph *(below)* shows the carbon-14

A calibration chart devised from studies of bristlecone pine tree rings by Hans Suess, Professor of Chemistry at the University of California, San Diego, corrects inaccuracies in the carbon-14 dating of ancient relics. The carbon-14 date—for instance, 2100 B.C. for Sneferu's pyramid—is worked on the top horizontal line, which is divided into thousand-year intervals. A slanting line is drawn downward to the right, paralleling the nearest grid line, until it meets the wriggly calibration curve; then another line is drawn downward to the left, again following the grid, to the horizontal line at the bottom. This point is the corrected date—for this pyramid, 2500 B.C., corresponding closely to historical evidence. Similarly, the carbon-14 date for the earliest period of Stonehenge, 2180 B.C., is corrected to 2600 B.C.; the 2500 B.C. date for the temples on Malta becomes about 3400 B.C.; and the megalithic tombs of Brittany, which had been carbon-dated at 3400 B.C., turn out to be still nearly a thousand years older.

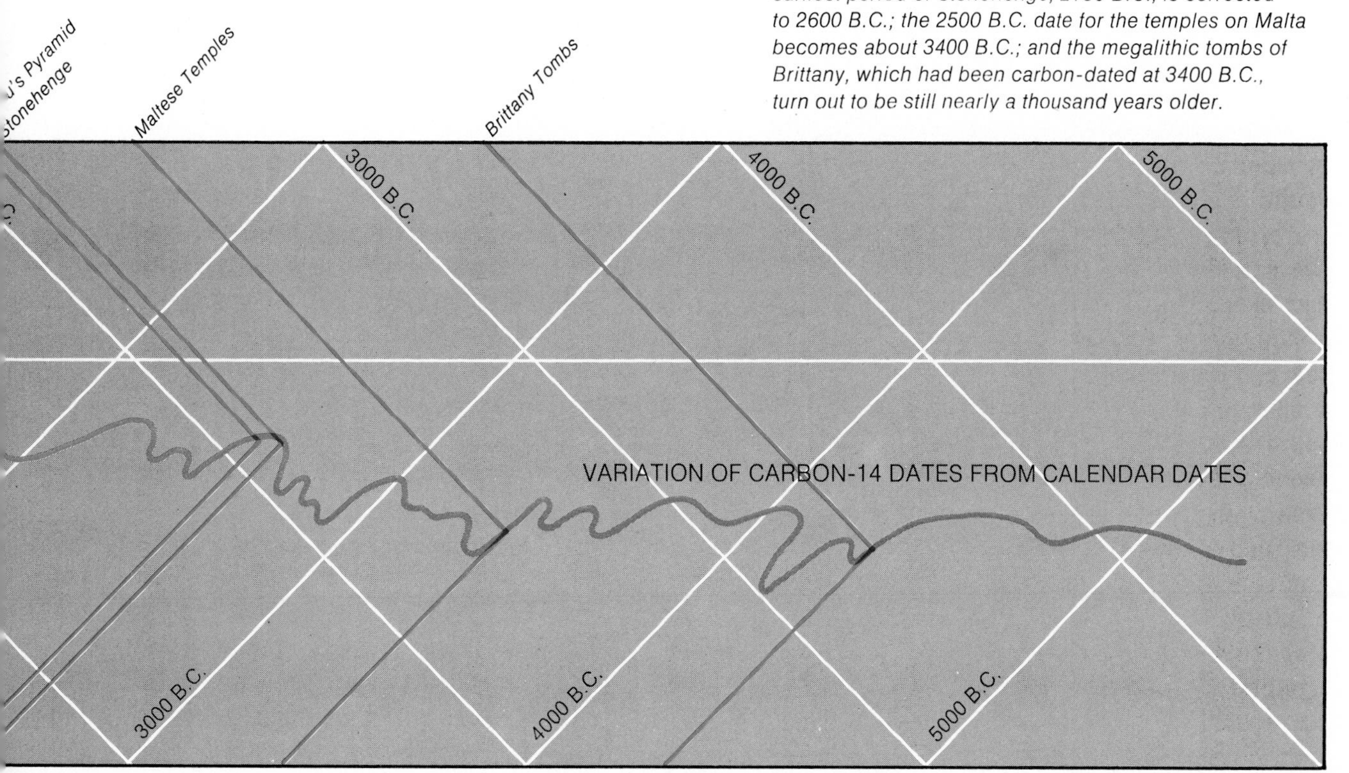

13 Ways to Tell Time Backwards

Fossils of man's ancestors, remains of lost civilizations, granite vestiges of the birth of the planet—the ages of nearly all of these mysterious discoveries can be told, thanks to a variety of techniques that tell time backwards, enabling archeologists to assign dates to relics of the past.

Of the 13 methods described below and in the chart opposite, the most useful are the so-called atomic clocks *(red on chart)*, whose "ticks" are precisely measurable transformations within atoms because they give fairly accurate dates for a wide range of materials, no matter where they are unearthed.

RADIOACTIVE DECAY CLOCKS

Carbon 14 is the best-known example of an atomic clock based upon radioactive decay. As described in the accompanying article, the element carbon 14 changes its atomic structure by the processes of radioactivity at a fixed, known rate—it "decays" into nitrogen 14. Other atomic clocks based upon radioactivity make use of the decay of potassium into argon, uranium into lead or rubidium into strontium.

The rate at which each of these elements decays is specified in terms of its "half life." In the case of carbon 14, half of a given amount decays in 5,730 years, half of the remainder decays in the next 5,730 years, and so on: its half life is thus 5,730 years. The other clock elements decay at much slower rates, so they can be used to date much older materials. Rubidium-strontium, a recently developed clock with a half life of 60 million years, has already been credited with dating the oldest existing rocks in the world: some granite from West Greenland that proved to be four billion years old.

FISSION TRACK

Fission track dating depends upon spontaneous splitting of atoms of the element uranium 238—a process similar to the one operating atomic-power plants—within certain natural glasses and minerals, such as quartz and zircon. The transformation leaves tiny scars in the material. By measuring the profusion of these scars, scientists are able to date the object accurately.

THERMOLUMINESCENCE

Thermoluminescence provides a clock that is dependent upon a transformation within certain atoms of the minerals that form clay. As clay is fired in the potter's kiln, the heat causes an unstable subatomic arrangement to settle into a more stable one. This process produces light; hence the name thermoluminescence. When the finished ceramic is removed from the kiln its atoms begin once again to return to the unstable form. This second process is the clock mechanism: when the archeologist finds the ancient ceramic and puts it into the fire again, the amount of light that is released lets him know how long the instability has been accumulating and thus how old the ceramic is.

Besides these atomic clocks, there are a variety of other dating techniques *(blue on chart)*.

TREE RINGS

One of the most widely observed of such phenomena is the addition of a new ring in a tree trunk with each year's growth. This regular annual process permits scientists to correlate the inner rings of young trees with the outer rings of old—or dead—trees. Thus, as the accompanying article points out, the tree rings of the bristlecone pine can be used not only for dating but for checking the accuracy of carbon-14 dates.

VARVES

A phenomenon strikingly similar to the growth of tree rings is the laying down, year by year, of varves. The word is Swedish and refers to the layers of sediment and silt in riverbeds and lake floors. The annual stacking of varves produces a sandwich effect which resembles, in cross section, a tree-ring sequence. The sediment of a varve itself—and anything that may have become embedded in it—can be dated simply by counting the number of varves above it.

STRATIGRAPHY

Yet another layering phenomenon that has long

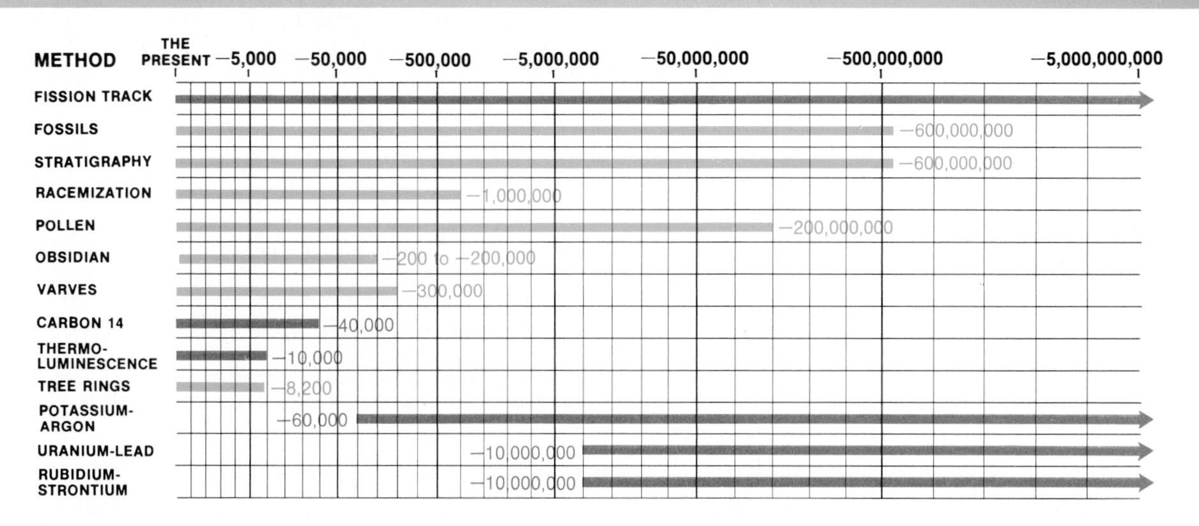

Major archeological dating methods are charted with the time-spans they gauge, ranging from the present to the birth of the planet. Those that depend on atomic processes are printed in red, those relying on other phenomena in blue. Each method has limitations as to what it can date directly. Carbon 14, for example, is generally used to date once-living organic matter, while thermoluminescence can date only inorganic clay.

been used as a dating technique is the sequence of sedimentary rocks. Tiers of geological strata in rock formations can be identified to give a rough idea of age. But since geological stratification does not occur at a fixed rate, this technique—known as stratigraphy—is not precise.

FOSSILS

Rocks can often be dated if they contain embedded within them fossils of once-living organisms. When such remains are found, and the period during which the organism flourished is known, the approximate age of the rock can be inferred.

POLLEN

In rocks, sediment or peat without fossil traces, grains of pollen are sometimes found. Botanists can associate various pollen types with the time-spans in which they flourished, and thus the objects in which they are embedded can be dated, again approximately.

OBSIDIAN

A more accurate dating technique, but one limited to objects and artifacts made of volcanic glass (called obsidian), is the measurement of water absorption. Since the rate of hydration in a given type of glass is fixed, the depth at which moisture can be detected in an obsidian arrowhead, for example, tells its age.

RACEMIZATION

Racemization is the newest dating technique, and a very precise one. It was announced in July 1972 at the University of California's Oceanographic Institute. Racemization depends on the peculiar behavior of amino acids—the building blocks of all living things—when they are subjected to light that is polarized, i.e., made to vibrate in one rather than all directions. If living amino acids are crystallized, they affect the polarization of an incoming beam of light by rotating it to the left. (For this reason, the molecules are called "left handed.") But when an organism dies, amino-acid crystals begin to realign, and as they do, incoming polarized light tends to be rotated to the right. This slow transformation into geometric mirror-image "right-handed" molecules is called racemization. Since the California scientists discovered that this journey through the looking glass takes about 60 million years before half of the left-handed molecules turn into right-handed ones, it serves as a new clock by which to tell when nearly any living thing died.

dates of the bristlecone-pine samples linked together in a continuous curve. The curve cuts across a horizontal line that indicates true dates. By noting how far the carbon-14 curve veers from the true date line at any point on the graph, scientists can tell at a glance whether and by how much carbon-14 dates are too early or too late. With this graph, the scientists were at last well on their way to solving the mystery of carbon 14's puzzling discrepancies.

What *did* cause these discrepancies in the first place? The answer seems to lie in the pattern of the discrepancies. From recent times back to around 500 B.C., the carbon-14 curve cleaves fairly closely to the true date line, wriggling back and forth across it. The discrepancies are frequent but small and they confirm the pattern discovered in the earlier survey with the old sequoia stump. But when the comparison extends beyond 3,000 years, the deviation becomes dramatic. The carbon-14 line diverges sharply from the true date line and departs farther from it as time recedes. By 2000 B.C., carbon-14 dates appear to be a couple of centuries too recent. By 3000 B.C., they are off by some 500 years. The error has grown to about 600 years by 4000 B.C. Between 4000 B.C. and 6000 B.C., carbon-14 dates are as much as 800 to 1,000 years too recent. What is more significant, the calibration curve shows that the original erratic carbon-14 dates that prompted the survey were not isolated instances. Just as the chemists and physicists had suspected, they were part of a long-range trend. And the scientists are now fairly certain that they know the reason for the trend and, accordingly, for the discrepancies.

The measurements, they believe, were thrown off because the test samples date back to an era when the global atmospheric level of carbon 14 was different from what it is today. Any organism living at a time when the atmospheric carbon-14 level was high would itself be proportionally rich in carbon 14 at the time of its death. Subsequent tests would therefore discover a relatively larger residue of carbon 14 and would result in a date for the specimen that would be misleadingly recent. Conversely, any specimen that came from an era deficient in atmospheric carbon 14 would have registered as too young. In short, carbon-14 deterioration—and carbon 14 used as a dating process—is constant. It was the original carbon-14 level that was not.

Thus the calibration chart also shows the relative changes in carbon-14 levels through the ages. The short-term squiggles of the calibration curve move back and forth across the true date line and appear throughout the chart, but the big long-term deviation starts at about 500 B.C. And what it indicates is that there must have been a larger amount of carbon 14 in the earth's atmosphere during that earlier period.

The carbon-14 method, then, had been supplying supposedly inaccurate dates not because it was a faulty clock. It had merely been measuring—in fact, quite accurately—the deterioration of a greater amount of carbon 14. The clock had simply been set wrong in some cases. The incorrect dates had resulted from the assumption that the atmospheric level of carbon 14 had been constant over the ages, at least during the past 50,000 years. The Suess calibration curve, however, offers definite evidence of past fluctuations—and at the same time provides the means of correcting for them.

WHY THE CARBON-14 CLOCK WENT WRONG

What caused the carbon-14 levels to rise and fall? Scientists are still theorizing. There seem to have been at least two conditions at work—one to produce the short-term squiggles, the other to account for the single huge long-term deviation. Suess and other scientists attribute the short-term squiggles directly or indirectly to rapid fluctuations in the sun's magnetic field and to the varying cycles of sunspot activity. Because cosmic rays are made up of charged particles, their impact on the outer atmosphere of the earth is modified by the strength of any magnetic field that gets in the way and tends to deflect them. Any increase in the fluctuations of the sun's magnetic field would tend to deflect the approaching cosmic rays, while a decrease would allow more of them to strike the earth's upper atmosphere and in the process create a greater amount of carbon 14. Moreover, astronomical records of the past activity of the sun seem to correlate with the squiggles on the calibration curve and thus lend credence to the theory.

There is also the possibility that short-term fluctuations may be caused by the earth's changing climate. Suess has suggested that solar activity might trigger both a climatic change and a fluctuation in the atmospheric level of carbon 14. There is also the possibility, suggested by some scientists, that the squiggles can be averaged out, perhaps by new computerized techniques, to produce a smooth curve and a revised calibration chart.

As for the long-term shift on Suess's chart, the Czech scientist Vaclav Bucha believes he has found the secret of this phenomenon—in the magnetic field of the earth itself. The source of this field, which surrounds the earth, is still not known but is thought to be linked with the earth's rotation. It is well known that this geomagnetic field has shifted in direction and intensity from time to time over the ages. There have been geological eras when the earth's magnetic poles have been completely reversed, as indicated by the incongruous magnetic alignment of iron oxide particles in rocks created during the period. Another indication that the earth's magnetic field shifts can be found preserved in magnetic iron oxide particles, such as those in the bricks used in the construction of ancient kilns. Iron oxide loses its magnetism under intense heat; as iron cools, its particles take on the direction and intensity of the surrounding magnetic field. The particles' magnetic alignment in the bricks thus reveals the direction and intensity of the earth's magnetic field when the kiln was fired and cooled for the last time.

On the basis of these and similar investigations involving ancient brick, tile, pottery shards, and wattle and daub, Bucha has managed to construct a curve that shows the earth's magnetic field intensity over the past 8,900 years, and the curve correlates to a remarkable degree with Suess's calibration chart for radiocarbon variations based on tree-ring dating.

Bucha has calculated the strength of the geomagnetic field of the earth over the past several thousand years, and he concludes that the field would have reached its nadir during the Fifth Millennium B.C.—about the very time, according to Suess's chart, when the atmosphere contained its highest concentration of carbon 14, causing the greatest inaccuracies in radiocarbon dates. Bucha theorizes that the level of carbon 14 in the atmosphere is directly related to the changing intensity of the geomagnetic field. If he is right, then the deviation should gradually diminish by 6000 B.C., and carbon-14 dates should once again be in agreement with true dates by about 10,000 B.C. This, of course, goes far beyond the present limits of Ferguson's bristlecone-pine calendar. But Suess's curve does appear to flatten out around 4500 B.C., as if preparing to turn upward again toward the true date line.

DOES CLIMATE AFFECT CARBON-14 DATES?

Scientists, too, are not dismissing the possibility that climate may in some way contribute to long-term fluctuations in carbon 14 by influencing the rate of exchange between the atmosphere and the oceans, which are the earth's two main reservoirs of carbon dioxide. When the ocean is cold, it releases less carbon dioxide into the atmosphere. As the ocean warms, proportionately greater amounts are released. Libby, however, considers this unlikely, since the climatic changes would have to be immensely large and last over long periods to affect the atmospheric levels of carbon 14 significantly. Other scientists, in turn, disagree with Libby; Paul Damon, for example, thinks that the climate may account for as much as 20 per cent of the observed fluctuation in carbon 14.

As the lengthy debate at the New Zealand radiocarbon conference in October indicated, the subject is still open to further investigation. Still, whatever the reason for its greater concentration, there is no longer any doubt that the radiocarbon content of the atmosphere has varied over the ages and the measurement of carbon-14 deterioration as a dating device has apparently been vindicated.

The biggest surprise of all in the correlation of carbon-14 dates with bristlecone-pine dates was the effect the new dates had on the diffusionist theory. For even when the proper allowances were made for greater concentrations of carbon

A leading critic of the diffusionist theory that Western culture traveled from the East is Britain's Colin Renfrew, shown here with some of the tools of his trade at the University of Sheffield, where he lectured in prehistory before going to the University of Southampton. As a graduate student, Renfrew became skeptical about the diffusionist claim that the prehistoric Spanish remains he was studying were influenced by the ancient Aegean culture, and his skepticism is now supported by the evidence provided by bristlecone-pine dating.

14 in the earlier periods, the carbon-14 dates, as corrected by comparison with those of the bristlecone-pine rings, indicated much more than ever before that many of the artifacts and monuments of Western civilization were built before those in the East that the diffusionists believed Western Europeans had copied. Furthermore, the more accurate dates have now reached beyond 5000 B.C., covering a great range of Europe's prehistoric cultures and monuments. Utilizing Suess's calibration chart, the Maltese temples come out at about 3400 B.C. *(pages 78-79),* far too early to have been influenced by Aegean styles of 1650 B.C. Instead, they evidently became the oldest freestanding monuments so far discovered. Stonehenge, whose first phase had been dated as late as 1800 B.C., now proves to be about eight centuries older, too early to have benefited from Eastern inspiration. Most of Western Europe's megalithic tombs are shown to have been built before 2500 B.C., long before their supposed Aegean prototypes. The tombs in Brittany, whose uncorrected radiocarbon dates had previously disturbed archeologists by appearing too ancient, now retreat still further, to before 4000 B.C. The copper culture at Vinca in the Balkans turns out, at 4500 B.C., to be more than 1,500 years older than the Early Bronze Age culture at Troy that was previously thought to have inspired it.

A CHRONOLOGICAL FAULT LINE

And as if to prove the proof of the bristlecone pine, the carbon-14 dates for Egypt, which had been too recent when uncorrected, now take a step backward to conform to the historical evidence. The Eastern chronology based on Egypt thus stands intact and unaffected by the new dating. But the diffusionists' carefully woven web of cross-cultural connections between the East and the West has been torn to shreds. British prehistorian Colin Renfrew, the leading antidiffusionist, likens the overall result to a geological upheaval, with prehistoric Europe displaced en bloc on one side of the fault line, and the Eastern Mediterranean world left undisturbed on the other side *(map, page 85).* The embarrassing task of rewriting history has just begun.

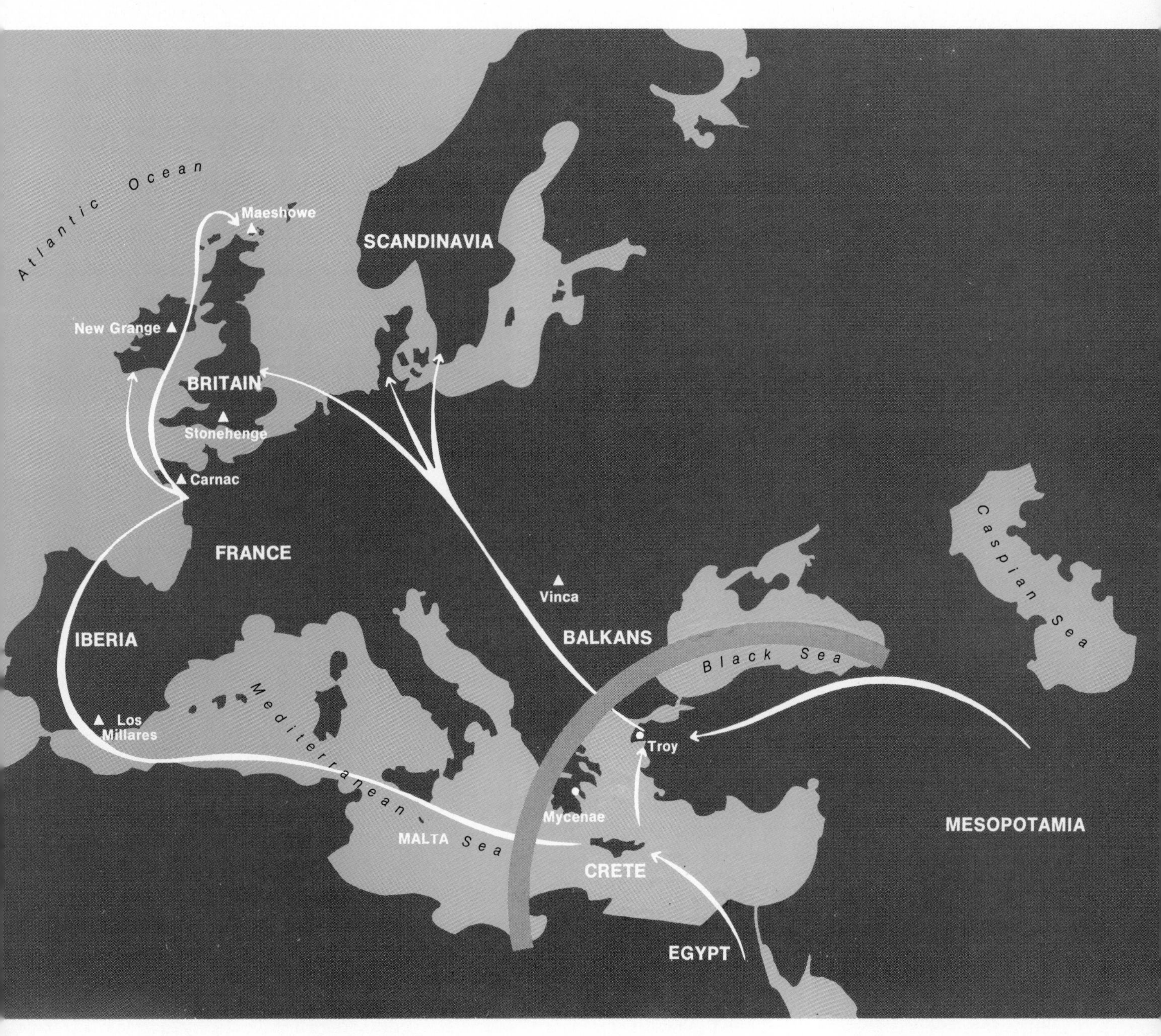

A map of Europe and the Middle East illustrates how civilization was supposed to have spread to Europe from origins in Egypt and Mesopotamia—the now discredited diffusionist theory, which seemed to be supported by carbon-14 dating but which was disproved when bristlecone-pine dating showed that some carbon-14 dates were off by hundreds of years. One of the routes of the presumed diffusion (arrows) followed the Mediterranean to Spain and extended to Brittany and Ireland.

Another route went up the Danube into central Europe, then to Britain and Scandinavia. But the newly corrected dates indicate that many of the artifacts of western European civilization were built before the Mideastern artifacts they resemble. The result, according to prehistorian Colin Renfrew, resembles a chronological fault line rupturing Europe's diffusionist link to the East. So, argues Renfrew, the Europeans must have developed most of their arts and skills on their own.

Indeed, the historians will have to rethink all their ideas about prehistoric Europeans: they turn out to have been far less barbarous than supposed; they evidently were capable of erecting elaborate temples and tombs, and of creating technically sophisticated societies long before the ancient Egyptians constructed the pyramids. There is, in fact, an ancillary bit of confirmation. Early European civilization had also been doubted because of the supposed illiteracy of these early people. Now even this long-standing assumption has been questioned, since archeologists have discovered, in scattered sites in the Balkans, clay tablets covered with mysterious incised symbols. They do not seem to be mere decorative designs, and scholars generally agree that they can only represent some primitive form of notation. The sites where they were found have been dated—by the carbon-14 and the tree-ring methods—at 5000 B.C. or earlier, a full 2,000 years before the oldest known form of writing in ancient Mesopotamia.

Have the tables been completely turned? Was Europe the leader rather than the follower on the path to civilization? Was it, in fact, Europe that originally inspired the East, instead of the other way around? Even though he disagrees with the diffusionists, Colin Renfrew does not go this far. It would, he says, merely "reverse the arrows on the diffusionist map." The truth, he believes, is that the monumental architecture, the smelting of copper and many other arts and crafts of early society were often discovered independently in different places and at different times.

Not least among the lessons learned from the bristlecone pine, according to Renfrew, is that it refutes the facile tendency to deduce historical connections from superficial but misleading resemblances. So the matter rests. That is, unless or until someone discovers that there is something very suspicious about those tree rings in the bristlecone pine.

The summer sun sets at Stonehenge, one of ancient Europe's most mysterious monuments, long thought to stem from Eastern origins. Revised dating, based on studies of bristlecone pines, now places the first stage of construction at 2600 B.C., far too early for Eastern influence—and makes Stonehenge a creation of the Europeans themselves.

Father of America's Parks

His name is hardly a household word, but in many of the major cities of North America, a family outing to the park is in effect a testimonial to the genius of Frederick Law Olmsted Sr., the creator of great public parks in Boston, Buffalo, Brooklyn, Rochester, Chicago, Detroit and Montreal. Such an outing would have been particularly appropriate in 1972, since it was the 150th anniversary of Olmsted's birth.

The first and greatest of Olmsted's string of parks is New York's Central Park, a haven of 840 green acres he landscaped foot by foot in the heart of Manhattan Island. Still very much as Olmsted designed it in the decade before the Civil War, Central Park reveals his prescient vision of the needs of a crowded modern city.

Olmsted foresaw the time when the park would be an island within an island, surrounded by "a continuous high wall of brick, stone, and marble" *(right).* He conceived of the park as an environment where city dwellers could enjoy, close at hand, a substitute for the open countryside. He mapped a plan *(pages 90-91)* that offered places for socializing and promenading, for play and recreation, and particularly for tranquil appreciation of water and woods.

Olmsted's creation was not a simple preservation of nature: when he conceived of the park, the land in the area was swampy and overgrown with brush. In effect he built a bit of nature, moving hills of earth, damming streams and draining swamps, and attending to the placement of more than four million trees, shrubs and vines. The project took 19 years. And today his Central Park remains a sylvan retreat from the city that has surged up around it.

High buildings rim Central Park's vine-covered rocks and trees today, just as Frederick Law Olmsted (inset) predicted in 1857 when he planned this refuge for urban man.

A Strip of Nature Artfully Planned

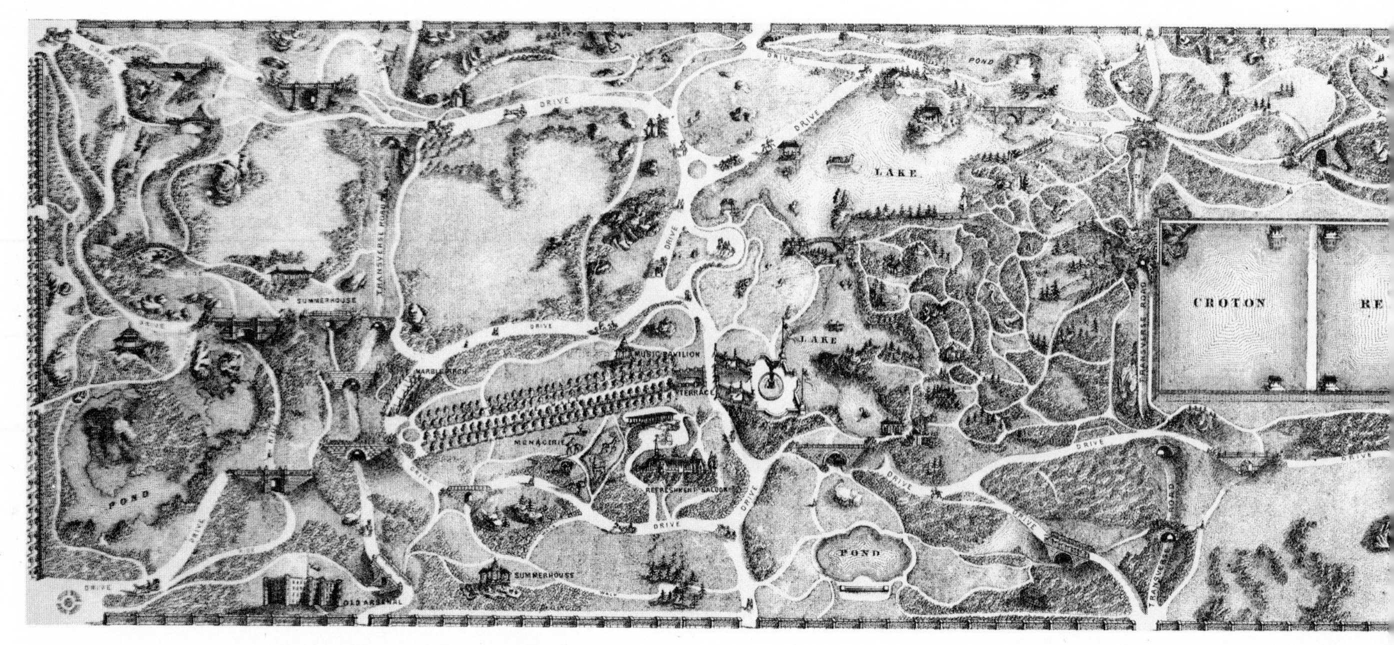

Olmsted's plan (above) was conceived in 1857 to make a "pleasure ground" of an unpromising one-half-by-two-and-a-half-mile stretch of real estate. His idea was to lead a walker from south to north (left to right) past a small pond (lower left) onto a long tree-lined mall (pages 92-93) climaxed by a terrace (pages 94-95) that gives out onto a large lake (page 96). He was forced to design around the old rectangular Croton Reservoir and to provide a larger basin as well. Beyond the lake he planned the thickly planted, most verdant areas of the park (pages 98-101).

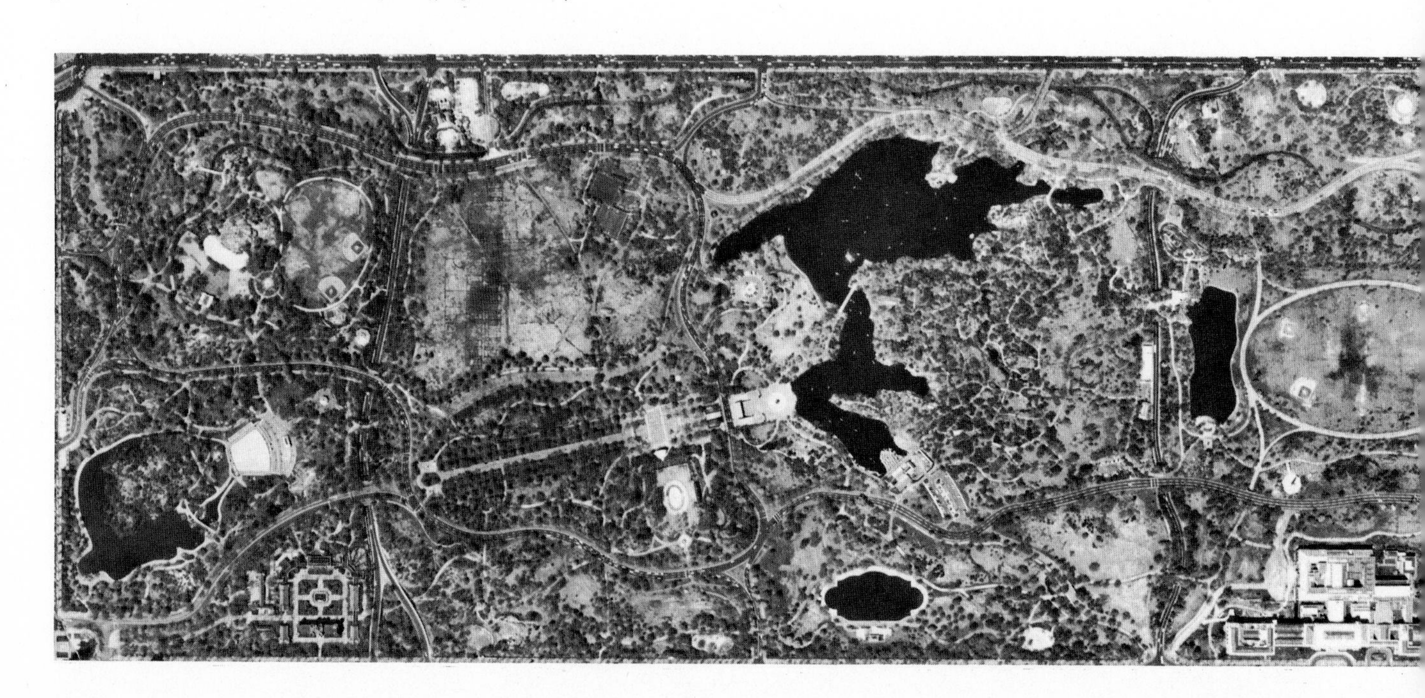

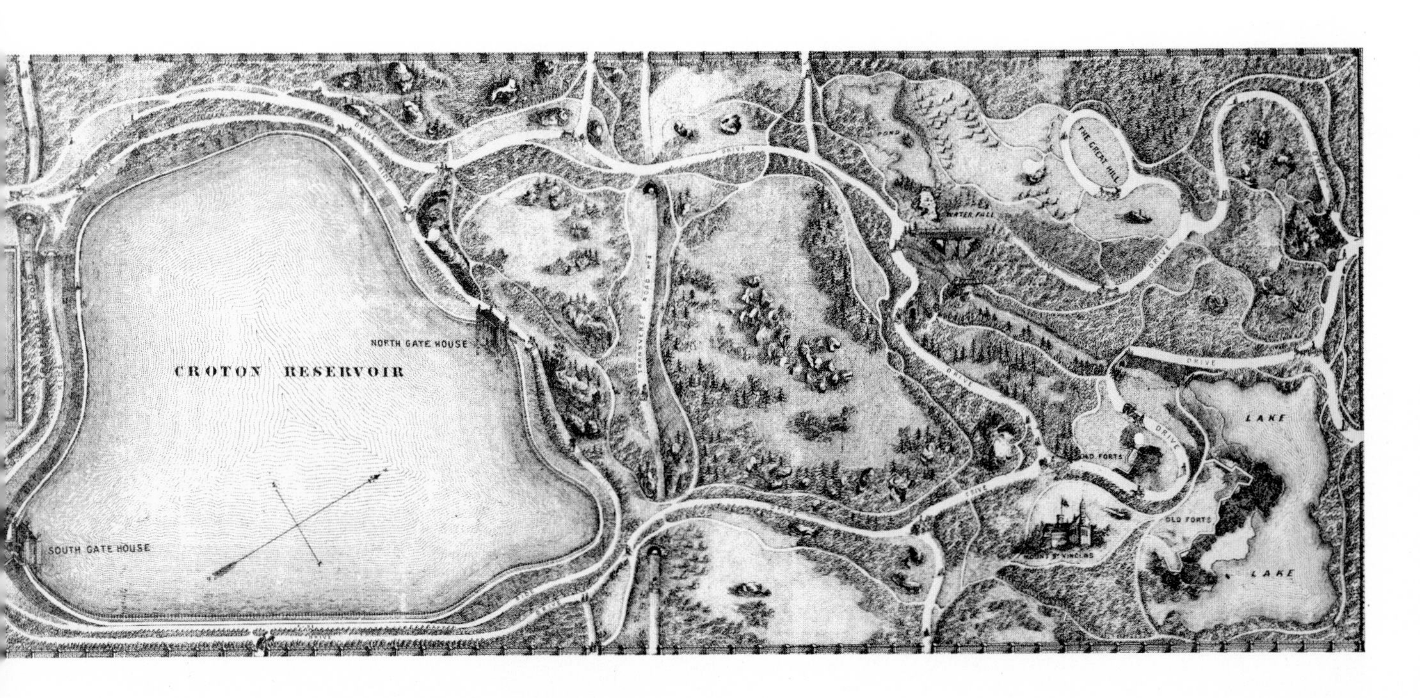

An aerial photograph (below) shows Central Park today, still much as Olmsted laid it out. The greatest change has been the filling in of the old reservoir to produce an oval playing field. Team games are now far more popular than in Olmsted's day, so many smaller grids and diamonds have been spotted around the park. Buildings, too, have encroached, notably the Metropolitan Museum (below the new oval field). Olmsted would not have approved; "Building can be brought within the business of the Park . . .," he wrote, "only as it will aid escape from building."

A Grand Mall for Promenading

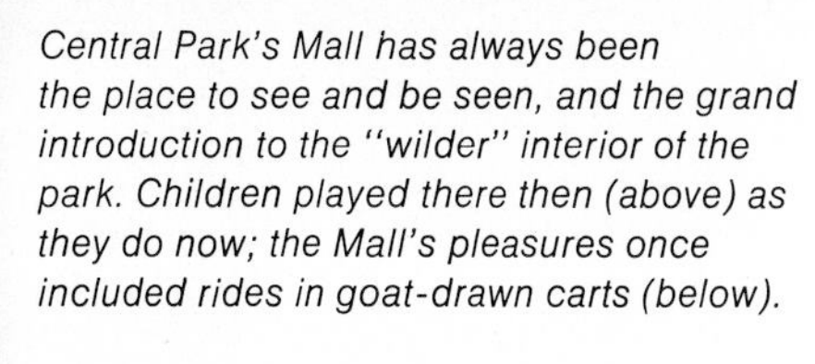

Central Park's Mall has always been the place to see and be seen, and the grand introduction to the "wilder" interior of the park. Children played there then (above) as they do now; the Mall's pleasures once included rides in goat-drawn carts (below).

At the end of the Mall, richly ornamented stairways descend to Bethesda Fountain, capped by "The Angel of the Waters," and the Lake beyond. In the past the focus of fashion (right), Olmsted's Terrace today (above) is a bit more plebeian, having suffered the addition of hot-dog stands and scrawled graffiti messages.

Olmsted's fellow artist Jacob Wrey Mould designed ornamentations for the soft stone of the Terrace (above).

An Open and Elegant Terrace

Man-Made Lake and Grotto

◀ *At the foot of the Terrace the Lake, which Olmsted had built, is one of the most popular parts of the park. In the last century (insets) swanboats rode on it in summer and skaters used it in winter. Today less elaborate rowboats move across its shimmering waters.*

The Cave (below) was once open and invited exploration; today timorous authorities have bricked it up (right).

On the north shore of the Lake is Olmsted's most intricately planned area: the Ramble. Planted with species native to the New York area, it attracts migrating birds, and shelters a variety of wildlife. The vegetation includes delicate Queen Anne's lace (left), inky cap mushrooms and tulip-tree blossoms.

Across the Lake a Walk in the Ramble

Turn-of-the-century New Yorkers prowl the paths of the Ramble, admiring the native plants and shrubs grouped in a man-made wilderness.

The pine warbler (left) is an early April regular in the Ramble, pausing on his annual northern migration. The squirrel is a permanent resident.

Pastoral Serenity in the Upper Park

The northernmost section of the park was designed on a more sweeping scale than the southern part. Olmsted gave it the look and feel of the countryside of his own time. He dammed a natural stream four times to create picturesque cascades (above). Today the stream has silted, but it still trickles through a vale of red oaks and white willows (right).

A wrought-iron bridge, designed by Olmsted's partner Vaux in a graceful lotus-petal style, allows walkers to cross easily over a sunken bridle path. The use of different elevations for different types of traffic was one of Olmsted's prime innovations. His sinking and screening of roads and paths help preserve the sweep and unity of the park.

Mind over Muscle

Rx FOR MIGRAINE, OTHER ILLS: A "THINKING" PROCESS

by Gerald Jonas

Rosemary Gianuzzi is almost completely paralyzed. As a consequence of a rare muscular disease that she contracted 11 years ago, she has no control over any of her skeletal muscles except those in her fingers, neck and face. Yet in the spring and summer of 1972, taking part in an experiment at New York City's Goldwater Memorial Hospital, Rosemary learned to control a set of muscles that most people cannot even sense, much less activate voluntarily—the mechanisms that regulate the rise and fall of blood pressure. Rosemary's remarkable feat of internal gymnastics will never, unfortunately, help her regain the use of her own paralyzed limbs. But it may speed the day when other people, suffering from such illnesses as chronic high blood pressure, will literally learn to heal themselves by controlling supposedly involuntary bodily functions.

Rosemary's teachers in blood-pressure control were Neal E. Miller, professor of physiological psychology at The Rockefeller University, New York, and his research associate, Barry Dworkin. They call the process visceral learning because it concerns the viscera—the organs and glands that normally operate without prompting from the conscious mind.

The notion that these organs and glands can be consciously controlled is not new. For centuries Eastern mystics have claimed the ability to order their internal bodily functions at will; and Western scientists are now corroborating those claims. Not only Miller's work, but a number of other research projects have shown that people with certain disorders can learn to control what goes on inside their bodies. All of these exper-

An attractive picture helps train a volunteer to regulate bodily functions once thought beyond conscious control. When he succeeds in lowering his blood pressure, the pleasing prospect of a lighthouse is briefly projected before him as a reward, to encourage further effort.

iments depend on training programs in which information on the state of internal functions —normally unknown to a human—is brought to the patient's attention.

The training used in these programs employs elaborate electronic monitoring and display devices that flash information to the patient in the form of colored lights, clicking sounds, fluctuating needles or pictures. Essentially, such training follows the same procedures as the trial-and-error tactics through which people learn to steer cars, carry tunes or place tennis balls with game-winning precision in the opposite court. The key to all trial-and-error learning is timely, reliable information about the consequences of one's actions. Without this knowledge a person can do nothing to improve his performance. With such information he can modify his performance, trying one thing and then another until he hits upon a successful response.

The information he gets thus influences his response—and this response in turn influences the information he gets, which further affects his next response. This circular process is known as feedback, and when used in visceral learning to influence biological functions, biofeedback.

In many learning situations feedback does not have to be very detailed. A person learning to sing does not have to know exactly how his vocal cords produce sounds of different pitch and timbre. All he needs is a clear indication of success or failure: he must be able to hear the sounds that issue from his throat.

But even this minimal consciousness of feedback is ordinarily missing when confronting the challenge of altering the performance of internal organs and glands. Where visceral functions are concerned, humans are totally in the dark—like a man, as Neal Miller puts it, trying to learn to play tennis at night with the lights off. All through the body small spontaneous biological adjustments are constantly taking place, adjustments that accommodate heart rate, body temperature and blood pressure to such things as changes in bodily posture, physical exertion or emotional stress. Yet normally, news of these biological adjustments never reaches the conscious levels of the brain, and most people faced with the need to make blood pressure go up or down would probably feel that they could not do it even if their lives depended on it.

It is this attitude that Neal Miller and many of his colleagues think may be out of date. Indeed, Miller himself believes that the traditional dividing line between "voluntary" and "involuntary" functions will begin to break down as medical technology reaches inside the body to reveal nature's own feedback system in a form that people can respond to. Miller believes that humans can learn to exert control directly upon the network of nerves that serves the so-called involuntary muscles. This is why Rosemary Gianuzzi was chosen as a subject. With her nearly total paralysis, Rosemary could engage in almost no "overt" muscular maneuvers to raise or lower her blood pressure.

CONTROLLING THE UNCONTROLLABLE

In the Goldwater experiment the feedback system devised by Miller and Dworkin employed a monitoring device no larger than a wrist watch. Strapped against the radial artery, on the underside of the wrist, it tracked fluctuations in the subject's blood pressure and passed this information along to a transducer that converted the alternations in blood pressure into electrical impulses. These impulses were then fed into an electronic programing system, from which they issued as a high-pitched humming sound. In Rosemary's case the feedback system was programed to emit a tone only when her pressure was at a certain predetermined level, and her instructions were simply "Keep the tone on." When she asked the natural question "What am I to do to keep it on?" she was told to concentrate on the tone, and let her brain and body do the rest.

In her initial training session, Rosemary's feedback machinery was set to produce its tone whenever her blood pressure increased. For 20 minutes the tone went off and on at more or less regular intervals, indicating the usual fluctuations in blood pressure. Then suddenly, as if her nervous system had figured out the game, the tone stayed on for over a minute as her blood pressure rose about one and a half times higher than normal. This was a much more dramatic re-

Neal E. Miller, a pioneer in the study of the control of internal, visceral functions, shows one of his special devices in a Rockefeller University laboratory. The instrument at the far left, a polygraph, measures the internal responses of rats confined in the cage at center.

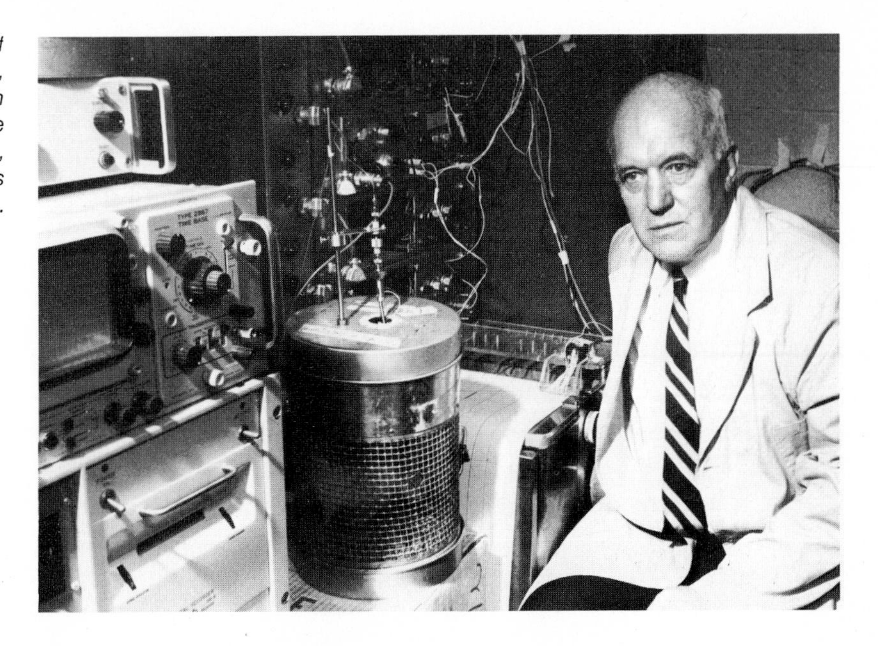

sponse than Miller and Dworkin had expected —and no one was more surprised than Rosemary herself. Asked to explain what she had done or how she had done it, she said she did not know.

Rosemary's feat in some ways resembles the kind of bodily control practiced by yogis, and scientists are well aware of the parallel. At the Menninger Foundation in Topeka, Kansas, for instance, psychologist Elmer E. Green has been working with an Indian yogi named Swami Rama as part of a far-ranging research program into unconventional methods of bodily control. Performing in a laboratory, monitored by a battery of instruments, the Swami has demonstrated that he can speed up his heart rate to five times its normal pace without moving any of his skeletal muscles or changing his breathing. He has also shown that he can produce a 10° difference in temperature between different parts of the palm of his hand. To do this, the Swami had to direct more blood to one side of his palm and less to the other by dilating one of the two arteries that feed the hand and by constricting the other.

When asked how he managed this remarkable degree of bodily control, the Swami, unlike Rosemary Gianuzzi, was able to supply an answer. He explained that he had spent 40 years educating himself. The first step toward such bodily control, he said, was to concentrate on what he called even breathing. He had practiced breathing slower and slower until he was able to take only one or two breaths a minute without any discomfort. For ordinary persons, such slow breathing is impossible because a respiratory rate as low as two breaths per minute causes the involuntary respiratory reflexes to cut in automatically to force air into the lungs, and no amount of conscious control can stop them. But the Swami had trained himself to approach this point very gradually, taking great care to exhale and inhale as smoothly as possible, so that he in effect could cross the border that separates voluntary and involuntary functions without alerting the reflex mechanisms. In this way he gained conscious control of such supposedly automatic functions of his body as breathing and arterial contraction.

Of course the fact that one or two yogis can learn to regulate the actions of their blood vessels does not prove that everyone can do so. After all, not everyone is able to learn to run the 100-yard dash in 10 seconds. Before Western scientists could be expected to take visceral learning seriously, they needed evidence that the talents of men like Swami Rama were not limited to a small population of "visceral athletes."

So far, the most convincing evidence that the

Swami Rama, an Indian yogi who can regulate his blood flow, heartbeat and brain-wave formation, lectures at the Menninger Foundation in Topeka, Kansas. The Swami's ability to exercise such control has given researchers an idea of man's potential for controlling his internal systems.

ability to master visceral learning is not a rare talent comes from a series of tests that Neal Miller and his associates conducted with white rats. These studies antedated the ones with Rosemary Gianuzzi, and in fact inspired Miller to test his theories on quadriplegic subjects like Rosemary. As a behavioral psychologist specializing in the learning process, Miller saw no reason why rats could not be taught to raise and lower their blood pressure, just as they have been taught to run through a maze or press a lever for a drink of water or a pellet of food. And if rats could learn to control their internal organs and glands, presumably men could too.

Miller knew that he could paralyze the rats so that no voluntary control could influence the result. If the rats did control internal organs, they would have managed some direct link between brain and organ.

Miller's experiment depended on the use of curare, the poison distilled by South American Indians from jungle plants. Curare completely paralyzes all the voluntary muscles of the limbs and torso, including the muscles used for breathing. Miller's rats had to be artificially respirated to keep them alive. But curare does not affect the five senses, and it does not interfere with the muscles that control the functions of the internal organs and glands.

In Miller's laboratory the deeply curarized rats were hooked up to monitoring devices that "rewarded" them for the correct visceral responses —by delivering an electrical impulse to the so-called pleasure centers of the rats' brains, for example. Not only did the rats learn to modify their blood pressure, but they also learned to modify their heart rates, their intestinal contractions, even the rates of urine formation in the kidneys. And in some cases the changes were large enough to suggest that visceral learning might have important medical applications.

While Miller was putting his curarized rats through their paces, other researchers were experimenting with the use of biofeedback techniques in the treatment of a variety of human ailments. Not surprisingly, a great deal of this research was focused on heart disease and high blood pressure, which together account for two out of five deaths in the United States every year.

The first indication that these techniques might be helpful in treating people with malfunctioning hearts came from an experiment conducted by Bernard Engel, a psychologist who is affiliated with the Baltimore City Hospitals and the National Institute of Child Health and Human Development. Engel was interested in patients with cardiac arrhythmias—irregularities in the normal pumping rhythm of the heart, out-of-step beating that in severe cases may lead to sudden death. In 1970, Engel and Theodore Weiss attempted to teach eight patients to stabilize their heart rates. In these patients the left ventricle of the heart, which normally expands and contracts about once a second, contracted prematurely. Some patients are conscious of the irregularity, reporting that it feels as if their hearts were "skipping a beat." But many patients are not, and Engel and Weiss proposed to help both types of patients deal with the malfunction.

REGULATING HEARTBEAT WITH COLORED LIGHTS

Formal training for the eight patients averaged out to about 30 sessions apiece; sessions were scheduled as often as three times a day, each session lasting about 80 minutes. The patient lay in a hospital bed, hooked into a standard electrocardiograph—a machine that tracks the rate of the heartbeat. The machine was connected to colored lights that registered green when the heart was too slow, red when it was too fast and yellow when it was beating normally. Initially the patients were asked to keep the yellow light on by forcing their hearts to beat slower or faster. Five of the eight patients succeeded—though there was no consistency in the way they said they did it. One patient speeded up his heart by thinking about "bouncing a rubber ball"; another thought about arguing with her children or running down a dark street. To slow down his heart, one patient reported that he just lay still and stared at the lights, while another explained that she thought about swinging back and forth on a swing.

During a second phase of the training the researchers rigged their lights to flash a special signal—red followed immediately by a burst of green—whenever the heartbeat was irregular. In this way Engel and Weiss hoped to draw the patient's attention to the faint but distinctive internal sensations that accompany an irregular heartbeat. With this information and the newly acquired ability to slow down or speed up his heart, the patient would then be able to correct irregularities whenever he felt them happening. The final stage of the training was to wean the patient from his dependence on the mechanical feedback system by gradually withdrawing the lights. First they were turned off every other minute, then for three minutes out of every four, then for seven minutes out of every eight. After that the patient was presumably able to go it alone, sensing his heart irregularities himself.

At the conclusion of the training period, four of the five patients who had successfully mastered the first phase were also able to master the second; and the fifth patient, although he never learned to sense his irregular heartbeat, had a more stable heart rate after the training.

Like many other researchers in biofeedback techniques, Engel thinks that the control methods used by his five successful trainees—despite their varying images of swings and bouncing balls—were much the same. From the physiological evidence, he believes that they learned to stabilize their heart rates by directly modifying the firing rate of the nerves that control the heart muscles. Whether the images brought this about, or some more subtle internal command was involved, is anybody's guess. In any case, as Engel acknowledges, even if they had known what they were doing, they would probably have had trouble describing it—since there are no handy labels for sensations at this physiological level.

A somewhat different approach to biofeedback training is being used at the Menninger Foundation by Elmer Green and his associates whose work with the Swami Rama demonstrated that the ability to control blood flow could be of great value to people with circulatory ailments. In seeking a way of teaching such control to patients, the method they hit upon did not require years of study in yoga, but combined biofeedback monitoring and display with a technique called autogenic training. The technique, which had long been used as an aid in relaxing, was worked out by a German psychiatrist, Johannes Schultz, in 1910. It consists of a series of verbal formulas that the patient repeats to himself to induce relaxation. A typical set of phrases suggested by Schultz is: "I feel quite quiet. I am beginning to feel quite relaxed. My feet feel heavy and relaxed. My arms and hands are heavy and warm. My hands are warm. Warmth is flowing into my hands, they are warm, warm. . . ."

Adapting these techniques, the Menninger researchers decided to tape temperature-sensing devices to the hands of their patients and, as they practiced autogenic relaxation, feed the slight changes in skin temperature onto an easy-to-read meter. As a patient's hands got slightly warmer, this fact would immediately be recorded on the meter.

Purely by chance, one of the earliest subjects in this "autogenic-feedback" experiment was a Kansas housewife who suffered from migraine headaches, which are generated by a circulatory malfunction—dilated blood vessels in the head. During one of the sessions in which she was practicing her autogenic phrases, the woman had a migraine attack, and the researchers sent her to sit quietly in a darkened room. But they did not unhook the woman from the biofeedback equipment, and two minutes later Green was astonished to see the temperature in her hands suddenly jump 10°, indicating that they had received a tremendous surge of blood. On questioning the woman, he found that her headache had vanished at just that moment. The event suggested to Green that there might be some connection between migraine headaches and a change in blood flow in the hands—and if this was so, then learning to "warm up one's hands" from inside might bring dramatic relief. Working on this theory, 70 migraine sufferers took part in a study in autogenic-feedback training, and more than two thirds of them ended up with warmer hands and fewer headaches. No one has been able to prove exactly why the treatment works, but apparently the blood vessels in the head and hands are on opposite sides of a cardiovascular seesaw: when the vessels in the hand contract, those in the head dilate—and vice versa.

After learning to control migraine with the help of the meters, some patients reported that their control was becoming more and more "automatic." Indeed none of them now needs a monitoring device at all. Early in her training, one woman discovered that her migraine headaches were invariably preceded by what doctors call an aura—in her case, an olfactory sensation. She imagined she smelled ammonia. When this happened, she went home, lay down and practiced her warmth-and-relaxation exercises for an hour—and the headache would disappear. After a few months, 15 minutes of exercising was long enough, and she could do the exercises while sitting at her desk. Now whenever the woman senses the aura, she simply gives a mental command, "Go back down, blood," and evidently her brain and body do the rest—for the headache passes.

HOW TO TURN OFF A TENSION HEADACHE

Presumably, any of the body's involuntary functions can be brought under control with biofeedback training—as can certain functions that are normally thought of as voluntary but are really only voluntary to a small degree. Most people, for instance, can wrinkle and unwrinkle their brow at will by contracting and then relaxing the frontalis muscle in the forehead. But there are people in whom this muscle, along with others in the scalp and neck, tightens up gradually under stress, unbeknown to them. They become very much aware of the result, however: a "tension" headache, as debilitating as a migraine headache, that can last for weeks and even months. Tension-headache sufferers may know the cause of their trouble, but even so they cannot normally relax their frontalis muscles—any more than a person with a Charley horse can unknot the cramped muscle in his leg. But in two recent experiments at the University of Colorado Medical Center, psychologists Johann Stoyva and Thomas Budzynski demonstrated that a chronically tense frontalis muscle can be coaxed into relaxing with biofeedback training.

Stoyva and Budzynski's monitoring device was

an electromyograph, which measures the electrical activity in muscles. The machine was set up to make clicking noises that increased in frequency with the amount of tension in the muscle —so that the subject could literally hear how tight his forehead was. The aim of the subject was to lower the click rate, and four of the six subjects who took part in the study learned to recognize the warning signs of muscle tension, and turn off most of their headaches. Those that do occur require far less pain-killing medication.

Ultimately, of course, the ideal source of biofeedback information is the brain itself, since the brain plays a decisive role in the regulation of every bodily function. The standard machine for monitoring electrical activity in the brain is the electroencephalograph, which picks up electrical impulses through electrodes taped to the scalp. But it is not always easy to correlate a particular "brain wave" pattern with a particular bodily activity. When such a correlation can be found, it ought to be possible to modify the activity at its source in the brain. The most dramatic example of such an application for biofeedback training was reported in 1972 by psychologist Maurice B. Sterman of the Veterans Administration Hospital in Sepulveda, California.

To begin with, Sterman identified a particular pattern of electrical activity in the brain waves originating in the part of the brain that controls movements of the skeletal muscles. This pattern, which has been named the sensorimotor rhythm, seems to be associated with muscular quietude —subjects produce the SMR pattern when they are awake but completely motionless.

In the initial stages of the investigation, Sterman used cats for subjects—because cats can be studied under carefully controlled laboratory conditions. He found that hungry cats could be trained to increase their SMR production if they were fed only when the pattern appeared. Instead of roaming their cages restlessly, they sat stock-still waiting for food. Other experiments with the same cats showed that after they had learned to produce the pattern, they were unusually resistant to drug-induced convulsions. This result prompted Sterman to try training epileptics, whose seizures are thought to result from a breakdown in the brain centers that regulate muscular activity.

The preliminary results of this phase of Sterman's research have been very encouraging. Substituting standard feedback signals—lights, bells, pictures projected on a screen—for the food offered the hungry cats, Sterman has taught three epileptic patients to increase their production of the "quiet" type of brain waves. In each case the training has lessened the number of epileptic seizures. In one case, that of a six-year-old boy, the results of the training have been astonishing. This boy, despite massive medication, had been suffering as many as 25 seizures a week. When brought to the laboratory by his parents, he was so drugged that Sterman doubted his ability to comprehend even the simplest instructions. Yet after six months of training, the boy had remained free of seizures for as long as four months and was able to get along with fewer anticonvulsive drugs.

ALPHA WAVES—A MATTER OF CONTROVERSY

The muscular quietude induced by SMR training is not to be confused with the kind of quietude that supposedly results from what is popularly known as alpha-wave conditioning. Sensorimotor rhythms emanate from a specific part of the brain and are correlated with a specific pattern of muscular activity. Alpha waves, by contrast, are recorded over a much wider area of the brain, and whether or not they correlate with any consistent pattern of behavior is still a matter of controversy. Most people produce alpha waves when they are relaxed or faintly drowsy, but cannot sustain them; the slightest motion or mental activity is usually enough to block the wave production. A harmless and pleasurable experience, the sustained production of alpha waves is relatively easy to learn with the assistance of an electroencephalograph. But there is no proof that the waves can profoundly alter the personality, making it more "free" and "creative," as some merchandisers have claimed. In 1972 more than 60 companies were marketing alpha-wave expertise. Some were selling sophisticated electronic equipment that went "blip-blip-blip" when the user produced alpha waves; hardware like

In this double exposure, the husband-wife team of Elmer and Alyce Green appear with an image of the control panel of an electroencephalograph, which they employ in studying body responses. The instrument makes a record (lower left) of electrical brain patterns, such as alpha waves, that let a subject know when he is successful in regulating such normally uncontrollable functions.

this can run into hundreds of dollars. At the other end of the scale were promises of "Alpha-Wave Training and Control Without Headphones, Equipment" for five dollars.

Perhaps because biofeedback research lends itself so easily to commercial exploitation, scientists in the field go to great lengths to avoid premature claims of success. Dr. Morton F. Reiser, editor of the journal *Psychosomatic Medicine,* cautions, for instance, that many of the studies in biofeedback therapy reported in his journal's pages are too limited to be conclusive. Except for the work on tension headaches, he points out, none of the studies have been conducted under the carefully controlled lab conditions that would rule out what doctors call the "placebo effect" —the curative consequences of simply being the object of a scientific experiment.

Neal Miller, whose daring theories have laid the groundwork for biofeedback research, would undoubtedly agree with these cautionary disclaimers. (No one is more aware than Miller of the pitfalls of biofeedback research; in April, Miller reported that he was having trouble duplicating some of his earlier experiments on curarized rats.) Yet Miller continues to believe that biofeedback techniques will eventually help scientists unravel the intricate network of interrelationships between brain and body that make the behavior of higher animals—even white rats—so extraordinarily flexible. And if and when this knowledge is acquired, the applications for biofeedback training may go beyond the treatment of disease, to the prevention of trouble before it starts. At the University of Colorado Medical Center, for instance, researchers Budzynski and Stoyva are already at work on a method of teaching people to slow down their metabolism at will —a talent that could have enormous survival value in a world in which everyone seems to be overstimulated, and thus fair game for biological breakdowns. But whether or not the average person learns to control his bodily functions to the same degree as Swami Rama, of one thing there is no doubt: biofeedback research is shedding new light on areas of human experience that have long been *terra incognita* to Western man.

The calm that accompanies the alpha type of brain wave has moved some—such as this group in an inflated 40-foot bubble in Los Angeles—to try to produce alpha with the help of a simplified electroencephalograph.

A New Age for Mass Transit

It could finally be the turn-around year for mass transportation. More and more automobile drivers continued jamming the cities; but suddenly there seemed to be a number of alternatives that should appeal to the most stubborn family-car commuter. One of the most attractive new examples of high-speed, comfortable mass transportation finally went into operation in 1972 after 15 years of planning and construction. When it is completed, this 75-mile rapid-transit system will link three California cities—San Francisco, Oakland and Berkeley—to one another and to suburbs expected to house seven million people within the next two decades. The Bay Area Rapid Transit System (promptly nicknamed BART) is the first all-new rapid-transit system built in the United States in over 60 years. But it is only one of many new conveyances shown off in 1972 in the hope of getting the commuter out of his air-fouling car and into a train, a bus or even a tube.

A spectacular display of such innovations was put on view at the country's first transportation fair, the federally sponsored Transpo '72, held in late May and early June outside Washington, D.C., at which designers showed off new, electrically powered, computer-guided cars to whisk the commuter around the city after mass transportation gets him there *(pages 117-119)*. For long distances, scientists were working on more radical proposals. In California, Rohr Industries was completing a prototype vehicle that would float on air and speed 60 passengers at 150 miles per hour. And physicists at Santa Monica's Rand Corporation were developing the farthest-out idea of all, even though it was proposed in 1905: the use of electromagnetic suspension to create a train that could ultimately fly through a transcontinental tunnel *(pages 122-123)*, and carry people coast to coast in less than half an hour.

Circles of light echo through the world's longest underwater transit tube, the 3.6-mile BART track beneath San Francisco's bay that will link the city to the East Bay area.

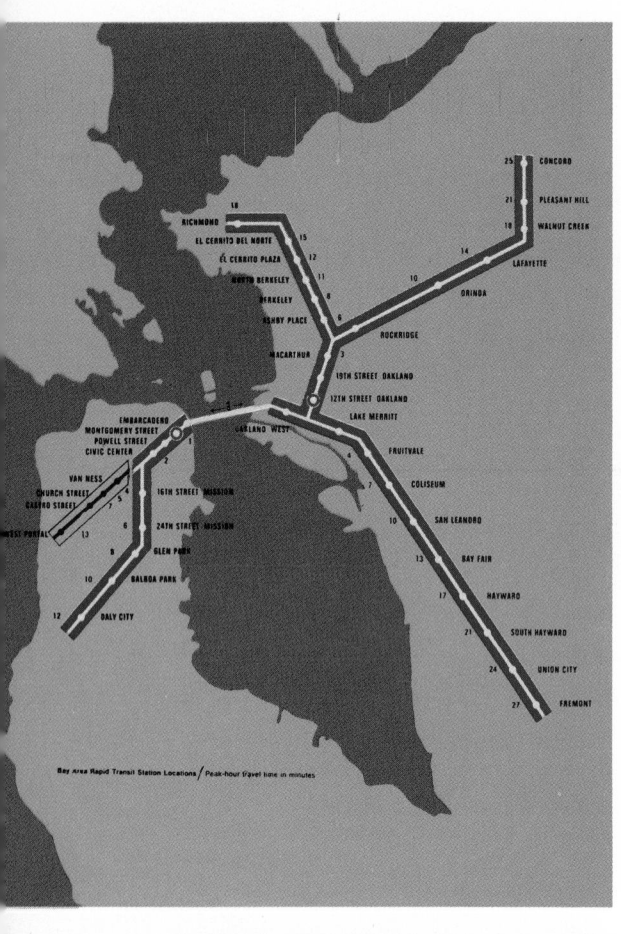

In a preview of rush hour, BART employees and their families crowd into an Oakland subway station (above) in preparation for a trial run.

Suburban lines (right), like this one outside of Oakland, speed over auto traffic and include miniparks planted under the elevated tracks.

The BART system (above) reaches antennalike arms over 75 miles of subway and surface tracks to 30 communities east of San Francisco.

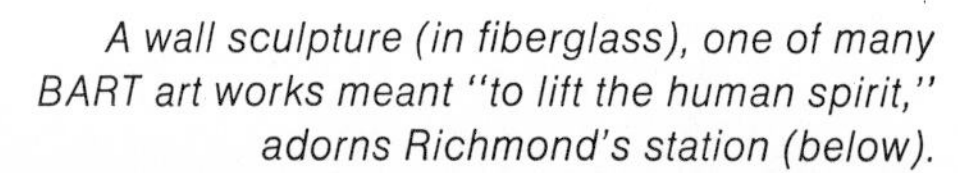

A wall sculpture (in fiberglass), one of many BART art works meant "to lift the human spirit," adorns Richmond's station (below).

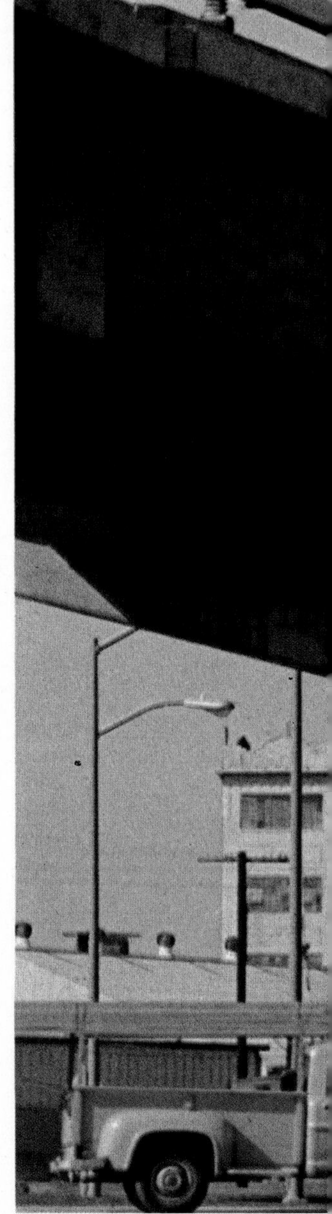

Moving Crowds in Style

Mass-transit experts long ago discovered that speed alone is not enough to lure the hardened automobile commuter out of his car. So the BART system in San Francisco was designed to compete with every comfort short of a limousine. Its 80-mile-per-hour electrically propelled vehicles travel smoothly on rubber-cushioned rails. The interiors have wall-to-wall carpeting and wide, cantilevered seats for as many as 72 people per car—enough to meet BART's expectation that all non-rush-hour and most rush-hour riders will be able to have seats.

BART was set up to be as efficient as it is comfortable. Everything from ticket selling to operating the trains is computerized. And while such functions as opening or shutting doors and starting or stopping trains are fully automated, an "attendant" rides each train, just in case.

Belts and Boxes for Short Hauls

A major problem for most mass-transit systems like BART *(previous pages)* is what to do with the commuters once they are dumped in the city's midtown. Vehicles for such short hauls inside the city are part of any balanced transportation network; today they are traffic-jamming buses and taxis, but transit planners have come up with replacements for the future. Their brain children, typically called PRTs (for Personal Rapid Transit systems), are electrically powered, computer-controlled carriers designed to move travelers through crowded areas like university campuses, airports or metropolitan centers. One people mover is already in use: the moving sidewalk *(left),* an invention that was first proposed in 1859, allows airline passengers a respite from the long walk between the parking garage and the terminal and can accommodate wheel chairs, luggage carts and infant strollers. The new sidewalk can carry up to 7,200 passengers per hour. Among the future people movers still being tested are the Insta-Glide *(below, left),* a system of two- to four-passenger cars that run on ground-level tracks; and the Monocab people-mover system *(below, right),* made up of six-passenger modules suspended from an overhead monorail.

The privacy of a driverless taxi is enjoyed by two riders in an Insta-Glide capsule (above). When the system is operational, a passenger will board a waiting car for a 40-mile-per-hour, nonstop trip to a spot near his destination.

◀ *Travelers use an inclined moving sidewalk (left)—the first to run uphill and down as well as horizontally—to cover the 445 feet between the parking garage and boarding area at Cleveland-Hopkins Airport. Such conveyor belts are well suited to airports because they also carry luggage.*

Above the flag-bedecked fairground of Transpo '72, a Monocab glides along its monorail (right). Its manufacturers view the thin monorail as an improvement over the wide, ugly tracks used by most present elevated systems.

Visitors to the Transpo '72 transportation fair take a ride in a prototype of a 24-passenger car that is controlled by a computer. The car is steered along a track by horizontally mounted wheels which run inside a trough.

The same track that serves the subway-type car shown at right also accommodates a 12-passenger bus (below), which can ride on the track as well as on an ordinary road.

The Vehicle for Rail or Road

In the event that the enticements of luxurious new trains and other "people movers" cannot get the motorist to leave his private car, the transportation researchers are working on a way to switch the car onto an automated transit system. New "dual-mode" vehicles will operate both on highways, under a driver's control, and on guideways controlled by a computer. They combine the speed and personal convenience of private autos with the safety and traffic-handling capacity of electronically guided transit. On highways they are run by gasoline engines, on guideways by fume-free electric motors.

A motorist would be able to drive his dual-mode car on a regular road to a guideway, where the car would be automatically merged into ongoing traffic. It would then be routed to the exit the driver selects, whereupon he would resume control. Or he could step out and send the vehicle back home or to a distant parking garage.

An arm that swings out from the fender of an experimental automobile hooks onto an electrified guiderail when the car leaves the roadway for an automated ride into the city.

High-Speed Trains That Float

In their quest for greater speeds, ground-vehicle designers are even abandoning the wheel. As speeds increase there is more and more stress on the track, causing maintenance and safety problems. So some designers have turned to vehicles that float in a guideway without touching it. Wheelless carriers will be capable of attaining speeds of at least 300 miles per hour. Some of them float on a cushion of air, sucking it into the vehicle from above and blasting it onto the guideway through compressors, in the manner of the Hovercraft vessels already used in ferry services. Others run on another cushion, this one made of opposing electromagnetic fields like that caused by two magnets repelling each other. And though some of these floating trains are driven by aircraft propellers, others employ electromagnetic force generated along the guideway to pull them forward—a "linear" electric motor that operates in a straight line instead of rotating.

Suspended on an air cushion and driven by a propeller, an Aerotrain reaches 186 miles per hour at Chevilly, France.

Lifted by magnetic levitation, the Transrapid, a German test train, is driven 105 miles an hour by a linear induction motor.

HOW TO RUN WITHOUT WHEELS

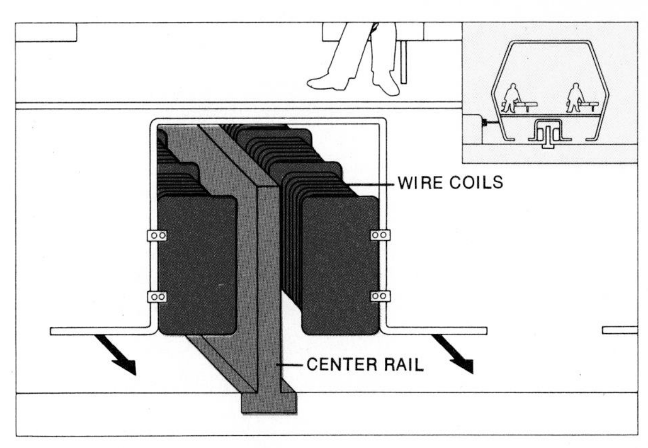

Linear induction motors use electric current to induce a strong magnetic field in wire coils fixed to the bottom of a vehicle. The field induces a corresponding field in the center rail of a guideway. The interaction between the two magnetic fields creates the thrust. Since the central rail is stationary, the thrust propels the vehicle forward.

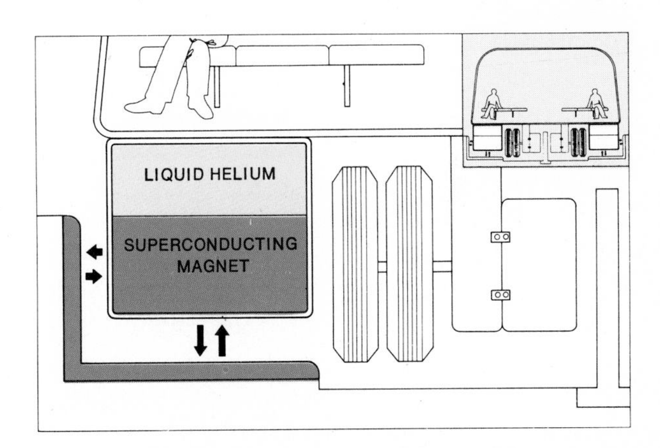

For magnetic levitation, coils—chilled to —452° F. so they lose all electric resistance and can handle tremendous currents—generate a magnetic force that produces an opposing magnetic force in an L-shaped aluminum guideway on each side of the vehicle. The opposing forces suspend the vehicle vertically and guide it horizontally.

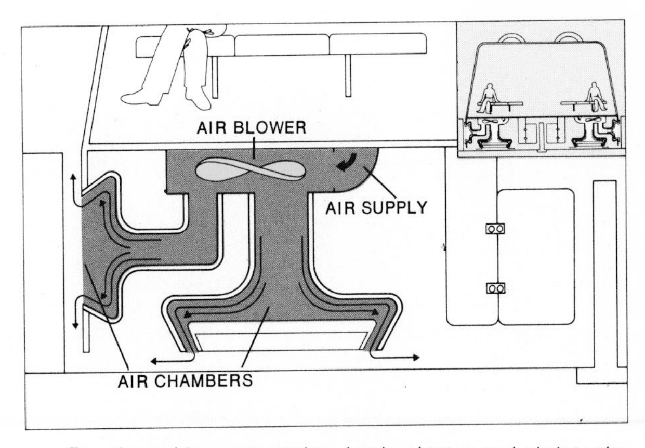

For air cushion suspension, intake ducts send air into the chambers in the lower part of the vehicle. The blower generates air pressure, which is forced through the chambers to the guideway. Pressing down and against both sides of the guideway, the pressure lifts the vehicle and at the same time controls its lateral movement.

Coast to Coast in 21 Minutes

The trip from Los Angeles to New York may someday be made in 21 minutes, at a speed of 14,000 miles per hour. The train that accomplishes this astonishing feat will run through a coast-to-coast tunnel. Electromagnetic forces will both provide thrust and support the vehicle *(preceding pages)* in its underground guideway—a tube that has been emptied of air almost to the point of vacuum to eliminate air resistance. So goes the Rand Corporation's plan for its projected tube train. A major problem, of course, is the prohibitive cost of such a 2,600-mile tunnel; but new tunneling devices *(below),* using heat to melt rock, may make such a project feasible. A similar high-speed train could also run in an aboveground tube. In fact J. V. Foa of George Washington University has long been at work on one. Foa's vehicle is propelled by a jet engine that pumps air from in front of the train to the rear, thereby creating thrust. This train would fly through a steel tube at speeds up to 500 miles an hour. The train would fit in a 15- to 18-foot-wide tube and would be supported by an air cushion between its pads and the tube walls.

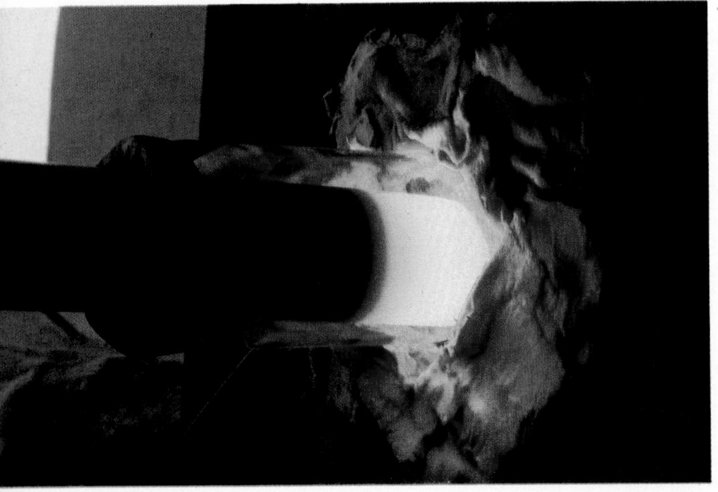

As viewed from the top of a tube, a model of Foa's train of the future (above) is seen head-on. The six-bladed propeller sucks air from in front of the train to the rear to drive the vehicle. In a side view (right), the propeller is moving too fast to be seen. The projections are guidance wheels but, in a full-scale prototype, projecting pads would eject an invisible cushion of air between train and tube to eliminate friction.

◀ *A tunneling device, its shaft heated to 2,900°F., melts through rock twice as fast as blasting methods. Penetrating 400 feet a day, it makes a hole accurate to within a thousandth of an inch.*

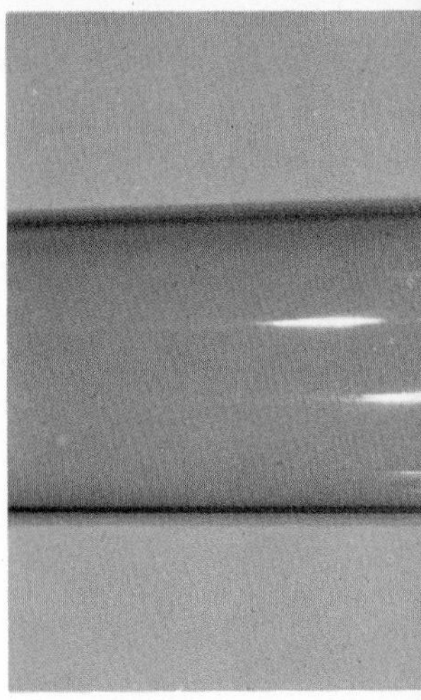

The Gray Whales' Comeback

PROTECTION PAYS OFF FOR SEALS AND SEA OTTERS, TOO

by William Weber Johnson

Every winter the most impressive of all known animal migrations takes place off the Pacific coast. It is the yearly southward migration of the gray whales, perhaps as many as 13,000 of them, from their summer home in the Bering Sea off Alaska and Siberia to their winter quarters in the quiet bays and lagoons of Baja (Lower) California's western coastline. Thousands of sightseers gather on bluffs and headlands from Monterey's Cypress Point to San Diego's Point Loma to watch the great 35-ton mottled-gray hulks churn along just offshore, their blowholes sending up plumes of vapor. It is one of the most awesome displays of animal might and majesty that can be seen today in the natural world.

It is doubly impressive because not long ago the gray whale seemed, like several other species of whales, to be doomed to extinction. But the gray has made a miraculous comeback. Further, enlightened steps have been taken to ensure its survival. In February 1972 the Mexican government declared Scammon's Lagoon, the grays' favorite Baja California refuge, a wildlife preserve where the whales cannot be harmed or even bothered by well-meaning whale watchers. It was the first time that any government had provided protection for a specific kind of whale in a specific habitat.

It also was an imperative step. One key to the survival of the gray whale has been the extreme isolation, the near emptiness, of the Baja Peninsula's coastline. Much of this coast is a forbidding desert of rock and shifting sand punctuated by the bays and lagoons favored by the whales. In these protected bodies of water the gray whale mothers have borne their young in safety, while

A sleek gray whale, one of several sea mammals coming back from near-extinction, thrashes the waters of Scammon's Lagoon, a whale refuge in Baja California. This underwater photograph was taken by Philippe Cousteau.

the other females have energetically endeavored to become pregnant themselves, sporting with the attendant males. In short, Baja's bays and lagoons have afforded the whales privacy and protection during the most vital periods in their life cycle, breeding and childbearing.

But every year Baja is becoming less isolated. Soon a modern highway will run from the U.S.-Mexican border down the entire 800-mile length of Baja, connecting its deserts and mountains with the dense population centers of Southern California. Tourism and other business will inevitably increase—a development that will be good for the economy of this rocky, sun-baked peninsula, but will hardly benefit the animals that have thrived in the heretofore sheltered wilderness.

For Baja has, by its very wildness, helped in the survival of a number of threatened species besides the gray whales. The northern elephant seal, thought for years to have become extinct, has been discovered alive and well on Guadalupe, an island belonging to Mexico that lies 180 miles off Baja's Pacific coast and is even more isolated than the peninsula itself. This island is also a refuge for the Guadalupe fur seal, only recently rescued from the brink of extinction. Elsewhere in isolated parts of the Pacific coast still another seagoing mammal, the sea otter, is just beginning to stage a comeback.

These remarkable recoveries by endangered species were celebrated by Carl Hubbs, a marine biologist who has devoted a lifetime of study to the seagoing mammals of the Pacific coast, in a speech he gave before a meeting of the United States National Wildlife Federation that was held in Mexico City in March of 1972. Dr. Hubbs lavished praise on Mexico for the creation of the wildlife refuges of Guadalupe Island and Scammon's Lagoon: "All hail to Mexico," Hubbs said, "for the . . . role it has played in the conservation of marine mammals."

A PRIMITIVE LOVE OF SHORES AND SHALLOWS

Two other key factors, aside from the isolation of Baja California's lagoons, have played a part in the comeback of the gray whale. One of them is an international whaling convention, signed in 1937, that forbids the commercial slaughter of the grays. But this by itself was no guarantee of survival. For example, the right whale was protected by the same agreement. But the right whale (so called by early whalemen who considered it the "right" whale to harpoon because after being killed it conveniently floated on the surface) has probably passed the point of no return. Whalers kept on killing them until today right whales can apparently no longer be counted among the resources of the sea.

Aside from the isolation of the lagoons and legal protection, the principal factor in the gray whale's survival lies in its nature and behavior. Most of the big whales are deep-water creatures, frequenting parts of the ocean that are remote from observation and regulation. But the gray whale, while it is capable of crossing oceans, prefers the shallows and the shores. Since so much of its life is spent in the patrolled territorial waters of Russia, Canada, the United States and Mexico—and even within sight of land—its protection is more easily enforced.

The reason for the gray whale's predilection for coastal waters and lagoons lies buried in its evolution as a species. Like all whales, the gray is descended from an ancestral mammal that deserted the land for a marine habitat about a hundred million years ago. The front legs became flippers and were used as stabilizers. Hind legs disappeared (although there are vestigial pelvic bones within the whale's body). Horizontal flukes, or tail fins, for propulsive power developed just past the end of the spine. Whales continued to take oxygen from the air—breathing through the blowholes in the tops of their heads. They continued to bear their young alive and to suckle them, as do all mammals.

But the gray, more than any other large whale, maintained an affinity for the land. A majority of the other cetaceans—whales and their relatives, such as dolphins and porpoises—prefer to inhabit the mid-ocean deeps. The grays, sticking to the shallows, appear to represent a primitive form in whale evolution, an intermediate stage between land animal and sea animal. Only the gray can tolerate water so shallow that its belly rests on the bottom—a situation that causes panic and death in other whales.

Gray whales migrate an astonishing total of some 12,000 to 14,000 miles each year, from the Arctic to the tropics and back. The main herd spends the summer feeding in the waters between Alaska and Siberia—the checked area in the map above. With the coming of autumn, the whales, perhaps 13,000 animals in all, start southward for five breeding and calving areas along the shores of Baja California and mainland Mexico (inset map). Their route (yellow lines) cuts through gaps in the Aleutian chain, then veers shoreward to hug the Pacific coast. The whales follow almost the same route every year; their annual arrival off any point on the coast never varies more than five days.

"Mudhole whaling" at its deadly worst is shown in this frontispiece from a book on marine mammals written by 19th Century whaling captain Charles M. Scammon, whose name was given to Scammon's Lagoon. Five mother ships ride the waters of a protected Baja California lagoon, while a dozen whaleboats scurry about slaughtering gray whales. The whale carcass in the foreground, staked with a flag to identify the ship whose crew killed it, attracts scavenger birds. The grays were easy prey in their nearly landlocked lagoon-refuges; more than 10,000 were harpooned during a 28-year period in the mid-19th Century.

Gray whales evidently once cruised the shorelines of the North Atlantic Ocean, and were far more numerous than they are now. The whale's bones have been found in parts of Great Britain, Sweden and the Netherlands. It is possible that the "scrag" whale that was hunted in the Atlantic until a few centuries ago was a gray whale. Today, however, the gray is found only in the waters of the North Pacific.

The gray is not one of the largest of the whales. Fully grown it may be from 35 to 50 feet long and weigh about 35 tons, the female being somewhat larger than the male. The blue whale, by comparison, is at least twice as long and can weigh eight or 10 times as much. The gray is nevertheless an impressive beast. Its basic color is black, but older whales are heavily mottled with patches of grayish white: barnacles cling to the whales' hides; when they fall or are scraped off, they leave behind this mottling of scar tissue. The overall effect is a shade of faded gray-black that looks ancient, as if the whales were scarred veterans of titanic wars in the deeps.

The gray is a member of the Mysticeti—or baleen—suborder of whales, as differentiated from the Odontoceti, or toothed whales. The latter, including the sperm whale, the grampus or killer whale, and the various dolphins and porpoises, are equipped with strong pointed white teeth and can eat a variety of marine life. The killer whale, in fact, preys on practically everything in the sea, including other whales. The Mysticeti are identified by the baleen, a fringed, bony structure in the jaw. They feed solely on the small organisms that can be gulped with sea water and then strained through the baleen.

GORGING ON AN EXPLOSION OF SCUDS

This specialized feeding method plays a part in the gray whale's yearly cycle. From late spring until early fall it eats scuds, which are tiny, distant relatives of the shrimp. During these months, scuds are incredibly abundant in the arctic and subarctic waters between Alaska and Siberia. The almost never-ending summer sun of the far north produces an explosive growth of food. And here the gray whales spend their summer, grazing the bottom of the sea, gulping three- or fourscore gallons of food-rich water at a time and then straining the scuds out of this sea-soup by pressing the tongue against the baleen. The food sieved in this way is then swallowed into the first of a series of four stomach cavities—at a rate of perhaps one ton of food a day. It is believed that the gray may eat the clock around, seldom pausing for sleep. In this summer feeding period the whale stores up huge quantities of blubber, a food reserve that must last a long time.

When the summer days shorten and the bloom of marine organisms withers, the gray whales head south. A few of them may follow the Asian coast to the bays of Korea. But the larger herd crosses the Gulf of Alaska and then, starting in the vicinity of the outlet of the Columbia River, swims southward following the coastline of North America. The trip totals between 5,000 and 7,000 miles. The whales seldom seem to rest, but cruise at a steady speed of about five knots (a speed they can more than double if attacked by killer whales or menaced by men), alternately surfacing, spouting and diving.

First come the females that were impregnated during the previous year's southern visit (gestation takes 12 to 13 months). These females are in a hurry to reach the quiet lagoons of Baja to give birth in calm waters. Then come the females that are ready for breeding. Some may have recently weaned a calf born the previous winter; others, younger, may be in season for the first time. As they approach the lagoons, they are accompanied or pursued by eager males. Since about half of the cows are pregnant during each of the southward migrations, there is about a 2 to 1 surplus of males to service the ready and available cows. Finally come the younger whales. Some of them are yearlings, making the southern journey for the first time. Others are older but still sexually immature (maturity is thought to be reached at about the age of eight).

Little is known about the gray whales' navigating ability, but year after year they steer the same course with very little alteration in route or in timetable. Some naturalists have suggested that the grays find their way with the help of sound-wave echoes, as do human navigators and many sea mammals—the dolphin, for instance. Others believe that the grays "spyhop" (thrusting about one third of the body out of the water) to orient themselves visually with known landmarks. But the gray's long-distance vision is questionable, at least in the air, so this too is uncertain. Still other investigators believe that the gray whale may use its sense of taste to detect the mouth of a river or the opening of a bay or lagoon, since water draining from the land would contain more sediment than the open ocean. And still another theory postulates that the whales know how to "read" ocean bottom contours. During migration the grays dive several times an hour, usually staying down three to six minutes, although they occasionally make a 12-minute plunge. Since there is general agreement that the whales do not eat en route, it is possible that they dive to follow familiar sea-floor topography.

Whatever guides them, the gray whales head unerringly for their migratory terminals in Baja California every fall, usually arriving in early January. Three principal bay-and-lagoon complexes in Baja lure them. Northernmost is Vizcaíno Bay, about halfway down the 800-mile-long peninsula, with its three branch lagoons—Manuela in the north, Guerrero Negro in the center, and Scammon's Lagoon, largest of the three and the most popular with the whales, in the south. About 200 sea miles to the southeast of Scammon's is San Ignacio Lagoon, second only to Scammon's in popularity. Farthest south is Magdalena Bay with a number of mangrove-bordered lagoons. A few of the gray whales go even farther, down past the tip of the peninsula at Cabo San Lucas and across the Gulf of California to lagoons on the Pacific coast of mainland Mexico. But a large majority of the whales stop in Baja California.

TITANIC THRASHING IN THE SURF

Breeding occurs along the migration route, but it appears to take on greater intensity when the whales near their destination. There is much rolling and thrashing of the great bodies in the swells and breakers at the lagoon entrances and just inside. Until the moment of sexual junction, the female may be attended by two or more suitors. But there is no belligerence to the rivalry of the males. When one of them is accepted, the others may stay around or calmly swim away to search for another mate.

A few of the already pregnant females give birth to their young along the migration route. The birth of an air-breathing creature underwater is a risky business at best. The whale calf must get to the surface immediately for its first breath of air. The dangers are of course heightened by a rough and rolling sea, and the bodies of young whales born—and lost—in rough water can occasionally be seen along the beaches of Baja California. But if the pregnant female is lucky, she reaches a calm shallow lagoon where she can help her calf get to the surface with her flippers or head. The calf is a sleek black creature, 12 to 17 feet in length and weighing in the neighborhood of 3,000 pounds.

The mother whale nurses the calf from two short nipples at the rear of her belly. The young whale seizes a nipple, and the mother, by contracting some of her abdominal muscles, shoots a jet of super-rich milk down the calf's throat, a gallon or so at a time. The mother whale's milk, laden with fat, is approximately eight times as rich as human milk. As a result, the young whale grows at a phenomenal rate during the winter months it remains in the lagoon.

But the young whale is the only one that eats well—or at all, for that matter. The adult whales have not eaten since leaving the north—not on the trip south, nor during their stay in the lagoons, nor will they eat regularly again, so far as anyone knows, until they get back to the rich sea pastures of the north. When they leave the southern lagoons in mid-February, the adult whales are wasted and gaunt from fasting, breeding and giving birth to the young, and their swimming speed is noticeably diminished. This strange pattern of alternate gluttony and apparently complete fasting is one of the many oddities about the gray that puzzle scientists. Whatever the explanation, the gray whale survives on this regimen—if left alone by man. But unfortunately it has not always been left alone.

From time immemorial the aboriginal peoples living on the Kamchatka Peninsula, the Aleutian Islands, Alaska and the Northwest coast have killed gray whales for meat and for oil. They have pursued the whales in frail, skin-covered open boats and killed them with primitive harpoons. But it has always been extremely dangerous and difficult work, and the natives' needs have been modest. As a result, the toll in whales was neither large nor threatening—until a century ago.

MUDHOLING FOR SPOTTED HYENAS

By the mid-19th Century, United States whalemen had set up commercial stations along the California coast to kill the migrating whales, and some whaling ships were pursuing their prey along the coast of Baja California, particularly in the lagoons of Magdalena Bay. Such hunting was called "mudhole whaling" because of the way the whales roiled the shallow bottom. It was not very profitable. The grays were regarded as inferior to the other great whales as a source of oil and whalebone. Further they could, when molested, become violent and destructive—particularly the females with calves. They butted whaleboats, using their heads, or smashed them to kindling with their flukes, sometimes killing or crippling sailors in the process. Whalers called them hard heads and devilfish, and their pursuit was not a popular enterprise. One veteran complained, "I shipped to go a'whalin . . . not to go into a duckpond to whale after spotted hyenas."

Then an ingenious Yankee whaling-ship skipper named Charles Melville Scammon found a way to make this sort of whaling safer and more profitable. In 1857 he worked his ship over a dangerous sand bar and through a treacherous pass into a desert-girt lagoon, then known as Ojo de Liebre—Jack Rabbit's Eye Spring—after a desert waterhole not far east of the lagoon. The lagoon stretched back into the desert for 30 miles—so that whale spouts seemed to be rising from the midst of an arid and sandy landscape. There were thousands of them. Scammon knew the hazards of mudhole whaling from bitter experience—the previous season some of his whaleboats had been smashed and their men crippled hunting grays in Magdalena Bay. But the abundance here in Ojo de Liebre was too much to resist. He armed his men with bomb-tipped lances and had them moor their whaleboats near shore. Here the water was so shallow that the grays could come close enough to be harpooned and killed, but not sufficiently close to damage the boats. The success was spectacular. Every receptacle aboard Scammon's brig, *Boston,* was soon full of oil. Ojo de Liebre became known to whalers—and to most English-speaking cartographers since—as Scammon's Lagoon.

Within a few years, scores of vessels were plying the coast of Baja California and the lagoons. So congested was the traffic that the whaleboats carried large painted insignia—stars, crescents, eyes, stripes—so they could be identified by their mother ships. The lagoons, where once the only sounds had been the whooshing of the whales' spouts and the splash of their breaching, were now a bedlam of rattling ships' gear, detonating harpoon bombs, and shouted dialogues in Yankee English, Portuguese and various South Sea Island dialects. The clear desert air became thick with smoke from the try-pots in which whale blubber was rendered into oil.

Scammon was a thoughtful man, at least by the standards of his time, and an observant one. He later wrote and published an authoritative book on the marine mammals of the North Pacific. He estimated that between 1846, when the initial mudhole whaling had been undertaken in Baja California waters, and 1874, when his book was published, 10,800 gray whales had been killed. There were then so few left that systematic pursuit was no longer worth the trouble. By the end of the century the species was considered to be commercially extinct.

The few gray whales that were left managed to reestablish themselves, although in considerably reduced numbers. Then in the 1920s and 1930s American and Norwegian factory ships resumed the slaughter. The whale population dropped again—more sharply this time, and the gray was thought to be doomed as a species and not merely commercially extinct. But then, in 1937, the International Agreement for the Regulation of Whaling put the gray on its protected list and banned any further killing except by the indigenous peoples of the north—Aleuts, Eskimos, Indians—who were allowed to kill them for their own use but not for sale.

Once more the grays miraculously managed to survive, and by the late 1940s their spouts again began to be seen in impressive numbers along the California coast. Carl Hubbs of the Scripps Institution of Oceanography, Raymond Gilmore of the San Diego Museum of Natural History and other marine biologists began making annual censuses of gray whales. The counts were based on sightings from shore and from boats and airplanes at the terminal Baja California lagoons. In recent years the gray whale population, extrapolated from these observations, is believed by some scientists to be increasing at the rate of about 10 per cent a year and may now number between 10,000 and 13,000.

Because of the grays' shore-hugging habit, they have been more closely observed in their natural state than any other whales. Marine biologists have followed them along the migratory routes and have watched them during the lagoon phase of their yearly cycle. Dr. Paul Dudley White, the noted heart specialist, has managed to implant electrodes, connected to an electrocardiograph, in a 30-ton gray whale in Scammon's Lagoon. He took a reading of 27 heartbeats a minute, which most whale experts believe is abnormally speedy, a whale's heartbeat usually being about nine per minute. The heart action was probably fast because the whale was excited by the presence of men and because it was grounded in a shallow part of the lagoon when the reading was taken. Dr. White has also made a number of attempts to implant wires in free-swimming whales, but so far without success. Gray whale carcasses have been dissected, analyzed and studied. Dale Rice of the U.S. Bureau of Marine Fisheries has made a thorough study of the gray whale's natural history. But still there are a great many mysteries about the animal.

A 4,300-POUND GIRL NAMED GIGI

The smaller cetaceans—killer whales, dolphins, porpoises—have been successfully studied in captivity, and even trained to become performers in amusement parks. But until 1971 there had been little opportunity to observe one of the larger whales under controlled conditions. In that year, a systematic effort to capture a gray was made by David Kenney, a veterinarian then

A southern sea otter, another mammal rescued from extinction, happily floats on its back munching shellfish that it cracks with a rock held on its chest.

◀ Sleek in its beautiful black pelt, a Guadalupe fur seal surveys the island sanctuary where its seemingly doomed species has made a comeback.

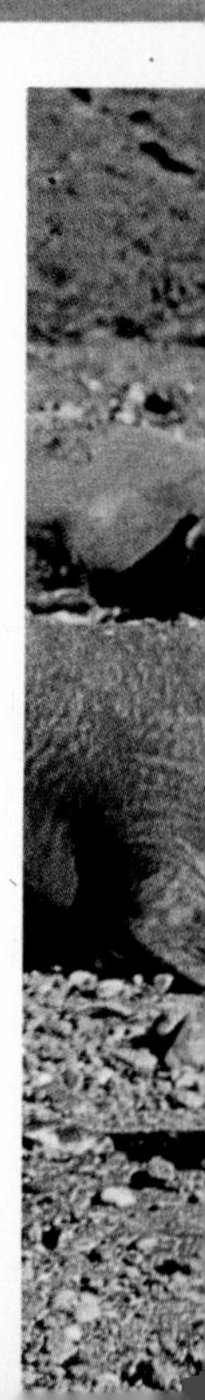

A bull elephant seal raises his trunklike nose to trumpet a challenge as he protects his harem. Several thousand elephant seals survive off Baja.

in charge of research and collections for Sea World, the San Diego aquatic park. Kenney managed to throw a net around the head of a young female gray whale in Scammon's Lagoon. The calf weighed 4,300 pounds and was a little more than 18 feet long. She was placed on an oversized stretcher, carefully lifted aboard a ship and taken to San Diego. Although on the record books the whale calf was simply identified as GW 12, she was named Gigi because, like the little girl in the musical-comedy song, she would presumably get bigger every day.

But Gigi did not grow at first. She was placed in a 55,000-gallon tank of filtered sea water, and during the first fortnight she lost 150 pounds. But then she began to thrive on a tube-fed formula made up of whipping cream, ground-up squid and bonito, cod-liver oil, brewer's yeast, vitamins, corn oil and water. She consumed the formula at the rate of 10 gallons a day. Within 10 weeks of capture, Gigi's weight was up to 5,525 pounds and she had grown one foot eight inches in length. Human attendants swam in the tank with her to keep her active, and she was given a friendly female Pacific bottle-nosed dolphin named Speedy as a companion.

Gigi grew and grew. She was twice moved to larger tanks, the final one being a million-gallon enclosure normally used for killer whale performances. She progressed from her formula to a diet of squid, which she would either take from human hands or scoop up off the bottom of her tank—and she gobbled up the squid at the rate of 1,500 pounds or more a day. Kenney charted her growth rate and calculated that after one year in captivity she would weigh about seven tons and would be more than 27 feet long.

It was an accurate projection, and on the first anniversary of her capture Gigi was returned to the sea—in March 1972. It was a time when the gray whales were expected to pass San Diego on their northbound migration, heading for the Bering Sea, and it was hoped that Gigi would, by instinct, join them.

But Gigi was not simply turned loose. She was branded for future identification, and a foam-rubber pad attached to her back was the base for a radio transmitter that would broadcast signals indicating her location, as well as the depth and temperature of the water. With this gear Gigi was expected to function as an independent oceanographic research vessel. She was gently derricked out of her tank in a synthetic fabric sling and placed on a thick foam-rubber pad on the bed of a 32-foot truck. She was then carried through the streets of San Diego late at night to avoid the distractions of traffic. The Naval Undersea Research and Development Center, which had been cooperating in the venture, placed her aboard a barge. It was towed out to the open ocean and in the morning Gigi was gently derricked over the side at a point where her migrating relatives could be seen not far away.

AIMLESS WANDERING, SHALLOW DIVES

The young whale inspected her new surroundings casually and appeared in no hurry to leave. Her movements seemed aimless and her dives were brief and shallow. It could be that she had no notion of how to dive deeper than the pleasant squid-strewn floor of her tank. Although her erstwhile custodians had expressed confidence, Gigi appeared at first to be somewhat helpless. Slowly she moved up the coast to the northwest, in the general direction of the Bering Sea. For a while she hung around off San Clemente. There encounters with an undersea forest of kelp, with which she had had no experience, damaged the antenna on Gigi's radio transmitter. Her last signals positioned her off Santa Cruz, California, about 400 miles from her point of departure; it had taken her almost eight weeks to get there. At this rate she would never reach the Bering Sea but might, instead, meet the other gray whales coming back south in the fall—if she survived. Gigi has not been seen since; if she is sighted she can be identified by a freeze-burn brand on her flank: a square with open corners.

Gigi played a unique and important role during her year of captivity. Carl Hubbs of the Scripps Institution said she might very well be the most important whale in history. Others said that what had been learned from Gigi had advanced the study of baleen whale physiology by as much as 10 years. Scientists, physicians, surgeons and engineers repeatedly tested and examined the

Stiffer Rules for Whale Hunting

With the gray whale apparently saved from extinction, popular and governmental attention focused on protecting the other breeds. The most dramatic gesture was a vote at the Stockholm Environmental Conference in June to ban all commercial whaling for 10 years.

But the vote was only a gesture, because the Stockholm assembly had no policy-making responsibility. A few weeks after the Stockholm Conference, the International Whaling Commission convened in London. The Commission, which could have banned most whaling if its 14-member governments had agreed, rejected the proposed ban, stating that "a blanket moratorium cannot be justified scientifically." Six of the nations—including Japan and Russia—voted against a moratorium on all breeds.

The Commission did, however, agree to tighten up on the quotas and restrictions that govern whaling, extending some measure of greater protection to all breeds. Among them:

—The fin whale, now the most seriously depleted of the breeds that are hunted. The stock of fins is only one third the breed-sustaining "replacement" level. The Commission reduced hunting quotas 38 per cent in the North Pacific and 34 per cent in the South Pacific.

—The blue whale, the world's largest creature. The Commission voted to make permanent its previous temporary ban on hunting blues. The blues thus become one of five breeds completely off limits to hunters. (The others are the right, gray, bowhead and humpback.)

—The sperm whale, now actually in excess in some areas of the Southern Hemisphere. The Commission refined its quotas on sperms to ensure that females and males are taken in equal numbers, and lowered the overall quota in the North Pacific by 8 per cent.

—The sei whale. Noting that its population is now at a safe level, the Commission lowered quotas only slightly.

Overall, quotas on every breed of whale were lowered by amounts from 8 to 38 per cent. And, significantly, the Soviet Union was persuaded to permit international observers aboard its antarctic whaling ships.

The United States had advocated a total moratorium on whaling, while the Soviet Union and Japan argued for breed-by-breed restrictions. America has no whaling industry at all; the Soviets and Japanese have large whaling fleets.

young whale, checking heart function, respiration, circulation and consistency of the blood, nutrition, digestion, susceptibility to parasites and disease, sound generation and so on.

Someday these findings will be untangled, analyzed and published. But several things are already clear. The gray whale, unlike the chattering dolphins and the singing humpback whale, had been thought to be mute or nearly so. In fact it was often called "the silent whale." Not Gigi. She made two different kinds of noises and made them frequently. One, apparently coming from the esophagus, was described as a crick or chirp or tap. The other, seeming to come from deep within the body, was variously described as a grunt and a burp. The gray whale's vision was also thought to be poor. Gigi's was excellent. Among her various human attendants in captivity she had certain favorites, and she could always recognize them, even when they changed to wet suits of an unfamiliar color.

The studies of Gigi are relevant to more than cetology. For one thing, they could add to our understanding of evolution and the adaptation of a species. The way in which whales and their relatives the seals, all of them onetime land animals, accommodated themselves to a marine environment and made superefficient use of oxygen and nutrients may have some message for men living in an ever more crowded world.

Of the other threatened sea mammals that have survived in California waters, the most spectacular is the elephant seal, the largest and most grotesque member of the fin-footed family, which includes all seals, sea lions and walruses. The males, strange monsters 16 feet long and weighing three tons, are distinguished by a trunk-like proboscis. When angered by the approach of a rival male, the elephant seal puts the end of the trunk in his mouth, producing a roar of defiance. When asleep, the seal's breath resonates in its trunk, producing a deafening snore.

Female elephant seals are about three quarters the length of the males, but are far less bulky, weighing only about one fourth as much. They live in harems under the belligerent guardianship of their polygamous mates. Their young weigh about 90 pounds at birth and grow quickly on the mother seal's rich milk. Many of the young, however, are victims of the older seals' incomparable awkwardness in love and war. Elephant seal rookeries are often littered with the flattened carcasses of young seals that got in the way. Still, the elephant seal was sufficiently prolific to build up huge populations on the islands and shores of both upper and lower California.

A DOCILE SOURCE OF BLUBBER

But the elephant seal, like the gray whale, was virtually wiped out by 19th Century hunters. It too stores up great quantities of blubber that can be melted down to oil. The huge seals were slaughtered in wholesale lots, often by the same men who pursued whales. The seals were easy prey—slow moving, docile, almost completely unafraid of man. Captain Scammon, discoverer of the gray whale hideaway in the lagoon named after him, also hunted for seals. By 1869, he said, the elephant seal was "nearly, if not quite, extinct." A few continued to be killed, but they became increasingly rare until in 1892 only eight elephant seals were found during a search of Guadalupe. In 1922 the Mexican government declared Guadalupe Island, one of the seal's favorite haunts, a wildlife sanctuary. This restriction is still in force. Because of its protection as many as 15,000 elephant seals now live on Guadalupe, with others on Cedros Island and the San Benito Islands off the Baja California coast, and even on islands off the U.S. California coast.

Guadalupe, which is about 280 miles southwest of San Diego, is also home for a smaller and considerably rarer pinniped, or fin-footed, mammal—the Guadalupe fur seal. These seals—identifiable by a pointed, almost collielike snout and oversized flippers—once numbered in the hundreds of thousands. Akin to the seals of the Bering Sea and the Chilean coast, the Guadalupe fur seal has a luxuriant fur coat, ideal in the days of sleighs and of open carriages for lap robes as well as for women's overcoats. For the sake of this skin it was slaughtered by the thousands. The Farallon Islands off San Francisco's Golden Gate were particularly busy hunting grounds. One American ship is said to have taken 130,000 fur-seal skins there between the years 1808 and 1810, and other ships took more than 70,000 between 1810 and 1812. Similar harvests took place on the islands off Southern California and Baja, Guadalupe Island being one of the most productive. Names of ships and dates are chiseled in chunks of black lava rock that once formed a hide storehouse on Guadalupe. They show that the island was visited regularly by seal hunters up to 1881. Then there are no more dates. The fur seals apparently were all exterminated.

In 1926, however, a fisherman found a small group of the animals on Guadalupe. Two were captured and sold to the San Diego Zoo. In 1954 Carl Hubbs, after a long search, discovered 14 fur seals on Guadalupe. The following year he located 30 and later found still more. The species had survived after all. The population, almost all confined during the summer breeding season to Guadalupe Island, now numbers at least 500.

The other sea mammal that has managed to come back from near oblivion is the sea otter, perhaps the most engaging of the lot. The sea otter is the smallest of the mammals that have taken permanently to the sea, and it still most closely resembles a land animal. Since it does not store up blubber, as do whales and seals, it is solely dependent on a thick fur coat for protection from the water and the cold. The fur is one of the richest and most luxurious in the world. In centuries past, Chinese mandarins and Russian czars were eager for it, for both warmth and adornment. As a consequence, few fur-bearing animals in the world have been so disastrously pursued and killed for their pelts.

Sea otters originally lived in a great ocean arc extending from Baja California in the south, up along the Northwest coast, out through the Aleutians and down the coast of Asia as far as northern Japan. Vitus Bering, the 18th Century Danish-born explorer who, in the employ of Russia, tried to find a new continent to the east of Siberia, became aware of these odd creatures in the northern seas. The animals were originally inquisitive and quite unafraid of man. Bering's men killed them easily for both food and clothing.

Otter pelts brought back by the survivors of Bering's ill-fated expedition started a fur stampede in the far north. Crew members on James Cook's unsuccessful search for a sea passage across the top of the North American continent in 1778 traded brass buttons and iron nails with the natives of Vancouver Island for sea-otter pelts. The shrewd sailors later found that the skins were worth a small fortune in Chinese ports. Spaniards collected otter skins along the California coast and traded them in China for mercury, needed for refining silver from Spanish mines. British and American ships cruised the North Pacific looking for sea otters, and in the process added considerably to the geographical knowledge of that hitherto unknown part of the world. Russia built a sketchy colonial empire in the New World largely because of the fur resources, but lost interest as the supply of fur-bearing animals diminished. By the time Alaska was sold to the United States in 1867, the sea otters were almost gone. In 1911 a fur treaty gave protection to the northern fur seal and, incidentally, to the sea otter. It apparently was too late for the otters; they seemed to have disappeared forever. But in the 1930s sea otters once more began to be seen in the Aleutians and along the California coast from Monterey south.

There is some scientific disagreement as to whether the sea otters in the Aleutians and those along the California coast are distinct subspecies. They are similar in appearance, but there are differences in behavior. The northern sea otter occasionally goes ashore and may even sleep there. The southern sea otter spends its life in the kelp beds offshore, never going ashore unless ill, injured or dying. The southern sea otter is also a tool user. It uses a stone as a hammer to knock shellfish loose from underwater rocks—among its favorites are abalone, clams and sea urchins. Surfacing and floating on its back, the southern sea otter will place the same stone on its chest and use it as an anvil to break up the shellfish before eating it.

The question of whether northern and southern sea otters are the same or different animals bears on their protection as an endangered species. Those in the south number a little more than a thousand and are fully protected. The northern sea otters are estimated to number 30,000. This is well beyond the danger point where there may be too few members of a species left to assure sufficient reproduction and survival. As a result, the numerous sea otters of the north are subjected to periodic controlled harvesting by wildlife officials, the reasoning being that such killing is necessary to avoid depletion of the food resources of their habitat.

URCHINS EAT KELP—OTTERS EAT URCHINS

Preserving the sea otter population interests more than lovers of nature. For this animal provides a classic example of ecology at work. The kelp beds where the sea otters prefer to live harbor a great variety of commercially valuable marine life. Moreover, kelp itself is an important economic resource. It is rich in algin, a substance that is widely used as a thickener and emulsifier in foods, cosmetics and paints. Ordinarily kelp is one of the strongest and fastest-growing organisms in the world. Cutting its leaflike blades for commercial harvest actually encourages it to grow faster. But sea urchins find kelp tasty fare and can quickly eat through the kelp stalks. One way to combat this destruction is to send divers down to kill the urchins by hand—smashing them one by one with hammers. But nature can do the same job far more efficiently. For sea urchins are one of the sea otters' most favored foods, and where the otter lives, sea urchins are kept under control and the valuable kelp beds thrive.

The interests of the paint and food industries aside, the sea otters are at least as great a public attraction along the California coast as the gray whales—a recreational and esthetic asset. They are easily seen from the shore. They are comical, playful—and the attachment between a mother sea otter and her pup, which she handles much as a human mother handles her baby, is one of the strongest in the animal world.

The gray whale, the elephant seal, the Guadalupe fur seal and the sea otter have several things in common. Each has, in the past, been hunted and killed to the very brink of extermination. And each has recovered and reestablished itself. Nature scores few victories over man's thoughtlessness these days, and most of them are subtle, unobtrusive things: fireweed blooming where a forest stood, grasses anchoring an eroded hillside. But the easily visible gray whales and the sea otters and the more isolated elephant seals and Guadalupe fur seals offer cheering evidence that endangered species, given a respite from man's depredations, can make a comeback and return to the land of the living.

A large gray whale rolls into a deep dive, throwing its flukes into the air. The markings on its side are barnacles, which leave gray patches when they are scraped off.

Atlantis: A Myth Redeemed

The legend of Atlantis, the lost continent, has haunted men since ancient times. The idea of a great civilization destroyed abruptly, its secrets reduced to myth, has tantalized searchers at least since Plato set down a classic description of it about 350 B.C.

But until recently most scientists have left Atlantis to the mythologists. Now, with the announcement of some surprising discoveries on the Aegean island of Thera, the lost continent is at last drawing attention from respectable scientists. If Atlantis was not actually found in 1972, its legend seemed largely explained.

According to Plato, Atlantis was inhabited by a powerful race skilled in art, engineering and agriculture. Suddenly, he wrote, "there occurred violent earthquakes and floods, and in a single day and night of misfortune" the entire island sank out of sight.

In many respects the civilization described by Plato had a parallel in the magnificent Minoan culture based on the Aegean island of Crete. It flourished during the Bronze Age and then, about 1500 B.C., declined. It was left for a Greek archeologist named Spyridon Marinatos to turn up the link between Minos and Atlantis. Digging in volcanic debris on Thera, north of Crete, he unearthed frescoes *(right),* pottery and, in the summer of 1972, paintings testifying to Thera's importance as a trading center—all part of a major Minoan city, with a civilization as sophisticated as Plato's Atlantis. What the findings suggest about the end of Minos is more dramatic. For like Atlantis, Thera apparently vanished almost overnight; about 1500 B.C. a volcanic eruption blew the island to bits and created tidal waves that wiped out the parent civilization on Crete. All that is left of Thera today are a few segments of rugged land embracing a deep gulf.

Wearing blue wigs through which their long hair emerges in snaky locks, two boys spar in a fresco found on Thera and reconstructed in Athens. The old plaster fragments recovered in the dig are rough, the restorer's work smooth.

A Culture Engulfed by a Volcano

◀ *Alternating stripes of dark lava and lighter volcanic ash and pumice, visible on the headlands of Thera's Akrotiri peninsula, were exposed when the island's center sank beneath the sea in the volcanic eruption 3,500 years ago.*

Lying in the middle of the Aegean, Thera and its sister islets were first formed as rocky fragments (yellow in inset) poking above the water. A series of volcanic eruptions caused them to grow into a single round island (white). In about 1500 B.C., when Thera was a Minoan outpost, a major eruption drained so much lava from below it that half collapsed, sending tidal waves in all directions. Only the parts shown in orange are above sea level today.

The volcanic explosion that left Thera's cliffs dropping sheer into the Aegean *(left)* must have been—to judge from the size of the collapsed land mass *(inset below)*—about four times greater than the blast that destroyed the Indonesian island of Krakatoa in 1883. Archeologist Marinatos theorizes that accompanying earthquakes and tidal waves probably wrecked important centers of the flourishing Minoan civilization. The tidal waves alone, moving close to 200 miles per hour, may have been 300 feet high when they slammed against the Minoan capital on nearby Crete. Minos, like legendary Atlantis, never recovered.

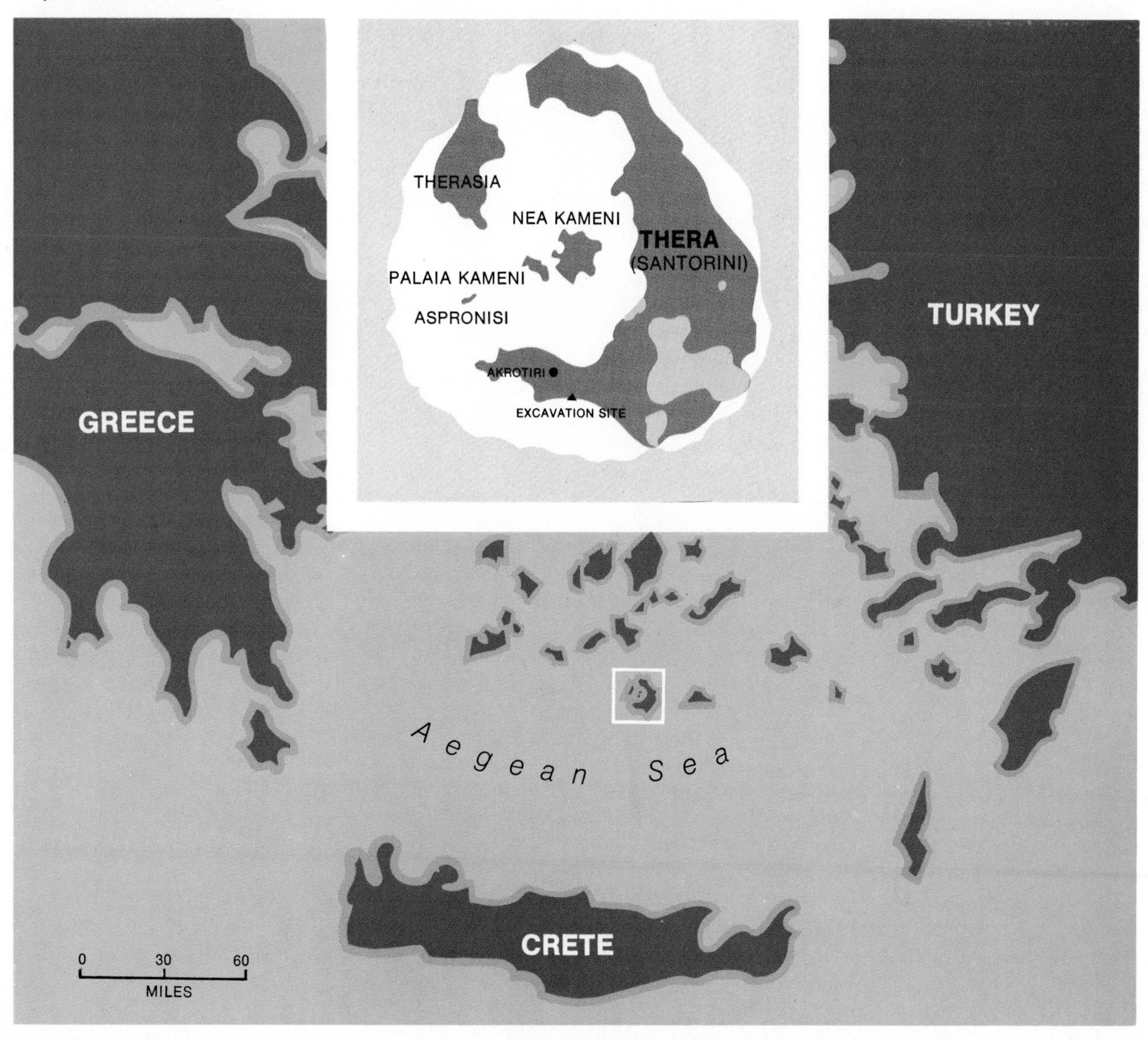

At the dig, excavation director Spyridon Marinatos (left) consults Constantine Eliakis on the placement of fragments of a fresco. Eliakis made the drawing behind them to suggest how the original fresco might have looked.

About eight feet wide, the main street of Thera's ancient city lies partly exposed. Low openings near the ground are windows in the crumbled walls. These buildings were originally three stories high; the top two floors were used for religious purposes, while ground floors served as storerooms.

Beneath the Pumice, a Lucky Find

The rediscovery of Thera's ancient glories came about after Spyridon Marinatos, Inspector General of Greek Antiquities, began to dig in 1967 near the town of Akrotiri, where the volcanic ash was only 30 feet thick rather than 100 to 165 feet as it is on other parts of Thera. "With God's help," he says, "the choice was very lucky." The excavators found themselves in the center of what had been a large town. Part had dropped into the sea when the volcano erupted. But the rest was well preserved. Under a mantle of volcanic ash and pumice lay streets, houses, rooms and furniture. No skeletons were found. Perhaps, speculates Marinatos, the earthquakes preceding the eruption warned the inhabitants to flee. But there remains the ghoulish possibility that "we will find the victims crowded on a beach where they tried and failed to board a ship."

The place where pots are found can reveal something about their use. These vessels were cached near a shrine and apparently had a sacramental purpose.

Nipples on the midsection of this graceful jug, its spout resembling a long-beaked bird, suggest it was used in fertility rites.

A long narrow vessel, decorated with swallows that are surrounded by billowing waves, probably was used for some sacred purpose.

Fitted with a neck, handles and foot of pottery, the vessel at right, made from an empty ostrich egg, was probably imported from Syria.

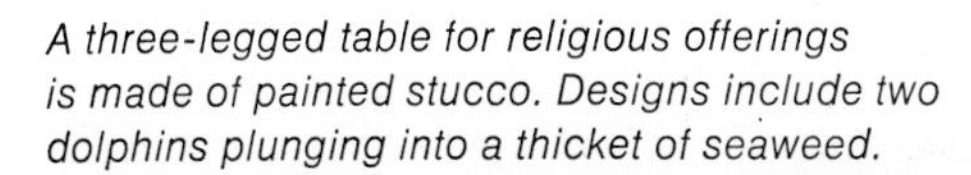

A three-legged table for religious offerings is made of painted stucco. Designs include two dolphins plunging into a thicket of seaweed.

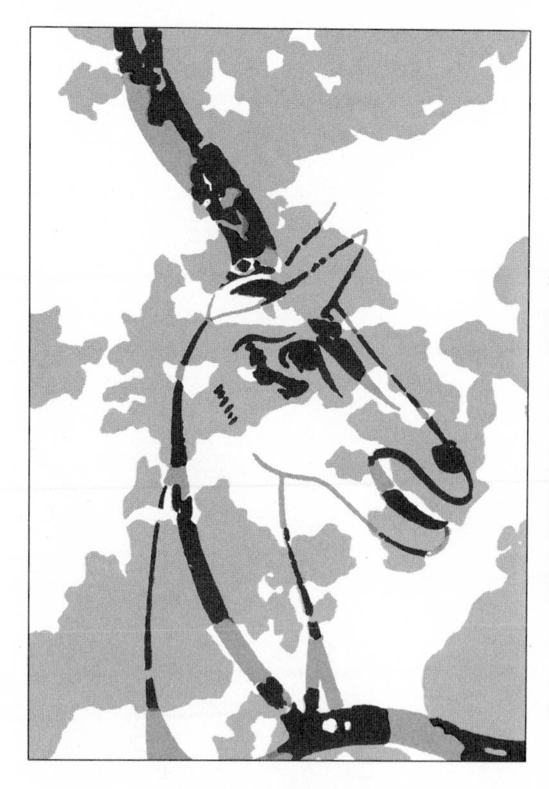

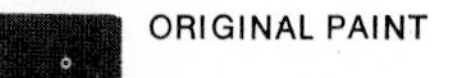

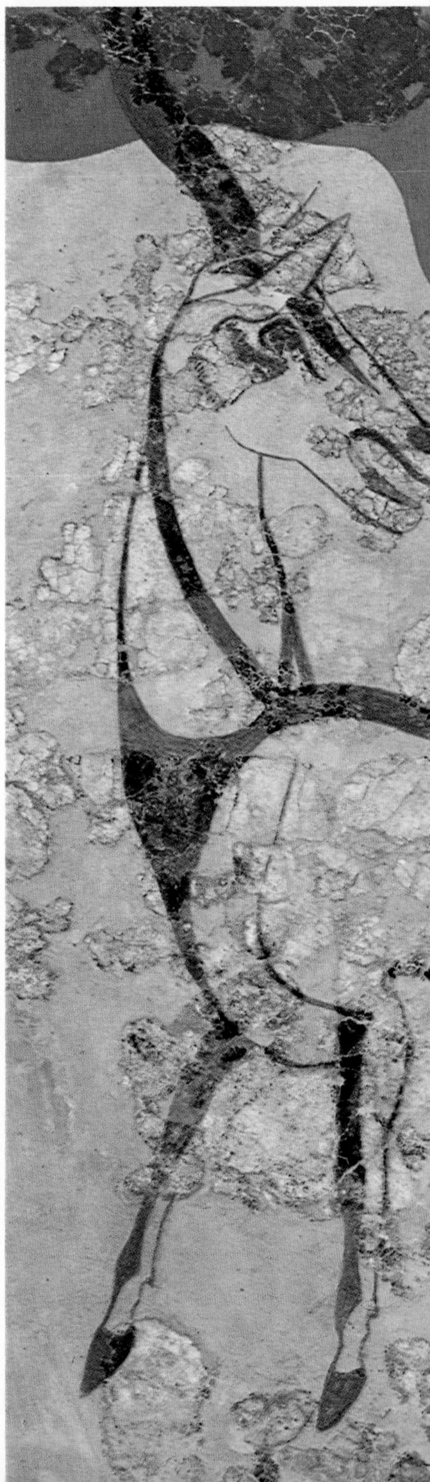

In the room where the boxing boys fresco (page 141) was found, excavators discovered fragments of a painting of antelopes, shown at right. Realized by a few sinuous lines, this kind of antelope is now found only in East Africa. The sketch above shows how restorers pieced together bits of rough plaster, filling in blanks conjecturally.

Broken plaster bearing pictures of seven or eight monkeys, life-size and painted blue, turned up in the rubble of a room. This one is partly restored.

Walls of Beauty and New Mysteries

Most striking of all the beautiful objects unearthed at Thera are the frescoes. Reassembled like jigsaw puzzles from thousands of plaster fragments, the wall paintings exhibit a grace reminiscent of Minoan works, but have a delicacy that sets them apart from other ancient Mediterranean art. Even the frescoes of the palace of Knossos on Crete seem stiff beside them. But they are as puzzling as they are handsome: many of the mammals, birds and even people they show are of types long since vanished from the Aegean—if indeed they ever lived there.

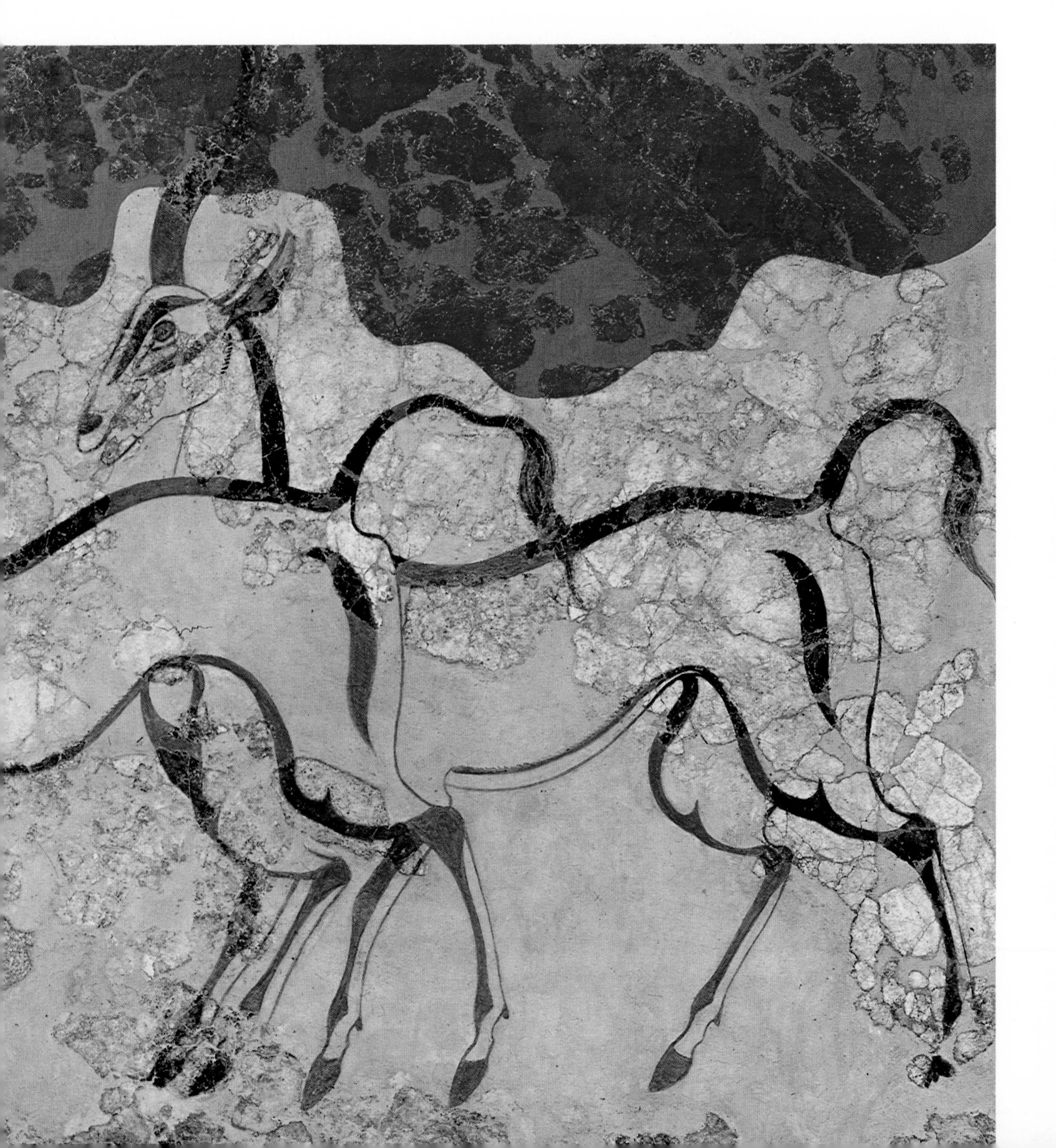

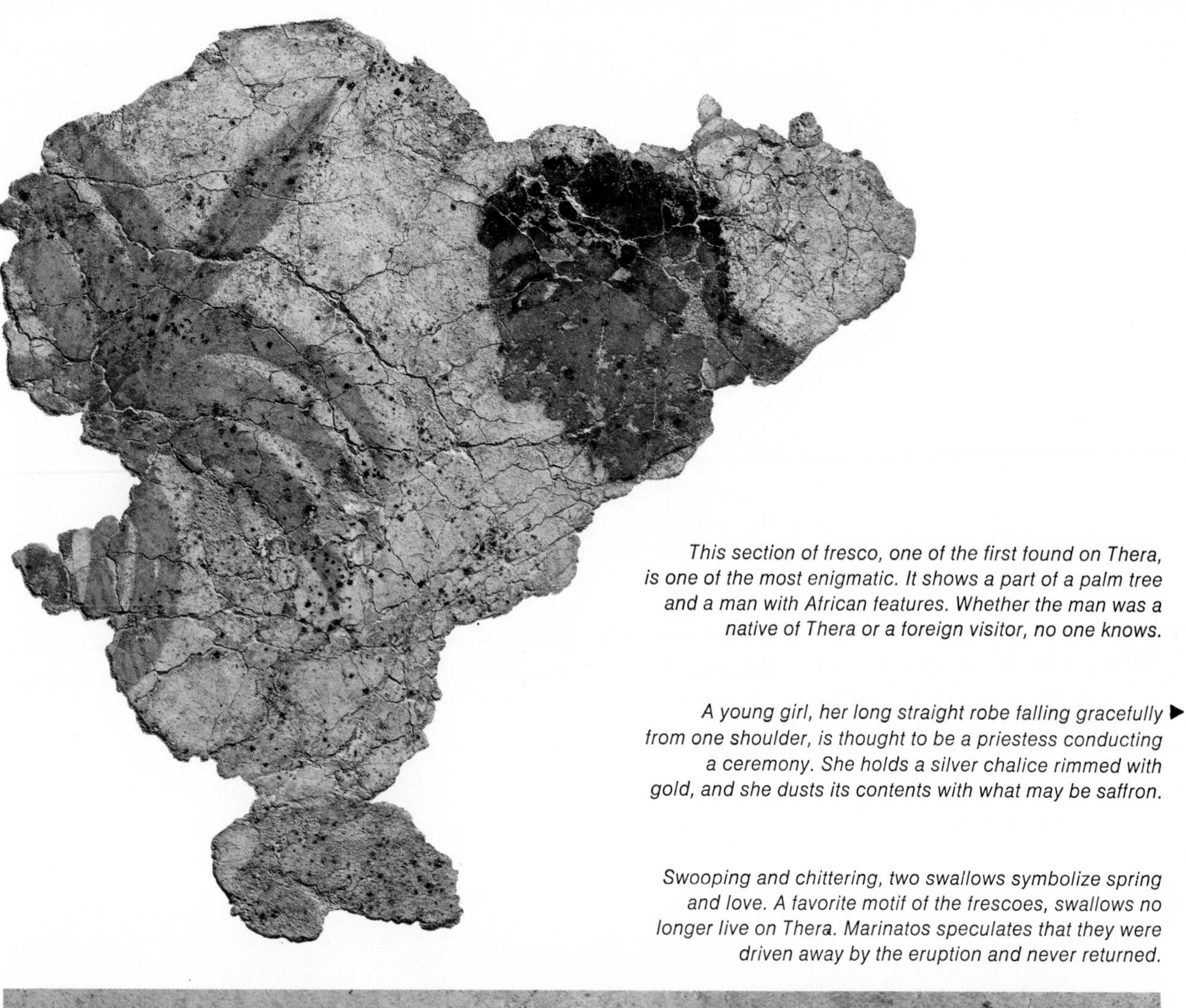

This section of fresco, one of the first found on Thera, is one of the most enigmatic. It shows a part of a palm tree and a man with African features. Whether the man was a native of Thera or a foreign visitor, no one knows.

A young girl, her long straight robe falling gracefully ▶ from one shoulder, is thought to be a priestess conducting a ceremony. She holds a silver chalice rimmed with gold, and she dusts its contents with what may be saffron.

Swooping and chittering, two swallows symbolize spring and love. A favorite motif of the frescoes, swallows no longer live on Thera. Marinatos speculates that they were driven away by the eruption and never returned.

Their rich colors shielded by volcanic ash that choked the buried chamber, frescoes from "The Room of the Lilies" were recovered almost intact, then remounted in Athens.

The Mechanical Heart

SUBSTITUTES FOR NATURE'S PUMP RUN ON ATOMIC POWER

by Rick Gore

The doctors, the designers, the technicians and the engineers had been working on such a device for nearly 10 years. Finally, on Valentine's Day in 1972, in a laboratory room in Boston City Hospital, a cow was kept alive for five hours by a partial artificial heart; the heart was powered by a miniature steam engine that worked on a single drop of water, and the engine was fueled by a tiny capsule of plutonium. With this final experiment, all the components of an artificial heart had been tested successfully in animals. Experiments like these, with individual components and later on with the entire assembled heart, will continue for at least three or four more years with laboratory animals. But if everything goes as expected, scientists at last will have perfected a machine that will replace the human heart. It will perform every function of the natural heart, and without the batteries or outside power source required by previous heart substitutes. It will allow its recipients to walk and run and get excited, and will automatically—by computer—meet the ever-changing demands for more or less blood flow, faster or slower pumping rates. And within the next decade, some say, this artificial heart will be ready for human beings.

Replacement of various body parts and the design of artificial organs have become commonplace of course; but until recently the duplication of the human heart seemed as difficult as a walk on the moon seemed not 10 years ago. The heart is a machine for moving fluids; in its fundamental working principle it is little different from the water pump in grandma's backyard. But in the sophistication of its design and in its ability to work, it is as far from grandma's pump as an au-

Resembling the natural heart, which is also a pump, this artificial organ, made of plastic on a stainless-steel frame, pumps blood through four Dacron-lined chambers.

Chief architect of the artificial heart is a scientist—Lowell T. Harmison of the National Heart and Lung Institute in Washington. In 1962 he began designing a mechanical heart substitute. It has taken 10 years and the work of many fellow scientists to develop the device that has finally been made to work in an animal.

tomated textile mill is from her knitting needles.

The human heart squeezes and relaxes 90 times a minute, 100,000 times every 24 hours, pushing more than 16,000 quarts of blood a day through the body's 60,000 miles of blood vessels. In spite of the bad publicity it gets from its frequently dramatic failures, it is superbly designed for its job. And it is remarkably able to speed up under stress, to slow down when demand passes, to adapt to the change in blood volume needed for extreme arctic cold or oppressive tropical heat. So to attempt to replace it with something man-made is one of the most audacious of modern science's often immodest ventures.

TO DUPLICATE NATURE, START WITH A PUMP

Since the heart is a pump, the scientists started by designing a pump. Simple enough. But this pump would need an engine to drive it; and the engine in turn would need a power source. Finally, to keep the mechanical heart in tune with the vagaries of human life—its ups, its downs, its spurts of activity, its tranquil times—some kind of electronic control system had to be devised.

Clearly this was a formidable assignment—one that would need the skills of biology, cardiology, hemodynamics (the science of blood flow), chemistry, physics, engineering and computer technology—as well as a large injection of common sense, imagination and money.

The team that finally succeeded in this intricate project consisted of a group of scientists at the National Heart and Lung Institute (NHLI) under the direction of Lowell T. Harmison. They had help from the scientists and engineers at Stanford Research Institute, Statham Instrument Inc., Thermo Electron Corporation, Aerojet General Corporation, Travenol Laboratories, McDonnell Douglas Corporation and many other institutions across the country. And somehow this conglomeration of experts has managed to solve the innumerable problems, develop an artificial heart and test it successfully in a living creature.

The need for such a heart is undeniable: each year heart disease claims more than 500,000 lives, and it is estimated that in the United States today there are 100,000 people who could benefit from a new artificial heart. Technologists have devised a wide variety of interim measures to help most of these people. Nearly every individual component of the heart can now be replaced or repaired. Artificial valves have been made by the thousands, in nearly as many designs as are found in an auto-supply catalogue. Pacemakers, to keep the natural heart beating rhythmically when its own internal regulators fail, have been implanted in thousands of people. Transplants, the hope of the late '60s, have faded from the headlines; nonetheless, 29 transplant recipients were still alive in 1972. A variety of heart pumps have also been developed. The heart-lung machine used in open-heart surgery is basically a pump; it drains blood from the heart and artificially oxygenates it outside the body so surgeons are enabled to operate on a clean and quiet heart. And booster pumps have been developed to take over the heart's work for a while, giving it a chance to rest and recuperate.

Perhaps the most famous, or notorious, of these was an eight-ounce plastic heart pump implanted in 1969 in Houston by the well-known surgeon Denton Cooley. The recipient was 47-year-old Haskell Karp, a man doomed to die of congestive heart failure. Cooley had intended a heart transplant, but no donor heart was available. To keep his patient alive until a heart transplant could be located, Cooley tried the artificial pump, a gas-driven device that got its power through two plastic tubes connected to a bedside console about the size of a refrigerator.

Some 65 hours after the artificial pump had been implanted, and while the pump was still going strong, a suitable donor heart at last became available. Cooley transplanted it to Karp. But Karp died 30 hours later. The operation, however, had been a calculated risk: the odds against the heart transplant would have discouraged all but a patient with no other hopes. In any case, the pump was not designed to work over a prolonged period. And even if it had been capable of working for years, it would mean a lifetime tied to that big bedside console. Many physicians are aware of what life on such an artificial device could amount to: quite a few people whose lives have been prolonged by artificial kidney machines have literally pulled the plug from the socket because of the unbearable psychological burden of dependency on "the machine."

The personality battle and the publicity that surrounded this surgical experiment were indeed unfortunate. The medical significance of the heart-pump installation was obscured by an intraprofessional quarrel between Cooley and another famous heart specialist, Dr. Michael DeBakey, who accused Cooley of prematurely using an insufficiently tested gadget that Dr. DeBakey said belonged to him in the first place.

Still, Cooley focused attention on the fact that an artificial pump could be put into a human body and could work for at least 65 hours. And the incident added impetus to the ongoing efforts to build an artificial heart that would not have to be powered from outside, and thus would not restrict its recipient to his bed for life. What was needed was a man-made duplicate of the human heart in all its functions and ramifications—a self-sustaining instrument that would work so precisely like a heart that after a while its recipient might even forget he had it, just as the normal person is oblivious to the rhythmic, constant, life-sustaining action of a natural heart.

The National Heart and Lung Institute had, in fact, been working on the components of a total artificial heart for seven years. The model that Harmison designed remarkably resembles a human heart in shape. Although it is bigger than most human hearts, it is not as large as severely diseased hearts (and such hearts are troublesome not because they are too big, but because they are inefficient). The new artificial heart does nearly everything a human heart does.

THE SOPHISTICATION OF THE HUMAN HEART

To see what the scientists were up against in thus imitating life, it helps to understand how the heart itself works. Consisting mainly of muscle tissue, it is divided into four chambers: two atria above, two ventricles below. The pumping cycle begins when oxygen-poor blood that has been used by the body enters the right atrium from the venae cavae *(diagram, page 160).* From the atrium the blood rushes through the tricuspid valve down to the right ventricle. The valve is one-way; blood moves through it, but cannot flow backward.

From the right ventricle the blood enters the lungs via the pulmonary artery, is enriched with oxygen and gets rid of carbon dioxide; then it returns to the heart. This time it goes to the left atrium through the pulmonary veins. From there it moves down into the left ventricle, then up and out through the aorta, to begin its circuitous journey through the body and back again: veins to atrium to ventricle to lungs to atrium to ventricle to aorta to body. For an artificial heart maker, this is chiefly an engineering problem, and a relatively easy one—compared, that is, with the difficulties of duplicating the heart's natural power supply and its ability to regulate its rate of action.

Because in order for the heart to pump, it must first have a constant source of energy—a fuel supply—to draw upon. The heart's fuel is stored in the sugars and oxygen carried by the blood; when the sugars and oxygen combine, chemical energy is released and this energy keeps the heart muscles in action.

But the action also has to be regulated. And the heart needs a separate power source to stimulate its pacemakers, the specialized tissues that do the regulating. The natural heart's pacemakers get their energy, in the form of electricity, when the salts of calcium, sodium, potassium and other chemicals in the blood and in the cellular fluid of the heart move back and forth across the cell walls, unbalancing the usual equilibrium between positive and negative electric charges.

In order to make the heart respond to the body's continuing demands for speeding up during exercise or anxiety—or slowing down during rest and relaxation—the pacemakers must be able to receive cues from the body. They receive these commands as a wide variety of highly complex and interrelated signals from the body's hormones and nerve impulses, and the pressure and flow of the blood.

The human heart, then, runs itself, energizes itself and paces itself. To achieve the same result with nonliving plastic, metal, rubber and other materials obviously requires the most sophisticated engineering. The challenge was, however, taken up by the NHLI and the laboratories around the country that have been working under contract to NHLI to invent, improvise and perfect the various technologies demanded by these stringent requirements.

The artificial heart they have finally produced consists of a stainless steel frame covered with silicone-rubber-like polyurethane and is divided into two atria and two ventricles. It has artificial valves between the left atrium and ventricle and the right atrium and ventricle—one-way valves as in the human heart. And it has all the appropriate artery and vessel connections, made of plastic tubing.

Nestled in the middle of this "simple" little pump housing is a control mechanism that makes the pump work. When a pulse of energy comes into the control system, it moves a tiny bellows against the inner wall of the right ventricle. This pressure squeezes the blood out of the ventricle through the pulmonary artery into the lung, as the natural heart does in making its first contraction against incoming blood. From the lung, the blood enters the left atrium of the heart, then flows through valves to the ventricular chamber. When that chamber fills, the tiny control mechanism squeezes the bellows against the left ventricle, ejecting blood (now full of oxygen from the lungs) out of the heart through the aorta to the body. Meanwhile, the pressure on the right side of the heart has subsided, letting the next rush of blood flow into the right atrium and ventricle.

The cycle is repeated over and over again: blood enters the right heart, bellows ejects it, the left heart fills, bellows ejects it; each emptying makes room for the next filling and activates the bellows for the next emptying.

OVERCOMING THE HURDLE OF BLOOD DAMAGE

One of the most difficult problems facing the heart designers (and the developers of the heart-lung pump before them) was how to move the blood around in an artificial environment without damaging it. Blood is a very delicate substance. In the body, blood cells are protected in their dangerous journey through veins, capillaries, liver, heart and so on, because the channels are lined with a material that does not damage blood. Artificial equipment is different; it must of necessity be made of harder, nonliving, nongiving stuff. So the artificial heart had to be carefully designed in such a way to ensure that none of its moving parts would touch during a pump stroke, to avoid crushing the blood cells as they passed through. The NHLI designers also discovered that blood damage could be minimized if the blood flow is steady and smooth, so that no drops or spurts in pressure could cause the blood to jet through or to eddy—both potential causes of pulling and tearing. Accordingly, the chambers are built to empty completely, so that no little pools of blood collect to stagnate.

Another difficulty the designers of the artificial pump had to confront was how to duplicate the heart's natural lining, for human blood tends to clot when it touches any foreign surface. (This was one of the greatest stumbling blocks in the design of the heart-lung machine.) Inside the natural heart is a cushion of tissue called endothelium that provides a smooth path for blood as it passes through the corridors of the heart. The NHLI team's answer to this ingenious natural design was to line the artificial heart with flocked Dacron velour, a velvety material like that of soft sport shirts and baby pajamas. This material is full of microscopic spindles—which may sound like an unsuitable surface for blood; in fact, when blood flows over the Dacron the spindles pick up bits of fibrin, a chief clotting agent in blood. The fibrin forms a kind of mat on which endothelium can grow—living endothelium no different from the natural lining of the living heart.

In cows, a heart with just such a lining has pumped for months with only minimal damage to the blood (even the real heart does a little damage to blood cells). It will take much longer testing to see if this lining is durable enough for humans; meanwhile, new materials are being tested in search of the perfect one. Harmison predicts that it will soon be possible to take out a small vein sample from a patient's leg a few weeks before surgery, strip out the endothelial lining, and use it to grow endothelium in the artificial heart even before it is implanted.

While the biologists and engineers were solving this problem, thermodynamics experts were working on the second major component required for the artificial heart system: an engine to supply the power that would squeeze the bellows against the heart's chambers. The heat engine was an obvious contender for the artificial heart. Though the engineers had a variety of choices, they elected to concentrate their efforts on two systems. One of these, the steam engine, was not exactly a new or unfamiliar piece of equipment. In a steam engine, water is heated to steam, the steam expands under pressure, and the expansion can be used to push something—such as the appropriate part of a pump.

AN ENGINE THAT WORKS ON A DROP OF WATER

But the steam-type engine devised for the artificial heart—by Fred Huffman at Thermo Electron in Waltham, Massachusetts—would be barely recognizable to the engineer of a locomotive or a steamboat. Actually called a tidal regenerator engine, the miniature machine made by the Waltham group produces no huge rushes of hot steam and, in fact, works essentially on one drop of water. This is how:

On signal from a computer, two magnets cause a miniature bellows to expand, pushing a drop of water from a reservoir up through a narrow column into a "boiler" *(diagram, page 161).* There the drop of water becomes steam. The steam is heated still further, and as it heats it expands until enough pressure builds up to push down on another tiny bellows. This bellows activates a piston that presses on still another bellows and forces hydraulic fluid out through a little tube. Now at last we get to the point: the fluid in this little tube flows through the feed line to that other bellows in the heart that compresses the ventricles and makes the blood move. As soon as the blood is pushed out, a sensor in the heart gives a signal, everything reverses itself, pressure drops back down again, and all is ready for the next stroke. Pressure up, heart pumping, pressure down, heart refills again, ready to be emptied by the next pulse of steam pressure against bellows against piston against bellows against feed line. Rube Goldberg couldn't do better.

But the artificial heart designers are cautious men. So they sought insurance by investigating a number of engine designs. In addition to the steam engine, the only other thermal engine to survive their scrutiny is the Stirling engine—a

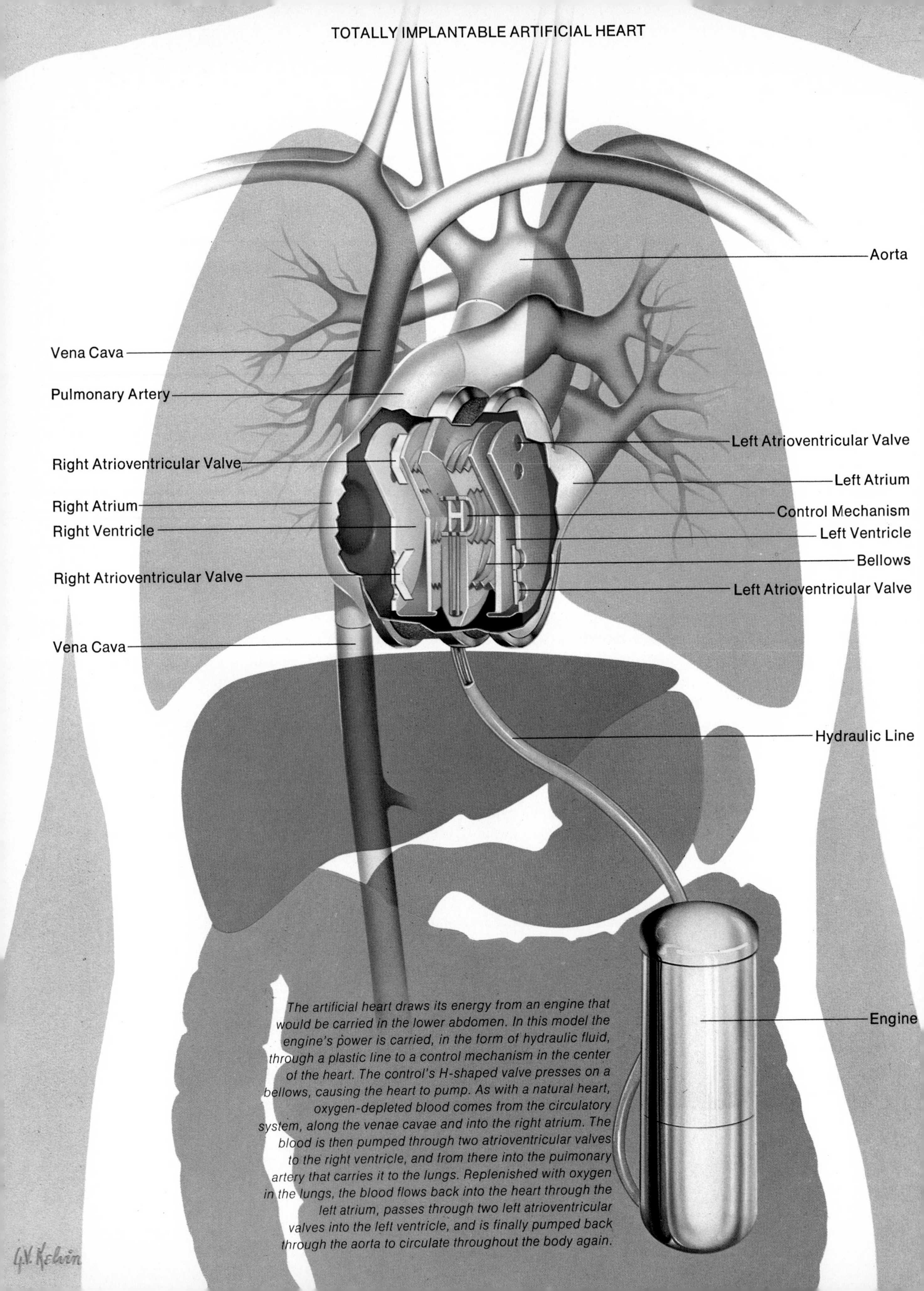

The artificial heart draws its energy from an engine that would be carried in the lower abdomen. In this model the engine's power is carried, in the form of hydraulic fluid, through a plastic line to a control mechanism in the center of the heart. The control's H-shaped valve presses on a bellows, causing the heart to pump. As with a natural heart, oxygen-depleted blood comes from the circulatory system, along the venae cavae and into the right atrium. The blood is then pumped through two atrioventricular valves to the right ventricle, and from there into the pulmonary artery that carries it to the lungs. Replenished with oxygen in the lungs, the blood flows back into the heart through the left atrium, passes through two left atrioventricular valves into the left ventricle, and is finally pumped back through the aorta to circulate throughout the body again.

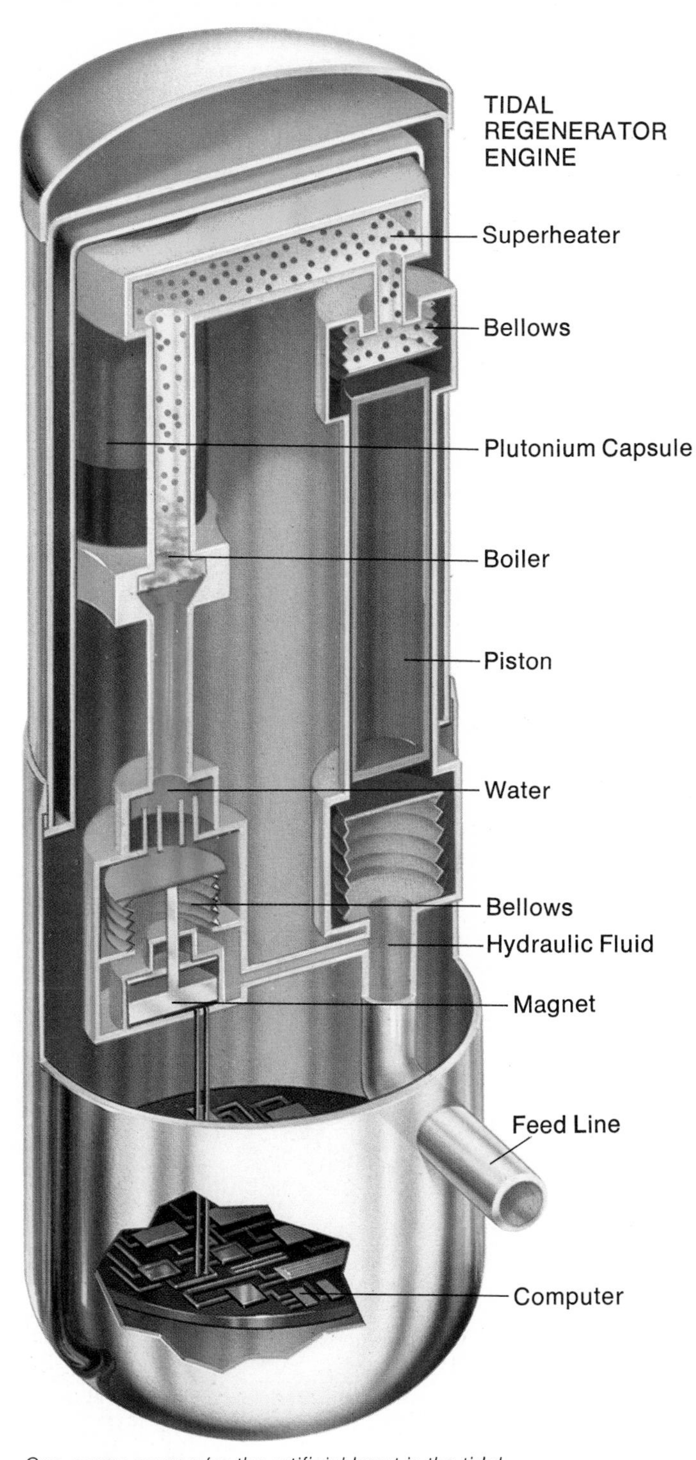

One power source for the artificial heart is the tidal regenerator engine, diagramed above (actual size). On signal from a computer, an electromagnet is activated to attract another magnet. The movement expands a bellows that forces a drop of water up a tube into a boiler where heat from radioactive plutonium vaporizes the water into steam. The steam is heated still further in a superheater. This steam then pushes on another bellows, forcing a piston downward against a third bellows that, in turn, sends a pulse of hydraulic fluid through the feed line to the artificial heart to power its next beat. The computer, timed to a normal heartbeat, sends another message, and the magnets separate. The bellows drops back and the steam condenses back into the original drop of water, ready for the next sequence.

An alternative power source for the artificial heart is the modified Stirling engine, diagramed below (actual size). At its center is a piston that slides in a helium-filled chamber. Plutonium above the piston heats and expands the gas, forcing the piston down. When the piston reaches the bottom of the cylinder, it forces most of the helium into the reservoir that is located at the bottom of the engine. The rest of the helium rushes into the bellows chamber under the piston, forcing the bellows to expand and drive the piston back to its up position. Because this cycle takes place 20 times faster than the normal heartbeat, a reservoir is needed to store the helium. When the heart needs more energy, it signals the diaphragm pump and a drop of hydraulic fluid, under pressure from the helium, spurts from its reservoir through the feed line to the artificial heart.

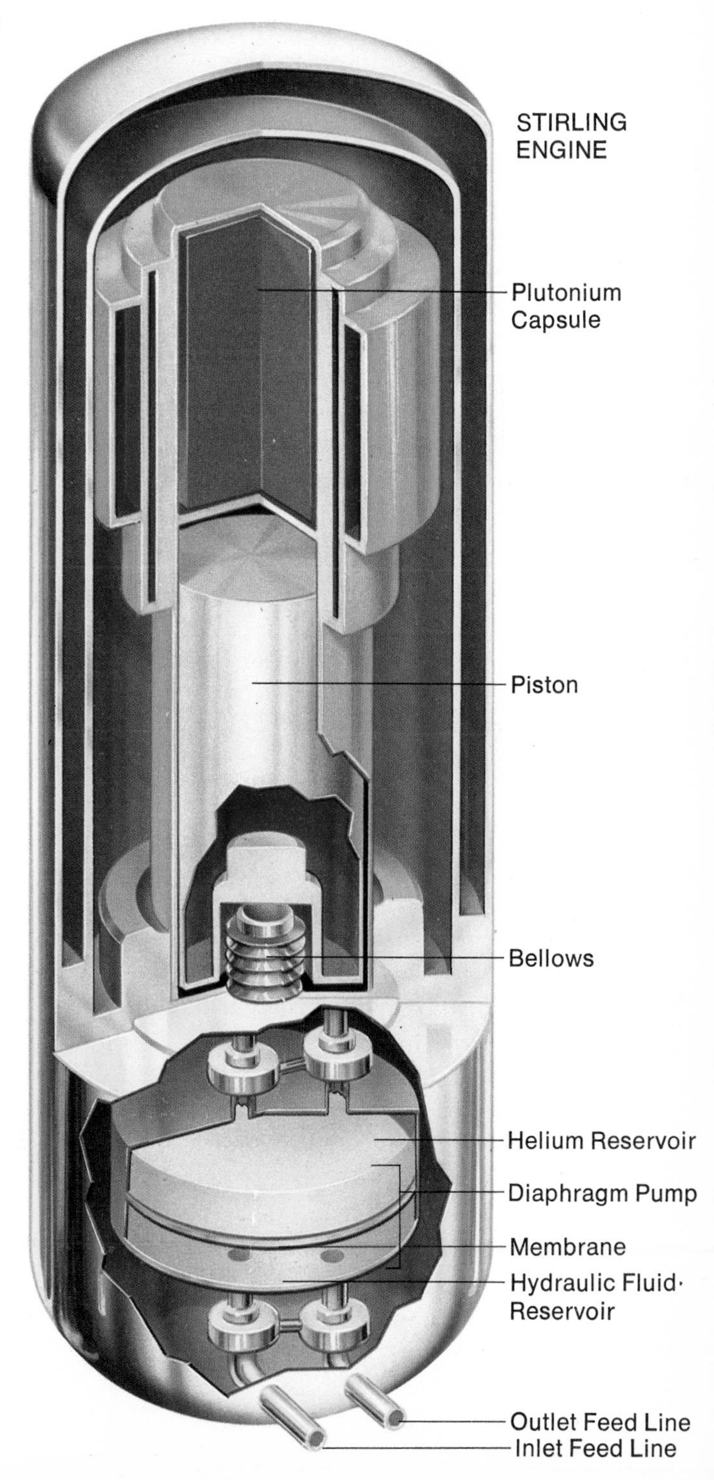

little-used, little-heard-of 19th Century invention.

When Robert Stirling patented his machine in 1816, the laws of thermodynamics on which his engine depended had not yet been worked out. Stirling was not an engineer by trade (in fact he was a 26-year-old Scottish clergyman); he was, however, aware of the danger of steam explosions, which were common in those early days of industrialization in England. Because his engine used hot air as the working force instead of steam, there was far less danger of explosion. The Stirling engine was widely used in England and America for a while, particularly in farm machinery, but it lost out when safer steam-driven devices were developed, and it gradually fell into oblivion. But in the last decade, Stirling engines have been making a comeback; engineers are developing test engines for underwater propulsion systems, power plants, spacecraft and nonpolluting cars. Late in 1972, the Ford Motor Company made a multimillion-dollar agreement with a Dutch electronics firm to develop a quiet low-pollution Stirling engine for automobiles.

Stirling's machine was unique when he invented it 150 years ago. Its simplicity of design and concept required few moving parts. In the typical steam engine, the working fluid is located in one place (as in a boiler) and flows to another place, where it performs its work—such as pushing on a piston. Most steam engines also require a condenser to convert steam into water so that the cycle can begin again. But the Stirling engine separates its hot and cool regions; at the hot end of the engine air is heated very rapidly. As it expands it pushes down on the piston, which does the work. As the gas cools it compresses; the piston returns to its starting position and the cycle is ready to begin again.

There are two 1972-version Stirling engines in the running for the artificial heart system. One is being developed under the direction of Mark Rudnicki of the Aerojet General Corporation of Sacramento; the other is being designed by William Martini at McDonnell Douglas Corporation in Richland, Washington. The two systems have some differences that are important to engineers, but basically they work the same way.

The Stirling engine consists of a cylinder filled with helium (rather than the hot air of the original Stirlings) that contains a floating piston. At the top of the cylinder is a pellet of radioactive material that heats the helium to about 1,200° F. This very hot helium expands rapidly, forcefully driving the piston to the bottom of the cylinder where the temperature is almost 1,100° lower. As the piston moves down, it forces some of the gas out through a valve on the cylinder floor into a storage reservoir. When the heart needs more energy, it signals the reservoir and a valve opens. Helium pressing on a membrane below it forces hydraulic fluid out through the open valve into a feed line that leads to the heart. Not all the helium is expelled into the reservoir on the downstroke; a small amount rushes into a bellows located underneath the piston and forces the piston back to its up position. At the same time another valve on the other side of the cylinder opens and recycled helium surges back in. Then the cycle starts all over again.

USING BLOOD TO ABSORB EXCESS HEAT

One big problem of both the tidal regenerator and the Stirling engines is that all the compression, friction and hot steam or helium could easily raise the temperature of the heart pump to as much as 150° F. That is high enough to severely damage human tissue. The engineers had an answer to this problem as well: they designed a metal heat-exchanging surface into the pump. The metal transfers the pump's excess heat directly into the blood as it rushes by. Like the water in the radiator of a car, the blood dissipates the heat throughout the body, preventing any one spot from getting too hot. The body's built-in temperature control mechanisms—the most familiar of which is sweating—take over at that point to dispel the excess heat.

So far so good. But if either the Stirling or the tidal regenerator engine is to be used for the artificial heart, it will need an internal fuel source to raise the temperature of that drop of water or that bit of helium. Searching for such a fuel, the NHLI scientists were led to nuclear physics.

A tiny amount of a radioactive isotope can provide enough heat to run a steam or gas engine nonstop for decades. Radioactive isotopes constantly toss off energy in the form of heat. One of the most attractive of these isotopes, from the viewpoint of the artificial heart designers, is plutonium 238, a close but more gentle cousin of the bomb material plutonium 239. In the open air, plutonium 238 gives off enough heat to burn a hole in a thick table in half a minute. It keeps on giving off this heat for a substantial amount of time—89 years to run down to half its strength, another 89 years to run down to half of that. Obviously that is quite long enough to keep an artificial heart pumping.

But could you put such a thing in a human body? It has already been done. Some 100 people in the world today are going to the grocery and going to their offices and taking care of their children with little capsules of plutonium 238 tucked into their abdomens. These people are the recipients of the first nuclear-powered pacemakers—the previously mentioned devices that substitute for a heart's faulty electrical system. Developed in a joint French-American industrial project, these pacemakers were approved by the atomic regulatory bodies of several European countries some time ago and by the United States late in 1972. The biomedical and surgical aspects are French; the electronics and wiring systems have been designed and produced by Medtronic, Inc., a Minneapolis firm that had pioneered in the development of conventional battery-powered pacemakers. The plutonium power sources are manufactured by Société Alcatel of France and that country's atomic energy agency.

Late in 1972, doctors at the Veterans Administration Hospital in Buffalo implanted the first four such units in American patients, all men in their forties and fifties. Until then the only recipients had been Europeans, because the American government had been cautious in granting its approval for the use of plutonium to power pacemakers. Nor, for a time, would the U.S. even allow European pacemaker bearers to enter the country. But in November 1971 the AEC did give permission for a European pacemaker user to visit America—Madame Jeanne Labatut, the chic and vigorous 50-year-old head of a photographic agency in Paris. She wore a conspicuous identity card bearing the international symbol for "radioactive material." Not that anyone considered her particularly radioactive, although she certainly might be called dynamic. Clearly, her colleagues could tell, the capsule of plutonium was not causing her to lose sleep or miss a step in her energetic, vivacious life.

TOUGH TESTS FOR A RADIOACTIVE CAPSULE

Plutonium, of course, does emit radiation, and a small amount of it, accidentally swallowed, could be deadly. But the two hundredths of an ounce that powers the pacemaker is safely encapsulated and emits little more radiation than color television sets. And to make sure the radiation would never escape by accident, the capsule was put through a strenuous series of tests. In Spain the reinforced capsules were shot against steel walls at 120 miles an hour. In France they were run over by buses and thrown into fires. In Germany police marksmen shot bullets at them. They did not break open.

For the artificial heart, similar tough tests were performed to ensure that no one would be exposed to radiation if some disaster occurred to the bearer of a plutonium energy source. The canister that holds the plutonium has been heated to 2,400° F. (1,700° F. is the peak temperature of a building on fire). The testers have exposed the canister to 10 tons of explosive force (more than has ever been measured in an airplane explosion) without rupturing it. They have guillotined it with 10,000 pounds of shearing force, without deforming it.

Another possible danger is to people who might be exposed to radioactivity after the death of a plutonium-powered heart bearer. In Europe, careful arrangements have already been made to keep a central registry of nuclear pacemaker users; their physicians will be expected to keep regular checks on their health and the status of their pacemakers, and to notify the central registry in case of death, so the pacemaker can be returned to the atomic agency for safe disposal. The assumption is that similar stringent requirements would be worked out for recipients of the atom-powered heart.

Not all conceivable problems associated with this use of plutonium have been solved. At the current stage of design, the amount of radiation leakage is slightly above occupational safety levels. It will have to be reduced, even though tests on animals have shown no acute effects from the current levels so far. Whether or not the plutonium capsule would pose any danger to the artificial heart user's genes is also very much under study. Most of the candidates for an artificial heart would be beyond the child-bearing age, and the others would probably not find it difficult to choose, if necessary, between life without children and no life at all.

Yet another type of engine, powered by electricity instead of plutonium, is under development by the NHLI team. So far it has been used mostly to run test-model artificial hearts while the scientists check out various aspects of its functioning: stroke rate, adaptation to sudden demands for blood and so on. But it has not been ruled out as a possible driving force for the final artificial heart, especially if the other engines present unexpectedly formidable problems. The electrical engine has one drawback. It would operate on batteries that would have to be recharged from outside the body. But, as the users of artificial pacemakers know, electric current at the proper voltage passes easily through the skin without damage, just as low-voltage X-rays pass through soft tissue and onto an X-ray plate.

POWERING A HEART FROM AN ATTACHÉ CASE

The owner of such an electrically driven artificial heart would, in a sense, be like any other rechargeable instruments, such as electric razors, portable radios and electric toothbrushes. He would be hooked up to a DC power supply that he could carry about in an attaché case. As Harmison describes it:

"The person could leave his house on DC power in the morning with 12 or 14 hours of energy stored in his attaché case. He would arrive at work, plug the attaché case into the wall socket and switch off the DC current. His heart would then be essentially running off the wall socket. Whenever he needed to get up and move around, he would switch back to DC, pick up his attaché case, and go."

So the designers have a pump, an engine to run it and a power source. What this adds up to is a device that could pump as steadily and regularly as a clock ticks—but, unfortunately, human hearts don't work that way. When a man runs to catch a train, his heartbeat may leap from 72 times a minute up to 200. In sleep, the beat may ease down to 40 or 50. It changes its rhythm as the rhythm of a person's life changes, from hour to hour, minute to minute, second to second, in response to a complex system of chemical and electrical changes in the body. To attempt to duplicate the control system that paces the human heart would seem daring, to say the least.

Once again the artificial heart team concentrated on what might be called the heart of the matter—its controls. The natural heart's control system is subtle, sophisticated and elaborate. It involves pressure and volume changes, nerve impulses and hormones. During exercise, for example, the heart is alerted by hormones and nerve impulses that express a higher demand for oxygen. The body meets this demand by sending a greater supply of blood from the veins back to the heart, where it is required to increase the fresh oxygen-rich supply going back to the body. And as greater amounts of venous blood pour into the right atrium and ventricle, the muscle fibers of the ventricle have to stretch to accommodate the incoming load. In order to get the additional supply of blood quickly into the body, the ventricle has to contract more forcefully. Special nerve fibers sense this higher pressure and cue the heart's pacemaker tissues that more speed is needed to handle the extra work.

This is oversimplified and doesn't occur in such a clear chronological order; everything actually happens almost simultaneously. But the main points are still increased pressure and flow, felt by nerve cells. Harmison reasoned that a device that could detect blood flow requirements and produce appropriate electrical signals could make the artificial heart respond with changes in rate and stroke volume to properly regulate the flow of blood through the heart.

In short, they needed a sensing device and a computer. Volume-sensitive devices have been around a long time; it was not too difficult to put sensors on the ventricles of the artificial heart.

The computer was another matter; even in this age of miniaturization it takes a flight of imagination to visualize a computer small enough to fit inside the body. But the technology is all there. The required computer circuit now fits onto a plate about the width and length of a Hershey bar. It is only a matter of time before the circuits can be reduced to the size of a dime.

PICKING A PACKAGE FOR A MAN-MADE HEART

With all four major components of the heart system well on their way to completion, Harmison and his team are developing three possible ways in which they might finally be packaged. First, an implantable heart that is resupplied with energy at regular intervals from outside the body. Second, and probably more desirable, an artificial heart pump with a separate power source implanted elsewhere in the body. (In nuclear pacemakers, for example, the plutonium power source is placed in the abdomen; about the size and weight of a heavy pocket watch, it seems to cause no discomfort and most pacemaker users forget it is there.) Third, a totally self-contained package, with pump, engine, power source and computer control all tightly compressed into a single artificial heart device.

While the third alternative sounds ideal, Harmison explains that it might be easier to make adjustments or repairs if the engine and computer were implanted in their own capsule in the abdomen. Detecting the need for such repairs is one of the simpler aspects of the problem. Computers of the kind that are already in use to diagnose auto engines electronically could be adapted to perform checkups on the artificial heart. This is already being done successfully with pacemakers: an electronic sensing device is merely placed over the chest and plugged into a telephone that is connected with a central computer laboratory.

The last critical step in the progression from the drawing board to use in humans is for the artificial heart to be tested for longer periods in animals. Harmison feels there are several major questions that must be painstakingly put to the proof in living creatures:

Will the whole body function normally with an artificial heart pump? How will specific organs —lungs, liver, kidney, brain—all respond to an artificially pumped blood supply? Will the damage to blood cells be minimal enough for good health? How will the artificial heart system respond over long periods to changing needs of the body? Will it react fast enough to sudden energy demands? Can the heat that the engine creates be indeed safely dispersed by the body without damaging tissue? And most of all, is the artificial heart totally reliable and safe?

These are big questions, and heart designer Harmison is well aware that a great deal more effort must be invested before all of them are answered. But the artificial heart innovators have already solved a series of complex medical, engineering and biological problems in remarkably short order. They *know* the heart will work: they believe it will work in humans—if not in this decade, then early in the next.

Summing Up the Year

A BRIEF REVIEW OF EVENTS, DISCOVERIES AND DEVELOPMENTS

ARCHEOLOGY

Three of the year's significant archeological finds concerned beautiful women of the past: the carefully preserved remains of a lady of the ancient Chinese court, new information about Egypt's enigmatic Queen Nefertiti and a statue of a young woman sculpted by a Sixth Century B.C. Athenian. Other archeological discoveries shed light on the origins of the Christian Gospel of St. Mark and on the prehistory of North America.

THE EARLIEST AMERICAN CALENDAR

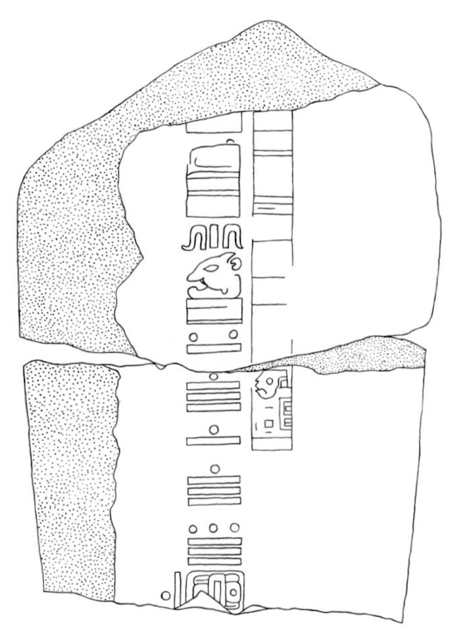

FRAGMENT PROVES OLMECS HAD CALENDAR.

The discovery of a missing chunk of intricately carved stone in Mexico's State of Veracruz finally established that, contrary to popular belief, the Maya, who ruled in Mexico and Guatemala from 300 to 900 A.D., did not invent the so-called Maya calendar. That sophisticated device, the stone fragment demonstrated, had been used by the Olmec, the founders of a civilization that existed some 300 years before the Maya. The piece of carved stone bore a date equivalent to 31 B.C.; that date proved significant on two counts. First, it placed the stone in the Olmec period (1200 B.C. to the Birth of Christ), and second, it proved that in order to date the carved stone, the Olmec must have had a calendar.

The find belatedly confirmed the deduction of Matthew W. Stirling of the Smithsonian Institution, who in 1939 unearthed part of a stone monument near the village of Tres Zapotes, site of an Olmec cultural center. After deciphering an incomplete column of mathematical symbols on the fragment, Stirling set the date at 31 B.C., well before the classical Maya era. Not until a Tres Zapotes farmer stumbled on another fragment of the same stone in February was Stirling's contention borne out. The farmer's find fitted Stirling's exactly and did bear a date corresponding to 31 B.C., the earliest recorded date in the New World.

A MASTER'S WORK FOUND

STATUES UNCOVERED NEAR ATHENS ARE THE FIRST KNOWN WORKS OF A MASTER SCULPTOR.

Greek archeologists exploring old graves in a field 25 miles from Athens unearthed two 2,500-year-old statues of painted marble that were immediately acclaimed by experts as masterpieces of the art of antiquity. One, of a young woman in a crimson, short-sleeved, pleated dress, has been identified as the only known example of the art of the Sixth Century B.C. sculptor Aristion of Paros. It was identified because it fitted a marble base, stored in an Athens museum, that bore the inscription "Aristion the Parian made me." Also carved in the base is a girl's name, "Phrasikleia." The other statue, of a nude young man, is similar in execution and material—Parian marble—and is considered likely also to be by Aristion. The young man, the archeologists theorize, may have been the girl's brother because the two figures were interred together face to face in the same pit; their family may have buried the funeral statues, it is thought, to save them from invading Persians about 490 B.C. The discovery of the statues is of particular importance to art historians and museum curators: heretofore the only physical evidence of Aristion's craftsmanship has consisted of four marble bases—one of them Phrasikleia's—from which the carved figures were missing. Now that the sculptor's style and technique are known, statues of hitherto undetermined origin may be identified as his work.

AN EYEWITNESS GOSPEL

A tiny fragment of papyrus no bigger than a man's thumbnail, from the Dead Sea Scrolls at Qumran, offered evidence that the Gospel of Mark was written before 50 A.D., or well within two decades of the Crucifixion. It therefore may be the work of contemporaries of Jesus who knew the disciples and perhaps witnessed the events the authors wrote about. Heretofore, modern Biblical scholars have assumed that the Gospels were written so long after the death of Christ that they must have been based on tales handed down via the beclouded memories of aged men. (The earliest known Gospel manuscript is dated at 135 A.D.)

The fragment of papyrus was one of 19 discovered in Qumran's Cave Seven in 1955, eight years after the first Dead Sea Scrolls had come to light. Scholars had dismissed these fragments as of only cursory interest; unlike the other scrolls, the 19 were in Greek rather than Hebrew or Aramaic. But they were dated: because of the Greek script's style, and the dates of coins found with them, they were identified as having originated between 50 B.C. and 50 A.D.

Pursuing Old Testament research at Rome's Pontifical Biblical Institute, Father José O'Callaghan, a Spanish Jesuit of Irish ancestry, was scrutinizing facsimiles of the fragments. On one, he could make out only 17 of the Greek characters in a five-line passage. But one group of characters looked to him like part of the word "Gennesaret," the Biblical name for a section of the region of Galilee and for the Sea of Galilee. The name recalled to O'Callaghan the passage in the Gospel of Mark relating to the miracle of the loaves and fishes. O'Callaghan turned to the passage in Mark, in its original Greek and set in five lines of from 20 to 23 characters each, the form in which the scrolls were written. He then superimposed the Greek passage on the facsimile of the fragment, like a tracing. The Greek passage fitted the fragment; and the 17 characters written on the fragment fell almost exactly in the proper places in the Gospel passage—thus indicating that some of the Gospel of Mark was written almost a century earlier than has been supposed.

FINGERPRINTS IN THE MARBLE

A new and better way to determine where a given piece of marble came from, reported in April, promised to resolve a multitude of archeological and artistic controversies: it may help date ancient sculptures since, between pre-Classical and Roman times, the Greeks shifted their quarrying from island to island at known dates. If the marble's birthplace is pinpointed, the period in which the stone was cut can be fixed, and it might even be possible to tell, for example, that a sculpture which has been debatably attributed to the Greek master Praxiteles (c. 370-330 B.C.) was only a Roman imitation carved centuries later.

Though specialists can generally identify marbles by content, color and texture, such signs afford uncertain clues. In the new technique, developed by the husband-and-wife team of Harmon and Valerie Craig of the Scripps Institution of Oceanography in La Jolla, California, minute samples of marbles are analyzed to determine their content of two varieties, or isotopes, of carbon and oxygen—carbon 13 and oxygen 18. The abundance of these two isotopes varies enough from one type of marble to another to fix a stone's identity as surely as fingerprints identify people.

BURIED TREASURE IN CHINA

Workmen digging excavation tunnels in Changsha, the capital of China's Honan province, unexpectedly brought to light a remarkable archeological treasure: a 2,100-year-old tomb that contained the extraordinarily well-preserved body of a noblewoman and a piece of silk seven feet long and three feet wide on which were painted scenes from legend and contemporary life. The body had resisted decay so well because it was protected so elaborately: it rested in the innermost of six coffins that had been buried under five tons of charcoal covered in turn by a four-foot layer of clay. The silk, also preserved in near-perfect condition, covered the coffin containing the body. An authority on Chinese art, Britain's ambassador in Peking, John Addis, described the painting as one of the most important discoveries in years. Also found in the tomb were nearly a thousand other relics of the Western Han Dynasty, which ruled part of China from 202 B.C. to about 25 A.D.

A BEAUTIFUL, POWERFUL QUEEN

The surviving sculptures of her attest that Egypt's 14th Century B.C. Queen Nefertiti was one of history's greatest beauties. Now, new archeological evidence indicates that she was also a major force in the reign of her husband, King Akhenaton, during the Golden Age of Egypt. University of Pennsylvania archeologist Ray Winfield Smith suggests that it was Nefertiti, and not Akhenaton, who conceived the world's first known monotheistic religion.

Smith made his deductions after assembling a gigantic jigsaw puzzle made up of photographs of 35,000 fragmented stone carvings that had been scattered across the Egyptian countryside (some were even found in Europe and the United States) for 33 centuries. Assembling a photographic reconstruction of part of the temple at Karnak built by Akhenaton,

Smith has discovered that the temple's carvings depict Nefertiti far more often than they do her husband. They show her as a goddess who was accorded equal rank with the king in religious ritual —unprecedented honors even for a royal wife in male-dominated Egypt. Smith points to a further piece of evidence: at Tell el 'Amarna, where Akhenaton built a new capital 240 miles from Thebes, an inscription relates that Nefertiti had her own ideas about the city's designs. No other queen had expressed views different from her husband's, and lived to have her opposition graven in stone.

ASTRONOMY

Confident that life, and possibly even civilization, exists on some unknown planet, astronomers took steps to pick up any signals or chance chatter on a giant radio telescope, and rocketed out a small picture plaque introducing earthman and his mate to any passersby in space. Meanwhile, more prosaically, scientists rediscovered an elusive comet and adjusted the world's time by one second.

BRINGING TIME UP TO DATE

June 30, 1972, was the longest day ever recorded since the bureau started keeping time in 1912. The world's official timekeepers, the Bureau International de l'Heure in Paris, added a second to June 30 at midnight Greenwich Mean Time, making that day 86,401 seconds long instead of the normal 86,400. They did it by slowing the clock at Britain's Royal Greenwich Observatory, with which national observatories everywhere coordinate time. The adjustment was necessary because the earth's rotation is slowing down and Greenwich Mean Time based on that rotation, was diverging from the time kept by the relatively new, but more accurate, atomic clocks. The difference is almost infinitesimal, but it was becoming crucial to navigators, astronomers and other scientists to whom superexact timing is essential. Greenwich Time and atomic time will be correlated again whenever they differ by as much as seven tenths of a second.

COMMUNICATION WITH THE COSMOS

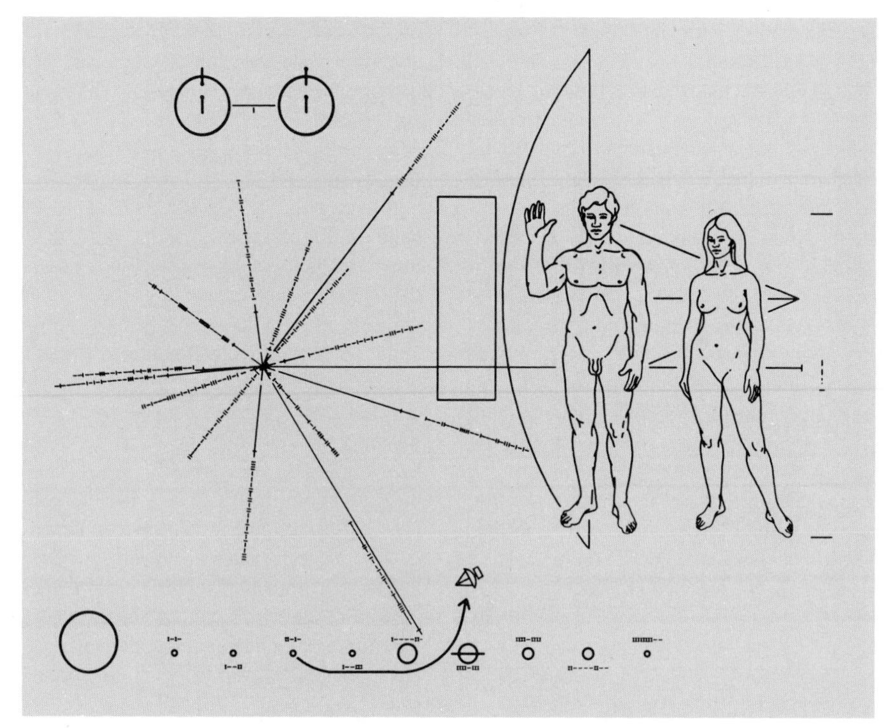

A PICTURE POSTCARD FOR SPACE DWELLERS, PLACED ABOARD PIONEER 10, TELLS ABOUT EARTH.

Are we alone in the universe? In 1972 scientists took two steps to get in touch with the life that they believe almost certainly exists somewhere else in space. One involved sending a message, a sort of greeting card from planet Earth, and the other involved cocking an electronic ear to listen for sentient signals.

In March the Pioneer 10 spacecraft headed for Jupiter and the outer reaches of our galaxy, carrying a graphic message in the form of drawings and diagrams *(above).* Etched into an aluminum plate, six by nine inches and coated with erosionproof gold, the drawings, conceived by astronomers Carl Sagan and Frank Drake of Cornell University and executed by Sagan's wife, Linda Salvman, tell where Pioneer 10 came from, when it left home and who sent it.

The symbol at the upper left of the plaque represents two states of the hydrogen atom, and the little vertical line between the two circles denotes the 21-centimeter-long wave of electromagnetic energy that the hydrogen atom emits. Any advanced society, the designers believe, would not only recognize the atom symbol, but understand that the line represents the atom's characteristic wavelength and that it is meant to serve as a scale. Below the atom, 14 of the radiating lines depict pulsars—stars that send out radio waves in pulsed rhythms —and their positions in relation to the earth. At bottom are the sun *(large circle at left)* and the planets; the bent line with an arrowhead pointing to a depiction of Pioneer 10 shows that the craft came from the third planet out from the sun and was ejected from the solar system by Jupiter's gravity. The man, with his hand upraised to show the unique opposed human thumb, and the woman beside him stand in front of a schematic sketch of Pioneer 10 to show their size relative to the vehicle.

The likelihood that anyone will ever get the message is admittedly slim. "The only chance of its being intercepted," says Sagan, "is if someone were to come out and grab it." If someone does grab it, the scientists are confident that he will be able to decipher it.

And what if all the while he has been trying to get in touch with us? Planet

Earth may be listening. The United States government announced plans in March to build a gigantic radio telescope with 10 to 100 times the power of current models. Part of the mission of the new telescope will be to overhear and monitor any signals sent out by an extraterrestrial civilization.

The VLA (for Very Large Array of antennas), consisting of 27 dish antennas, each 85 feet in diameter, will sprawl over the Plains of San Agustín, New Mexico, in a vast Y, each arm 13 miles long. Mounted on railroad tracks, the antennas will be easily movable for sharp focusing. The cost of listening for a cosmic call: an estimated $76 million.

That such expenditures are believed worthwhile was made plain in a survey published in June in which 23 leading astronomers supported the VLA program. As one of the astronomers has said, "Each passing year has seen our estimates of the probability of life in space increase, along with our capabilities of detecting it. More and more scientists are recognizing that contact with other civilizations is no longer something beyond our dreams, but an inevitable event in the history of mankind that will occur perhaps in the lifetime of many of us."

A MISSING COMET FOUND

A comet named Tempel 1 is supposed, according to the astronomers' calculations, to orbit into sight of earth every five and a half years. When Tempel 1 disappeared after its last sighting in 1879, astronomers began rechecking their calculations. In 1972 (which should have been a Tempel sighting year) two astronomers solved the mystery. It seemed that 19th Century astronomers had failed to take sufficient account of the effect of Jupiter's gravity on the comet, and miscalculated its course.

Using computers, Brian Marsden of the Smithsonian Observatory and fellow comet-watcher, Joachim Schubart, analyzed the 19th Century observations and plotted Tempel 1's course. Sure enough, the comet was sighted where the calculations said it should be, and Elizabeth Roemer of the University of Arizona got two pictures of it on January 11, 1972.

BEHAVIOR

In a study that seems bound to stir controversy, one researcher claimed that education, of whatever kind, had little effect on an individual's prospects for social or economic success in life. Other behavioral studies indicated that the age of sexual maturity is influenced more by social than by physical factors, and that mankind's biological clock regulated by the sun's rising and setting can be reset to make a 20-hour workday comfortable.

WHY GIRLS GROW UP FASTER

In the past century the age at which Occidental females mature sexually has dropped three to four months every decade—in 1870 girls matured at 15.6 years, in 1970 puberty came at 12.5—a change that has puzzled biologists. Now a team from the North Carolina Department of Mental Health, headed by Dr. John G. Vandenbergh, reports that mice experiments have disclosed two factors affecting the date of a female's first ovulation —the level of protein in the diet and the degree of contact with males. Each factor had some influence alone, but when social stimulus was combined with a diet high in protein, maturity was accelerated. Isolated females on an 8 per cent protein diet matured at 37 days and those on a 24 per cent protein diet at 35 days. But when females on the 24 per cent diet were given male cagemates, they matured nine days earlier than the isolated ones on 8 per cent protein.

FREE FROM THE SUN'S SCHEDULE

To study the natural rhythms of the body, a French scientist confined himself to a cave for 205 days, cut off from the sun, society and his wife. Seven months later he emerged, ebulliently claiming new insight into man's capabilities.

Michel Siffre was trained as a geologist, but for a number of years his passion has been to show that man could liberate himself from the rhythms and cycles imposed by the 24-hour solar day. So in February Siffre descended 150 feet into a cavern near Del Rio, Texas, to begin developing his own natural body "clock" uninfluenced by any clue of sunshine or night chill. Mostly he found himself staying awake and active for 20 hours, then sleeping eight. But twice, for periods of a week or two, Siffre slipped into 48-hour cycles, working and puttering about his cave without fatigue for about 36 hours straight, then retiring to rest for 12 hours or so.

Trailing cables from electrodes in his partially shaven head and other parts of his body, plugged into a computer, the 33-year-old cave dweller spent much of his time studying his own reactions and reflexes, testing his heart rate, blood pressure, grip strength, alertness and so forth. He read scientific works and kept a diary. He cooked and ate frozen meals developed originally for U.S. astronauts —pronouncing them "of the quality of a top restaurant." Back in Paris at year's end, still plugged into a computer to monitor his readjustment to day and night, Siffre believed he had proved that man can work longer than the normal solar rhythm dictates.

"Personally," Siffre explained afterward, "I am interested in the study of time from the philosophical point of view. But the applications of my experiment are many. From a military point of view, for instance, it is very important to establish that man can be awake and operate efficiently for long periods of time. In another field, that of flying, it's important to find out why sleep patterns are disturbed by transatlantic flights."

CAVE LIFE RESETS THE BODY'S CLOCK.

A NEW LIE DETECTOR

Invented by three former army intelligence officers, a device said to distinguish between truth and falsehood in the human voice—even if the speaker is being heard on radio or television—was unveiled in June. Unlike the conventional lie detector, or polygraph, which measures the subject's involuntary physical reactions—such as sweating, rate of heartbeat and rising blood pressure—to direct questions, the new machine records and analyzes the speaker's voice. When a speaker is relaxed, his voice contains inaudible tremors that disappear when he is under stress. A graph produced by the new briefcase-sized device, called PSE (Psychological Stress Evaluator), shows the presence or absence of these tremors, the inventors claim. As with the polygraph, PSE does not answer the question as to whether or not stress and lying are inseparable.

PSE was employed in four Maryland trials. Its findings resulted in the acquittal of one man on a murder charge and of two persons accused of issuing bad checks. In the fourth case, a shoplifting suspect pleaded guilty after his voice seemed to have betrayed him.

DOES EDUCATION PAY OFF?

A controversial study, published in October as millions of children settled into another school year, sought to explode two cherished assumptions about learning and American society. Sociologist Christopher Jencks, an associate professor at the Harvard Graduate School of Education, said his investigations disclosed (1) that improvements in school programs do not commensurately improve educational achievement, and (2) that schooling is only tenuously connected to economic success in later life.

Jencks and his associates spent three years assembling and analyzing information on all the major schemes to improve schools: preschool programs like Head Start, increased school budgets, racial desegregation, compensatory programs for the poor. They examined standardized test results of children who were beneficiaries of such programs, as well as of those who were not. The reforms and special programs did not significantly increase the children's test scores, Jencks concluded, and added that what they managed to learn was mostly a function of their personalities and the predispositions that they brought with them to their first day in school.

Jencks also studied the correlation between formal learning and later economic success. He found the connection tenuous. The data Jencks brought together suggested to him that measurable qualities—such as equal schooling, environmental background and I.Q. factors—had no more than 25 per cent influence on a person's eventual prosperity. Fully three quarters of a person's future position in life Jencks attributed to luck and personality and on-the-job competence.

Jencks's study, published under the title *Inequality,* seemed certain to draw widespread criticism. Even before official publication, the book was faulted for its dated data, and for the questionable practice of using a computer to solve equations that were a mixture of fact and assumption. Some educators felt that Jencks's voluminous collection of data was actually insufficient. "We are just beginning to learn what questions to ask in education, let alone coming to any conclusions," said James Guthrie, Associate Professor of Education at the University of California at Berkeley. And Stanford Associate Professor of Education Henry Levin added, "We have only the crudest understanding of the actual forces creating differences in people's abilities. It's like analyzing what is beauty. You can study fingernails and knuckles, but this would have nothing to do with the overall concept of beauty."

BIOCHEMISTRY

Harvard University biochemists isolated a chemical associated with tumors; if the chemical's effect on the body could be blocked, cancer might be inhibited. On another front in the war on cancer, the Soviet Union and the United States began to collaborate on cancer research. And biochemists in California found that bacteria have a rudimentary intelligence.

ISOLATING A CANCEROUS CHEMICAL

A first step toward the possibility that malignant tumors can be starved into harmless dormancy came with a discovery by a Harvard research team. The team's head, Dr. M. Judah Folkman, said in March that he and his associates had identified and isolated a chemical secreted by cancerous cells that is vital to tumorous growths.

The chemical, which is called the Tumor-Angiogenesis Factor, or TAF, triggers the production of tiny new blood vessels, or capillaries. Once a tumor reaches the size of a pinhead—one to two millimeters in diameter—it cannot spread unless a network of such capillaries develops to supply it with nutrients and to remove its waste matter.

Folkman and his associates are now attempting what may be a far more difficult accomplishment: counteracting or inhibiting the development of TAF, since if a tumor cannot grow, it becomes indefinitely inactive.

BRAINY BACTERIA

Bacteria have some kind of memory and vary their behavior on the basis of past experience, according to a report published in August by two University of California (Berkeley) biochemists, Robert Macnab and Daniel Koshland. For a simple single-celled organism a mere 1/10,000 of an inch long, this seemed a pretty heady accomplishment.

The two scientists explained that they found out about the bacteria's intelligence by observing swimming patterns. Normally bacteria swim through liquid in a somewhat erratic, tumbling fashion. But when a dollop of nutrient, such as sugar, is added to the liquid, the bacteria straighten out and swim smoothly through the nutrient slick, reverting to their undirected swimming style after a few minutes. This variation in swimming styles in response to stimulus suggests a rudimentary intelligence.

Macnab and Koshland then tried transferring the bacteria abruptly from their sugar-rich solution to a poorer solution and observed that the bacteria tumbled about in a wildly agitated way, as if trying to find a way back to the previous stream. Apparently the minute organisms "remembered" their lost sugary world.

U.S.-SOVIET WAR ON CANCER

American scientists profited quickly from the agreement reached in May between President Nixon and the Soviet leaders in Moscow to promote cooperation in cancer research between the two countries. In August the Russians agreed to share their research on leukemia, the deadly blood cancer, which they had reportedly induced in monkeys and baboons after inoculating them with blood taken from human leukemia patients. The transfer of the disease from man to primate, earlier attempted without success by American researchers, raised what one scientist called a "strong suggestion" that a leukemia virus may have been isolated, and strengthened hopes that an antileukemia vaccine might be developed. In November a United States medical mission went to Moscow to obtain some of the Russian viral material. By year's end, American researchers were trying to duplicate the experiments.

BOTANY

Cell fusion, a basic step in the reproduction of living tissue, was achieved in the laboratory, raising the prospect of new life forms tailored to order. A tobacco hybrid was the first product of the new technique, but the success suggested that more dramatic vegetable hybrids could lead to valuable food crops. In other botanical news, a possible antidote was found for Dutch elm disease, which kills some of America's noblest trees.

PLANTS BRED IN A TEST TUBE

The new science of test-tube genetics invaded the plant world and scored a notable success. In August, biologists at Brookhaven National Laboratory in Upton, New York, unveiled a hybrid tobacco plant that had been conceived in a test tube and raised in a laboratory. Cells from two species of tobacco leaves were soaked in chemicals called enzymes that ate away the outer cellulose walls to expose the inner genetic material of the two types of tobacco cells. These cell innards were then placed in a sodium nitrate solution and stirred until some of one species fused with cells of the other. When these crossbred cells were placed in laboratory flasks, they grew vigorously, forming plant shoots after several months. Grafted onto the stem of one of the parent tobacco plants, the hybrids developed into fine, healthy mature specimens that were—unlike so many crossbred strains—capable of reproduction. This new test-tube cell-fusion technique could theoretically lead to the development of fertile hybrids of food crops that will grow like weeds to help increase the world's food supply.

CLOSER TO CURING THE ELM

A REMEDY FOR DUTCH ELM DISEASE MAY PREVENT BEFORE-AND-AFTER SCENES LIKE THESE.

Lovers of the shady, stately American elm may once again take hope that a remedy has been found to fight Dutch elm disease. This plague arrived in the United States 42 years ago in a shipment of logs imported from Europe, and last year alone it killed half a million elms. Continually frustrated in their attempts to control the disease, botanists, tree surgeons and homeowners have tried everything from DDT to Epsom salts, but without success.

The disease is actually a fungus carried by an elm-bark beetle that bores into healthy elms. As the fungus develops, it enters the sap streams of the tree, inhibiting movement of the life-sustaining fluid. As the tree rots, it becomes the breeding ground for new generations of beetles that go on to spread the fungus to living trees.

The new and somewhat expensive solution to the problem ($75 per tree) is a two-part program that was endorsed by the U.S. Department of Agriculture in March: spraying the elms in early spring with the pesticide methoxychlor, which is lethal only to the beetles, and spraying again in June or injecting the tree trunk with a chemical called Benlate, to kill the fungus itself. The method has been tested for two years in a Milwaukee suburb, and the mortality rate for the elms there dropped more than half.

DEMOGRAPHY

Whether the campaign for zero population growth had much to do with it or not, the population boom seemed to be waning. In the United States the birth rate sank to a level that could eventually stabilize the population. In other lands similar trends were noted. Even in the most tradition-bound, attitudes toward family size seemed to be changing.

TOWARD ZERO POPULATION GROWTH

Demographers noted a worldwide trend to smaller families in 1972. The statistics suggested that population-explosion alarmists of recent years may have overstated their case.

In the United States the birth rate during the first half of 1972 dropped to 2.1 children per potential mother. This is what demographers call the replacement level, a birth rate that equals the death rate. In fact the United States birth rate has been declining toward this level for 14 of the past 15 years, and the mid-1972 rate was the lowest on record.

However, the United States is still a long way from the stabilized replacement level that is known as zero population growth. This is because of a "bulge" in the population—an especially large pool of young women in the crucial child-bearing years. Though they want and plan fewer children than their own mothers did, their sheer numbers ensure that while the individual birth rate will be lower, the total of new lives produced will exceed the number that death will delete from the population. Indeed, so youth-skewed is the present United States population that young families would have to maintain the current low birth rate for up to 70 years before population growth actually bottomed out at zero.

In the United States, at least, the plummeting birth rate has been credited to better techniques of contraception. Dr. Charles Westoff, co-director of the authoritative National Fertility Study, says, "It seems clear that the immediate explanation for the decline in the birth rate has been a decline in unwanted births, in turn a consequence of the dramatic improvement in the use of more effective methods of contraception." Dr. Westoff reports that 65 per cent of American couples employ contraception.

The United States is not alone in slowing the growth of its population. In Europe the birth rate is dropping nearly everywhere; births are fewer than deaths in France, West Germany, Sweden, Denmark, Finland, Portugal, Czechoslovakia and Hungary. Even in countries outside Europe and North America there are hopeful signs of a population turnaround. Stanford University demographer Dudley Kirk believes he has identified at least six areas where the traditional pattern of large-sized families is consciously being reversed: Hong Kong, Ceylon, Puerto Rico, Chile, Singapore and Taiwan. Kirk's findings are supported by Reinert T. Ravenholt, director of the Office of Population at the U.S. Agency for International Development. Says Ravenholt, "I believe that a powerful world response to the population explosion is occurring. I have the intuitive feeling that we are halfway to the top of the hill."

DRUGS

Even more than anyone had realized, America seemed a nation endangered by drugs. Alcohol in excessive amounts was sloshing a decade off the life-spans of some 10 million people. And 45 million tobacco smokers beclouded not only their own lungs but the lungs of their nonsmoking neighbors. Other drug dangers lurked in the antiseptic hexachlorophene, banned in the United States; and in isoproterenol, an inhalant that killed thousands of asthmatics abroad.

TOBACCO'S DEADLY GAS

Smoking endangers the smoker—a fact that everyone knows by now, or ought to know. But what was not appreciated, until the Surgeon General pointed it out in his 1972 report on smoking and health, was that smoking in an enclosed room or automobile endangers the nonsmoker as well as the smoker. The harm comes not from the still unidentified cancer-causing agent in tobacco, but from a long-recognized component of tobacco smoke—the deadly gas carbon monoxide. It enters the blood stream, usurps the place reserved for oxygen in the blood and forces the heart to pump harder to supply needed oxygen, thereby straining a weak heart. The reduction in the flow of oxygen also impairs mental acuity and physical reactions.

Federal air quality standards recommend that public exposure to carbon monoxide not exceed 35 parts per million for a maximum of one hour in an entire year. But according to one study, two packs of cigarettes smoked in an average room produce 50 parts per million.

THE MOST ABUSED DRUG, ALCOHOL

The federal government zeroed in for an attack on what it called the country's most abused drug. An estimated 95 million Americans drink, and 9.6 million are alcoholics or heavy drinkers whose habits shorten their own lives by 10 to 12 years, the Department of Health, Education and Welfare said. These drinkers cause 28,000 traffic fatalities a year—half of the total—cost employers $10 billion a year in lost work time and burden the taxpayer with $5 billion in expenditures for welfare, medical services and property damage. HEW proposed a comprehensive effort to coordinate federal, state and local programs for prevention of alcoholism, and treatment and rehabilitation of alcoholics. The campaign would be directed by HEW's National Institute on Alcohol Abuse and Alcoholism, whose $84.5 million appropriation for 1972 was six times as much as the government spent on alcoholism the previous year.

A DEADLY CURE

Although it received little publicity, a mysterious epidemic killed thousands of asthma sufferers in Europe, South America, Australia and New Zealand during the 1960s. Trying to solve the mystery, British doctors suspected that one of the drugs used by asthmatics might be to blame; but they could not isolate it. Finally in July a Johns Hopkins' epidemiologist, Dr. Paul D. Stolley, found the killer.

Because the epidemic did not affect the United States, Canada and several other countries, Stolley had looked for differences between the drugs administered in the stricken areas and those used in the epidemic-free regions. He found that isoproterenol, packaged as an aerosol spray, was manufactured in Britain in solutions five times as strong as permitted by United States and Canadian law. Isoproterenol, helpful in small doses, can be fatal in excessive amounts. Stolley called the epidemic "the worst therapeutic drug disaster on record." Total cost of his investigation: $250.

EXIT FOR HEXACHLOROPHENE

In September, after almost a year of hassling, the Food and Drug Administration said its apparently final word about the germ-killing chemical hexachlorophene, used in hundreds of widely sold soaps, deodorants, baby lotions and other preparations. The word was no. Specifically, the FDA ordered that all cosmetics and nonprescription drugs containing more than 0.1 per cent of the substance could no longer be manufactured.

The FDA's injunction was based on growing evidence that large amounts of the antiseptic killed not only germs but vital brain cells as well—lethal damage to the brain stem was found in laboratory test animals and newborn infants. Studies of babies routinely washed with hexachlorophene soap in one New York City hospital showed that the chemical was being absorbed through the skin into the blood stream. In France the death of more than 30 babies was linked to talcum powder with an accidentally high concentration of the chemical.

As some manufacturers of hexachlorophene products began to switch to one of two substitutes, triclocarban (TCC) or tribromosalicylamate (TBS), there was some question about the finality of the FDA's final word. Hexachlorophene had proved a very valuable antiseptic, particularly in protecting babies from staphylococcal infections that spread with ease through hospital nurseries. Hospitals faced with outbreaks of epidemic proportions got a reluctant okay from the FDA to use hexachlorophene as a last resort—but not on burned or denuded skin, not on mucous membranes and not over the entire body.

ENVIRONMENT

The United States banned DDT, made some progress in cleaning the air, and was subjected to less radioactive fallout. But the nation's waters grew dirtier, and its citizens learned that some unpleasant contaminants routinely slipped into food products. Concern for the environment inspired an agreement between the U.S. and the U.S.S.R. to work together on pollution studies. In Rome, another environmental problem, traffic vibration, caused authorities to bar tourists from the crumbling Colosseum.

A BEE MENACE FROM BRAZIL

A new species of vicious South American bee that has stung to death at least 10 people and countless animals in Brazil posed such a threat to the rest of the hemisphere that in July the National Research Council of the National Academy of Sciences recommended that a blockade of chemical traps be set up across the narrowest section of one of the Latin American isthmuses. The "killer bee" is the result of an experiment that failed when Brazilian scientists, in an attempt to produce a docile superhoneybee, set out to cross an aggressive but hardworking and highly productive honeybee from Africa with the gentler but lazier European bee already in residence in South America. But in 1957, twenty-six of the African queen bees escaped and interbred with native wild bees, producing such rapacious offspring that today all the native bees have disappeared.

The new breed has spread from Brazil throughout most of Argentina and is now headed north at the rate of 200 miles a year—which could bring it to the southern United States in 10 or 15 years. While the National Research Council proposed quarantine measures to fight the new menace, hybridizers, undaunted by their inadvertent creation of the killer bee, suggested a different alternative: crossbreeding its aggressive traits out.

A 99 PER CENT BAN ON DDT

Ten years after Rachel Carson charged in her book *Silent Spring* that DDT was an "elixir of death" for fish, birds and animals, and a possible threat to man himself, the federal government's Environmental Protection Agency prohibited almost all use of the pesticide in the United States after December 31, 1972. DDT may still be applied to green peppers, onions and sweet potatoes, because no other effective chemical protection for them has been found, but those crops consume only 1 per cent of the 14 million pounds of DDT hitherto sold every year. The EPA order also permits emergency use of DDT to cope with epidemics, and allows its export to continue because of its effectiveness against carriers of malaria and typhus.

Growers of cotton, peanuts and soybeans, who have accounted for the major domestic use of DDT, are expected to substitute methyl parathion—a compound that, unlike DDT, is known to be very poisonous to humans, but one that, again unlike DDT, quickly breaks down into other harmless substances.

AIR IS BETTER, WATER IS WORSE

The government's Council on Environmental Quality reported in August that America's air is improving while its water grows murkier. The panel credited controls on smokestacks with the abatement of air pollution. Between 1969 and 1970, the most recent period analyzed, emissions of carbon monoxide were reduced 4.5 per cent and particle emissions 7.4 per cent. The Council reported that pollution of the nation's waterways and shores is not being reduced—in 1971 the United States had 5,435 more polluted stream miles than in 1970.

But there was even hope for dirty water: late in the year Congress overrode Nixon's veto of a water pollution bill that authorizes $24.6 billion over three years to clean up the nation's lakes and rivers.

A DROP IN RADIATION LEVELS

Concentrations of radioactive fallout in human beings have dropped almost sixfold since nuclear testing in the atmosphere was prohibited by treaty in 1963—so announced the Brookhaven National Laboratory at Upton, New York, in August. Over a dozen years the laboratory has repeatedly examined the radioactivity levels in 910 persons, measuring their bodies' content of the fallout substance cesium 137: in 1964, when radioactive fallout was at its peak, the average was 110 picocuries (a standard unit of radiation measurement) of cesium 137 for each gram of normal potassium in the body. By 1969, the average level had dropped to between 18 and 20 picocuries, where it remains. The laboratory did not examine the subjects for concentrations of strontium 90, another dangerous product of fallout, because it is not detectable by external measurement, but the assumption is that this concentration has dropped drastically as well.

U.S.-U.S.S.R. COLLABORATION

The Soviet Union and the United States agreed to mount 30 cooperative ventures directed at coping with environmental problems. The initial understanding was drawn up by Presidents Nikolai V. Podgorny and Richard M. Nixon in Moscow during the May summit conference. And in September, representatives from the two countries signed an agreement and sat for the first meeting, again in Moscow, of their ambitious-sounding Joint Committee on Cooperation in the Field of Environmental Protection.

Among the ventures announced were:

- Urban air-pollution curtailment, with Leningrad and St. Louis as test cities.
- A study of lake pollution, using Lake Baikal in Siberia and Lake Tahoe between California and Nevada as models.
- A study of river pollution, analyzing the Delaware, the Potomac and two Soviet rivers yet to be designated.
- Urban environmental projects, comparing conditions in Leningrad and another Soviet city (to be selected) with those in San Francisco and Atlanta.
- Refinement of earthquake forecasting techniques, concentrating on the Pamir Mountains in the Central Asian Republic of Tadzhikistan and on the San Andreas Fault in California.

Though the representatives of the two countries carefully refrained from mentioning the possibility, there was talk in scientific circles that earthquake prediction tests could provide a new scheme of distinguishing between natural earthquakes and underground nuclear test explosions. Perfection of such a method might eventually lead to a foolproof way of monitoring nuclear weapons tests and thus provide a solid basis for the outlawing of such armaments.

MANURE RECYCLED INTO FEED

America's cattle produce far more manure than farmers have need of as fertilizer. So two corporations and the U.S. Department of Agriculture are studying a novel application of recycling: turning cattle manure back into feed. In August some promising experimental successes were announced.

In Casa Grande, Arizona, the General Electric Company opened a demonstration factory that processes the dried manure of 100 head of cattle—some 340 pounds a day—into 120 pounds of powdered high-protein feed. The recycled manure is tasteless, odorless and reportedly as nutritious as the soybean or fish meals that now comprise the normal diet of cattle and chickens.

The process accomplishes this recycling by fermentation, using a strain of bacteria that biochemist W. Dexter Bellamy isolated from buffalo droppings and dead plants around Old Faithful geyser in Yellowstone National Park. The manure is mixed with water and fed into fermentation tanks, where it is subjected to high temperatures like those around Old Faithful, 130° to 140° F. At these temperatures the bacteria transform the fiber in the decaying matter into a residue rich in protein.

Another corporation, Hamilton Standard, has developed a similar method that is claimed to be even more efficient. Its fermentation employs the bacteria already in the manure, and in the fermenting process enough methane gas is generated to provide the fuel needed to heat the fermentation tanks.

LITTER THAT SELF-DESTRUCTS

While throwaway containers pile up ever higher in a mess that threatens to last almost forever, a new type promises to provide the convenience of disposability without littering the landscape. In July, a California-based fast-food take-out chain began using a plastic cup lid that reintegrates into the environmental cycle.

The lid contains a chemical catalyst that causes a reaction between the ultraviolet rays of the sun and the resins that are a raw material in the plastic. The molecules in the resins heat up until they eventually separate. Then oxygen breaks the molecules down further into carbon dioxide and water, which are consumed by microorganisms in the soil. Depending upon how much catalyst the lid contains and how much sunlight it gets, it will crumble into a near-invisible powder in 90 to 150 days. In six months no trace of it will exist.

The demand for such self-destructing containers was underscored by evidence that nature needs all the recycling help it can get. In September, a team of chemists at Pennsylvania State University announced that, according to tests they had recently conducted, it will take a century for tin-plated cans to disintegrate—provided they are subjected to the elements. Aluminum cans will disintegrate into particles the size of a grain of sand in about 500 years. And glass, one of the oldest-known container materials, is the least destructible of all: inasmuch as glass beads 4,000 years old have survived intact from ancient Egypt, chances are that beer bottles discarded today will endure as shards and slivers until well beyond the year 6000.

A COSTLY RED TIDE

Most "red tides"—caused by a wild proliferation of ocean algae—are harmless, but in September a poisonous alga, *Gonyaulax tamarensis,* infested New England coastal waters, turning the waters reddish brown and contaminating mussels and soft-shelled clams. Within a week 33 shellfish eaters were taken ill, two of them so severely that they were confined for a time to iron lungs. The poison, for which there is no known antidote, can kill humans by paralyzing their muscles so that breathing becomes impossible. While all those sickened recovered, the Food and Drug Administration ordered the recall of all the clams and mussels shipped from Massachusetts, New Hampshire and Maine—beginning with those shipped 10 days before the first appearance of the red tide in early September. By early October the algae had all but disappeared, but the FDA's recall had brought economic hardship to the New England shellfish industry, which put its losses at one million dollars a day.

ITALY'S MOLDERING MONUMENTS

ENDANGERED COLOSSEUM AND CATHEDRAL ARE SAVED BY SCAFFOLDING AND AN AUTO BAN.

Rome is "tumbling like a landslide." That was the news in September from a Roman authority who added to the growing apprehension over the preservation of ancient treasures in many parts of Italy. The government is already taking some action. It partially closed the most renowned landmark of Imperial Rome, the 1,900-year-old Colosseum, because visitors were in danger of being struck by pieces of masonry that had been loosened by heavy rains and vibrations from auto traffic. Parts of the nearby Forum were also closed after a 300-foot section of wall along the First Century B.C. Sacred Way fell to rubble; weakened by an intrusion of brambles and weeds, it had also been battered by autumn rains.

In Milan the pillars that uphold the roof of the 600-year-old *duomo* were reported to be sinking into the ground at the rate of a tenth of an inch annually. And when inch-thick marble chunks began falling from pillars supporting the apse in September, the city banned all automobile traffic around the cathedral.

In Florence the famed Doors of Paradise of the Baptistery of San Giovanni, created in the 15th Century by Lorenzo Ghiberti, became so grimed from car exhaust that their figures were almost unrecognizable. City officials, reluctant to move the doors into a closed place, considered sealing them in glass. It was too late for any outdoor technique to protect the four bronze horses atop Venice's 11th Century Basilica of St. Mark. At year's end, so eaten away by pollution that they could no longer resist the canal city's smog, they were being readied for removal to an indoor location with controlled temperature and humidity.

HAIR IN THE PEANUT BUTTER

Processed foods are allowed to contain rather more substances than their labels list—among them rodent hair in peanut butter, rodent droppings in popcorn, fly eggs in canned fruit juices, insect fragments in chocolate and bits of worm in canned corn. The Food and Drug Administration disclosed that for years it has maintained ceilings on permissible contamination, but had kept them secret for fear processors would merely meet the requirements instead of striving to surpass them. The FDA explained that it had publicized these limitations under pressure from consumer groups, and argued that it could not make its regulations more drastic because "even with modern technology, all defects in food cannot be eliminated."

Such small amounts of contamination are not dangerous, nor do they affect a food's taste or appearance, said the FDA solicitously. *Bon appétit!*

GEOLOGY

Earthquake-prone areas got encouraging news from several developments in the prediction of earthquakes and from an earthquake simulator that will make it possible to test large-scale models of buildings. There was less-welcome news about Niagara Falls, whose rock cliff is crumbling at an increased rate. Experts warned of small avalanches and recommended a $38-million operation to save the tourist attraction.

TRYING TO COPE WITH THE QUAKE

Three important advances in techniques for coping with earthquake danger were disclosed in April: one is expected to expose weaknesses in building design and the two others to permit the forecasting of tremors as long as three months before they occur.

The tool for improving construction is the biggest and most sophisticated earthquake simulator ever constructed: it was unveiled at the Berkeley campus of the University of California on April 18, the 66th anniversary of San Francisco's catastrophic quake. Unlike earlier simulators, which could accommodate only relatively small models of buildings, the new computer-run device can subject a 40-foot-high, 60-ton structure to the motions of quakes whose characteristics have been recorded.

The testing machinery consists of a 20-foot-square, 45-ton slab of concrete supported by a cushion of compressed air. Driven by four 150-horsepower motors that apply hydraulic pressure, seven rams shake the slab upward and from side to side simultaneously, as much as 12 inches horizontally and up to four inches vertically, equaling the violence of a major quake. The simulator, its designers claim, will make possible the construction of more nearly quakeproof buildings, bridges, overpasses and dams by revealing potential weaknesses in the tested large-scale models.

A week after the simulator's unveiling, an earthquake symposium of the National Academy of Sciences learned of a new quake-prediction system developed by Russian scientists. The method depends on the fact that there are two kinds of earthquake waves that normally travel at different speeds. One type, known as a pressure wave, ordinarily travels faster than a so-called shear wave. By using sensitive new detectors in areas where earthquakes are common, Russian seismologists have discovered that several weeks before a quake, a change is registered in the ratio between the speed of the pressure waves and the speed of the shear waves. When the two waves regain their characteristic ratio, a quake follows. The most violent tremors measured to date have provided as much as three months' warning. Taking advantage of this phenomenon, American scientists are examining Russian methods to see if they are applicable to the prediction of quakes in the United States, where the crustal movements that lead to earthquakes are somewhat different.

Another totally different approach to predicting quakes is a result of the controversial underground nuclear test at Amchitka Island in November 1971. Two geophysicists at the National Oceanic and Atmospheric Administration, W. P. Hasbrouck and J. H. Allen, report from data collected during this test—a cataclysm closely resembling an earthquake —that 30 seconds after the explosion had been triggered, the intensity of the magnetic field over Amchitka increased significantly and the change appeared to be permanent. While they are still attempting to determine the cause of the magnetic increase, the NOAA scientists have concluded that a sudden high magnetism reading is a portent of violent rumblings beneath the earth's surface.

DANGER AT NIAGARA FALLS

THE PROFILE OF NIAGARA, DOOMED BY ROCK FALLS, MAY BE SAVED BY INTERIOR CABLES.

After three years of investigation by a joint Canadian-U.S. survey team, an interim report was presented in March with a recommendation that the two governments invest $38.5 million in shoring up Niagara Falls, whose rock walls are now dangerously crumbling.

Erosion has always nibbled away at the Falls: during the last 600 years over half a mile has been gouged out of the cliffs. But in recent years there has been a series of rock collapses from the cliffs surrounding the Falls, and geologists have become concerned about the instability of the cliffs, which provide the vantage points for the 10 million tourists who visit the Falls annually.

In 1969 the U.S. Army Corps of Engineers "turned off" the American Falls, diverting them with a dam while they explored the face of the cliffs. In the three years of inspection the engineers found deep fissures in the rock masses around the Falls, which could cause small avalanches, endangering any visitors in the vicinity. The engineers have recommended that funds be allocated to shut off the Falls once more, shore up the face of the cliffs and install sensors within the rocks to warn of any impending breaks.

MEDICINE

The year's medical innovations included an operation to flush hepatitis virus out of the liver, the use of radios to help nerve-damaged patients and the building of bones from coral. New ways were devised to fight meningitis, venereal disease, polio, gallstones and a lung defect that snuffs out the lives of newborn infants. An epidemic of rabies in many animal species—skunks, foxes and bats—prompted the development of a new vaccine, and animal doctors were also concerned about the spread of a dog disease called canine heartworm caused by a parasite carried by mosquitoes.

NEW WAYS TO FIGHT GONORRHEA

A faster, more efficient blood test and a new drug treatment are the latest weapons in the accelerating attack on gonorrhea. Authorities on venereal disease have long lamented that there was no cheap, quick method for determining the presence of the ailment, particularly in women, who usually display no outward symptoms until months after infection. The new blood test, announced in April by researchers of the New York State Health Department, involves examining a drop of blood through a microscope on a slide that has been treated with antigens from gonorrhea bacteria. Infected blood produces a reaction that can be seen under ultraviolet light. Since the test requires only two hours of laboratory work it promises to make mass screening far more feasible.

Meanwhile, a "one-minute treatment" for gonorrhea promised to be used much more widely than it had been, thanks to a strong endorsement in an April issue of the influential British medical journal *The Lancet.* The treatment consists of a single, oral dose of two grams of ampicillin (a form of penicillin) and one gram of probenecid (to increase the effectiveness of the penicillin by preventing its excretion through the kidneys). *The Lancet* credited it with a cure rate of better than 95 per cent.

The two developments were urgently needed, for gonorrhea, seemingly under control in the decade prior to 1957, continued to spread ever more rapidly since then. The nation's Center for Disease Control in Atlanta reported an estimated 2.5 million cases in 1972.

A PRENATAL LUNG TEST

The respiratory defect that killed President John F. Kennedy's infant son Patrick Bouvier in 1963 afflicts some 50,000 American babies every year and proves fatal to half of them. Now a simple test, announced in May, enables doctors to anticipate the problem before the baby is born and take countermeasures to prevent it. The ailment, HMD (for hyaline membrane disease), amounts to immaturity of the lungs. It occurs when the lungs' tiny air sacs lack a vital chemical compound that appears when the lungs reach maturity. This substance, called a surfactant, prevents the air sacs from collapsing and sticking together and suffocating the child.

Researchers at the University of California have discovered that if the surfactant is present in the fetus' lungs, it will appear in the amniotic fluid in which an unborn child floats. The test consists of drawing a teaspoonful of amniotic fluid from the mother, mixing it with alcohol and shaking it in a vial until it bubbles. If the bubbling persists after 15 minutes, the surfactant is present and the child's lungs are mature. If the bubbles quickly subside, the surfactant is absent.

Two remedies are then possible. One is to inject the mother with drugs to delay birth, thus giving the child's lungs time to mature. The other method is to deliver the baby on schedule and, if the baby shows signs of respiratory distress, to insert a tube into its windpipe. The tube carries compressed air and oxygen to partially inflate the baby's lungs, like two small balloons, so that the lungs cannot crumple together. Thus the baby can begin to breathe through the tube during its first few critical days of life, until the immature lungs have time to produce a sufficient amount of surfactant to function completely unassisted.

SALT WATER TO SAVE A LIVER

In an unprecedented surgical procedure, Air Force doctors pumped away all the blood of a young sergeant whose liver had been largely destroyed by viral hepatitis, and substituted salt water, which flushed away poisons that were preventing the liver from healing itself. After 10 minutes the doctors withdrew the saline solution and replaced it with fresh blood from carefully matched donors. Throughout the operation the patient remained chilled to 85° F., a temperature that retarded the body's functions so effectively that the brain, although deprived of blood, survived undamaged. The bold surgery was performed at Wilford Hall Air Force Medical Center in San Antonio, Texas, on March 31; three days later the patient, Sergeant Tor Olson, 22, who had been in a coma before the operation, was feeling well enough to sing hymns in bed and was impatiently awaiting release from the hospital.

Since that pioneering effort, there have been about a half dozen similar operations in various parts of the country, all of which have been successful.

A SOLVENT FOR GALLSTONES

An experimental treatment for gallstones, using chemistry rather than surgery, was tested with some success at the Mayo Clinic in Rochester, Minnesota. A gallstone is usually formed when the blood substance cholesterol, together with calcium salts and bile pigments, solidifies in the gall bladder, the organ that stores bile needed to help digest fatty foods. The gallstones become extremely painful when they travel out from the gall bladder and lodge in the bile duct, and often have to be taken out surgically; some 15 million Americans have gallstones and 350,000 operations are performed each year to remove them.

The chemical alternative to surgery being tried at the Mayo Clinic depends on the fact that the most common gallstones develop when the bile is abnormally rich in cholesterol and low in a substance called chenodeoxycholic acid (CDC)—a natural body chemical that prevents cholesterol from becoming solid. To dissolve gallstones, Drs. Rudolph G. Danziger, Alan F. Hofmann, Leslie J. Schoenfeld and Johnson L. Thistle administered doses of CDC to 16 patients. In four patients the gallstones entirely disappeared; in five, they shrank; but in seven the stones remained unchanged —for reasons that the doctors are as yet unable to explain.

HUMAN CELLS FOR VACCINE

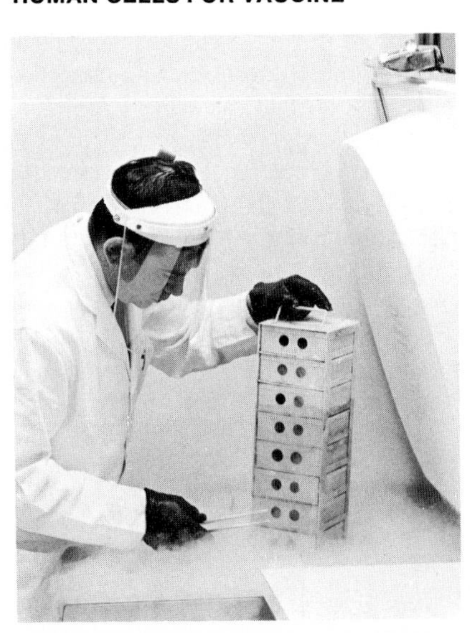

SAFER POLIO VACCINE GETS DEEP-FROZEN.

The use of human cells for the culture of polio vaccine was approved by the National Institutes of Health for the first time, in a step that promises to make prevention of polio—and eventually of other diseases—safer and cheaper. Human cells had not been employed previously because of the mistaken belief of the Federal Division of Biologics Standards that they might harbor a cancer virus. Until now all polio vaccine produced in the United States has been grown in the kidney cells of monkeys, long used for polio research. But monkey kidney cells may carry as many as 20 different viruses that can infect people who handle them as well as those injected with vaccines made from them. Because of the danger of viral contamination, the government required that a new cell culture be used for each batch of vaccine and insisted on exhaustive tests.

Using cells taken from a single aborted human fetus obtained from Sweden, Dr. Leonard Hayflick, then of Philadelphia's Wistar Institute and now at the Stanford University School of Medicine, developed a culture that, unlike those of monkey origin, was entirely free of viruses. Called WI-38 because it was the Wistar Institute's 38th culture, it will be multiplied for mass production of human virus vaccines, making cultures so pure they can be used repeatedly and will need only periodic testing.

CURBING A KILLER

A new vaccine has sharply limited the incidence of the deadly infection of meningitis among its most frequent adult victims, military recruits. An inflammation of the membrane covering the brain and spinal cord, meningitis is caused by a germ called meningococcus that spreads through the respiratory tract: recruits living in close quarters thus have been particularly vulnerable—as many as 30 died annually. But in June the U.S. Army reported that Dr. Emil Gottschlich and Dr. Malcolm Artenstein of Walter Reed Army Research Institute had developed a new vaccine that had produced heartening results: only 13 cases and one death had been reported in the eight months preceding the report.

BONES OF CORAL

One of the difficulties that doctors have had in trying to replace human bones was finding a substance that was equally porous so that bone tissue would adhere to it. Now an unusual solution has been proposed by R. A. White of the State University of New York Upstate Medical Center in Syracuse: it involves the use of porites, a reef-building colonial coral, which have pores of exactly the right dimensions to encourage fusion with tissue. In the past, alloys have been used. But the lack of pores discouraged permanent adherence, and all attempts to roughen their surfaces failed because it proved impossible to make pores of exactly the same size as human ones.

Although its pores are the right size, coral cannot be used directly. For one thing, it is not nearly as strong as human bone. White suggests, however, that the coral surface could be used as a cast from which to copy the desired configuration in ceramic. The ceramic "bone" would then be fitted with an internal metal rod, thus adding the desired strength to the essential porosity.

ELECTRICITY AS A BONE HEALER

While scientists were searching for the perfect bone replacement, doctors were trying to determine whether electricity could speed the healing of broken or defective bones. Last year their efforts paid off dramatically for a 14-year-old boy, a patient at New York's Downstate Medical Center, and promised eventually to save victims of bone fractures months of discomfort and shorten the time lost from school or work.

From birth the boy had suffered a rare condition of the tibia, the main bone of the lower leg: instead of firm bone, he had wobbly, cartilagelike tissue on which he could not stand. Bone grafts worked for a time until the boy fell and fractured his leg; subsequent bone grafts and other measures failed to heal the break and amputation seemed the only recourse. So Dr. Leroy S. Lavine decided to try electricity, which stimulated the healing of damaged bones in laboratory rabbits. He implanted tiny platinum electrodes in the boy's tibia on either side of the fracture, hooked them to two D-cell flashlight batteries and kept a small current flowing to the electrodes almost continuously. After four months, X-rays disclosed that the fracture had healed: the boy is walking normally today. The explanation for the phenomenon, surgeons believe, is that the electric current attracts calcium ions, the body's bone builders.

A LOCAL DOG DISEASE SPREADS

Pet owners have long been aware of the danger of distemper; but recently a new threat to canines has appeared. Its name is dirofilariasis, or heartworm disease; it has been prevalent in the South and is now spreading to other sections of the country, causing a canine health problem of national proportions.

When one of the more than 50 species of mosquito that carry the larvae of this parasitic worm bites a dog, it can inject the larvae into the dog's tissue. The larvae develop into young worms in the dog's muscle and fat; after three months the young worms migrate to the heart where they grow to be six to 15 inches in length. Their effect can prove fatal.

Symptoms of heartworm are coughing, fatigue, fainting and heart murmur. The disease can be diagnosed by means of a blood test; and if the test results are positive, an arsenic derivative can be administered to kill the adult worms, while still another drug can rid the dog's circulatory system of any larvae. There is also a preventive medicine, diethylcarbamazine, which can be administered daily from the beginning of the mosquito season until two months after the season is over. But it has dangerous side effects if the dog is already infected with heartworm; so he should be tested before taking the medicine.

So far there has been little indication of heartworm threatening other pets—or the pet owners themselves.

AN UPSURGE OF RABIES

If a friendly fox approaches in field or forest and appears to grin, do not pet it. Run—and report the incident to the police or health officers, because the animal may be rabid. Rabies has become epidemic, and wild animals are the most common carriers, the U.S. Center for Disease Control disclosed in May.

Contrary to popular belief, the center's doctors point out, rabid animals do not always appear furious, but are likely to be listless and at least partly paralyzed. The best hope for controlling the disease, often fatal among wild animals, lies in an oral vaccine that is still undergoing tests at the center. It would be applied to bait, and when consumed would immunize the animal against rabies.

Another, more drastic, control measure was put into use in Latin America, where vampire bats kill a million cattle annually. In a project underwritten by the Agency for International Development, the bats are trapped in nets and smeared with petroleum jelly mixed with rat poison—a drug that prevents blood from clotting. Then the bats are released to return to their nests, where they preen themselves and their fellows. When they ingest the anticoagulants, they die of internal bleeding. In the test areas cattle bites by the bats were almost totally eliminated in two weeks.

BREATHING BY RADIO

Two miniaturized radio receivers have made it possible for a totally paralyzed accident victim to leave his iron lung. A team of doctors at Yale University's Department of Surgery reported in March that the patient had so severely damaged his spinal cord in a racing-car smashup that he could not even breathe—while his brain was not damaged, it could not get the signal through to his diaphragm to expand and contract his lungs.

Fortunately, however, the two phrenic nerves in the neck, which activate the diaphragm on the brain's command were intact and unharmed. So Dr. William W. L. Glenn and his associates substituted for the brain's commands rhythmical signals from a transmitter the size of a cigarette pack located in the patient's pocket. The radio signals are picked up by two receivers implanted inside the patient's neck. Each receiver, a little bigger than a silver dollar, is connected to the phrenic nerves, stimulating them to operate the diaphragm. The patient, who was formerly confined to a mechanical respirator, now is able to get about in a wheelchair to attend to business—and to watch the auto races.

METEOROLOGY

Earth-circling satellites spied a new kind of storm activity over the mid-Atlantic where tropic and temperate zones meet, and meteorologists labeled it a neutercane. Elsewhere at sea, a string of automated buoys were launched in the Gulf of Mexico to monitor offshore weather. In the skies, airborne lightning-tamers defused the build-up of electrical storms, while on the ground a system was devised for broadcasting timely warnings of impending flash floods.

NEW NEUTERCANES

Thanks to the all-seeing eyes of orbital weather satellites, a new type of storm has been recognized in the mid-Atlantic. It was given the name "neutercane" by the National Hurricane Center's director, Dr. Robert H. Simpson, because it has some characteristics of the tropical hurricane and some of the temperate-zone frontal storm.

A hurricane gets its energy when warm water vapor condenses. The condensation releases heat, which rises in a whirling motion to form the circular pattern of that tropical storm. The frontal storm of the temperate zones develops when fast-sinking cold air collides with warm-air masses. The neutercane develops in the same way a frontal storm does—and it does not depend on warm water vapor condensing, as a hurricane does. But it can quickly take on the spiraling characteristics of a hurricane if it is surrounded by congregations of clouds. The neutercane usually has very low pressure and light rainfall; its winds, though generally not as severe as a hurricane's, form similar upward-spiraling columns of warm air. The neutercane is considerably smaller, though it moves at almost the same speed. Once in a while a neutercane can turn into a hurricane, as in the case last summer when Neutercane Bravo became Hurricane Betty. Most of the time, however, it remains an intense, violent squall that inexplicably never arrives at the mainland. For that reason, the neutercane was not recognized by meteorologists as a separate type of storm, with its own designation, until the advent of the weather satellites.

LIGHTNING FIGHTERS

Among the most daring young men of the year was a team of meteorologists from the National Oceanic and Atmospheric Administration who spent six weeks last summer "bleeding off" the electrical energy in storm clouds in an attempt to prevent lightning, which annually causes hundreds of deaths and many disastrous forest fires. The lightning fighters, flying a World War II B-26 bomber, tracked down thunderheads in the skies over Colorado and steered their plane through the turbulence in the lower level of the clouds. There they opened a tiny vent in the plane's belly in order to release a stream of aluminum-coated glass fibers, called chaff. Each fiber, acting as a conductor, helped to bleed away the excessive electrical charge from the center of a storm and in this way prevented the fierce build-up of lightning-strength clouds.

Their success as measured on the plane's voltage meter was dramatic. On one occasion, for instance, they flew into a cloud that initially registered 70,000 volts per meter and, after only two chaff-spreading passes through the cloud, they lowered the reading to 20,000 volts. On a different occasion, it took them only 10 minutes to reduce a 300,000-volt storm cloud to a reading of zero.

WARNING OF FLASH FLOODS

"I knew it was raining hard but . . . there didn't seem to be any real danger," said a survivor of the flash flood that almost destroyed Rapid City, South Dakota, in June. Indeed, a major reason for the devastation caused by the flash floods is their suddenness; they strike before their victims sense trouble. But after four years of work, the National Weather Service announced in May development and installation of a system that signals flash-flood warnings one to four hours before the cresting waters come raging down. The system works like a float in a toilet tank, rising with the water. The sensing device, installed on a bridge foundation or a piling in an area with a history of flash flooding, activates an electrical circuit if the water rises to a predetermined danger level and sounds an alarm in a police headquarters, or some other center that is manned 24 hours a day. Each system costs only $2,500 to $4,000 to install and little to maintain. The first went into operation in Wheeling, West Virginia, on May 10 where the Wheeling Creek had repeatedly flooded the surrounding counties every spring for the last 10 years. The promising new sensing device has since been installed in Wooster, Ohio, Plainfield, New Jersey, and Rosman, North Carolina.

MONITORING THE DEPTHS

ENGINEERS ADJUST SENSORS ON DATA BUOY.

A jaunty scarlet-and-gold buoy rolls and bobs like a cork in the hurricane-season waves, 225 miles off the Mississippi Gulf Coast. Along the 9,500-foot length of mooring chain securing the buoy to the bottom, electronic gauges measure water pressure, temperature and a dozen other characteristics of the deep sea. This information, fed to a cable running up the mooring line and then combined with other data such as air pressure and wave height, is recorded on magnetic tape, stored and transmitted through a 24-spoke antenna. At a data-receiving station in Miami, Florida, meteorologists extract, study and process the data that have been transmitted via computer.

The antenna-laden buoy, which was launched on June 14 by the National Data Buoy program, is part of an effort to apply to seabound sensing posts the monitoring technology of space satellites —and thus achieve a wide variety of practical benefits. The Commerce Department, which funded the program, has deployed three unmanned buoys in the Gulf of Mexico and plans two more there, plus a sixth off Alaska's coast, providing a continual read-out of data from the marine environment of these areas. Most of the data will help improve weather forecasts. The offshore oil industry will be a particular beneficiary since more accurate forecasts will enable it to batten down for heavy weather advancing on its Gulf drilling rigs. The buoys will also monitor water pollution. And no doubt Navy antisubmarine and mine warfare researchers will be tuning in to the same signals from the deep.

PALEONTOLOGY

Two sets of footprints excited interest among paleontologists in 1972. One set seemed to have been made by a Stone Age human child. The other set was attributed to some much earlier creature evolved midway between stream swimmer and land crawler. Elsewhere, students of the dinosaur had some huge new bones to analyze, and two possible clues for the dinosaurs' extinction.

FOOTPRINTS FROM THE PAST

Two sets of ancient footprints, discovered fossilized inside rocks on opposite sides of the globe, promise to answer questions about evolution that have long puzzled experts. One set, found in Africa, may reveal the appearance of the skin and flesh of Stone Age man—characteristics that until now could only be guessed at. The other set, in Australia, gives the first view of the crucial intermediate stage in the development of the feet of land animals from fishes' fins.

The African discovery—a human footprint, fingerprints and a series of pits in the ground, all at least 500,000 years old—was made by anthropologist Mary D. Leakey in Tanzania's Olduvai Gorge, the fossil-rich site where she and her husband, the late Louis S. B. Leakey, earlier found human and manlike remains going back at least two million years. The footprint, apparently a child's, and the fingerprints were in pits that had been scooped by hand from sand now hardened into stone. According to one authority on prehistoric human anatomy, P. V. Tobias of the University of the Witwatersrand in Johannesburg, the prints "would seem to be the first evidence we have of the nature of the soft tissue anatomy of early man." The pits, the largest three feet across and a foot deep, are connected by channels four inches wide and four inches deep and were dug, Mrs. Leakey believes, to catch rainfall.

The Australian discovery, much older than the African one, was a chance find on a vacation trip. In September 1971 the late Norman Wakefield, a biology professor and paleontologist, set out at the age of 52 with two friends to trek the Genoa River area of Australia's Victoria State. He intended a nostalgic revisit to a region where, 25 years earlier, he had found some previously unknown species of plants. Wakefield kept the results of his sentimental journey secret until August 1972, when he revealed that among them was the discovery of animal footprints 355 million years old—the earliest ever encountered.

Wakefield's discovery was embedded in rock along the river and included 19 marks of hindfeet and 19 more of forefeet, some so well preserved that the toes and webbing could be identified. A second rock path beside the first contained marks left by a belly or tail, with depressions on either side where feet had touched; that animal, Wakefield believes, must have been half-swimming in shallow water. A third trail, 15 feet from the others, contained 20 footprints over a space of three feet, ending at a rock wall.

The prints' most significant aspect, their age aside, is the angle at which they are turned. The feet and toes point outward at right angles, indicating that the animal was at a stage of development between an ancestral fish equipped with backward-stroking, paddlelike fins and a four-limbed animal with forward-moving feet. Wakefield kept his discovery a secret from all but a few scientific associates for almost a year, for fear sightseers might destroy the site. He disclosed it only after the rock slabs containing the impressions had been lifted out by helicopter and flown to a Melbourne museum for exhibition.

80 TONS OF WORRIES AND CHILLS

A PALEONTOLOGIST DUSTS OFF A RECORD FIND, THE WORLD'S BIGGEST DINOSAUR BONES.

Remains of the biggest dinosaur of them all were dug up in Colorado. Meanwhile, scientists propounded two new ideas to account for the strange, sudden disappearance of dinosaurs.

Two shoulder blades, a pelvis and five vertebrae—the largest dinosaur bones ever identified—were unearthed during the summer in Colorado's Uncompahgre National Forest. According to the leader of the excavating team, paleontologist James A. Jensen of Brigham Young University, the find indicates that an 80-ton, 50-foot-tall dinosaur, measuring 100 feet from nose to tail, prowled the area 150 million years ago. The remains may represent an altogether unknown species, larger than any previously discovered. However, the bones do resemble those of Brachiosaurus, a big four-footed plant-eating reptile known to have inhabited the same general area. Jensen speculates that the supersized dinosaur may have drowned in the floodwaters of the prehistoric stream bed in which the remains were found.

The puzzle of the extinction of all dinosaurs also produced two novel explanations in 1972: The first postulates that dinosaurs died out because of emotional stress induced by overcrowding. Heinrich K. Erben of Bonn University, reporting on an analysis of some dinosaur eggs found in nests in the south of France, stated that some of the shells were so thick that the embryos inside must have suffocated, while others were so thin as to have left the embryo unprotected. Erben traces the abnormal shell formations to deficiencies in hormones caused by the emotional stress of overcrowding. When much of southern France was desert, the dinosaurs were forced into oases where jostling for food and space enervated the dinosaur mothers, causing them to produce unhatchable eggs.

The second theory about the death of the dinosaurs has them being eliminated by overexposure to cold in an abrupt change of climate. The proponent of this theory, Robert T. Bakker of Harvard University's Museum of Comparative Zoology, argues that because the dinosaurs were both hairless and huge they would have been vulnerable to cold—just as hairless elephants and rhinos are today. Too big to burrow into the soil for warmth at a time when, many geologists believe, the earth suffered a brief but intense cold spell, the dinosaurs—so Bakker suggests—died from being chilled.

PHYSICS

The unusual composition of ore from an African uranium mine brought to light evidence of a hitherto unknown phenomenon: a naturally occurring nuclear chain reaction. And a long-debated implication of the theory of relativity was demonstrated when two globe-circling clocks showed that, exactly as Einstein had predicted, the faster timepieces travel, the slower they keep time.

CLOCKING THE TIME

It took just two jet flights around the world to show that Einstein seemed to be right about one of the most controversial implications of his theory of relativity: that an astronaut traveling at extremely high speed to a distant star and back would return home younger than a twin brother who had stayed on earth. This effect would arise, the theory holds, because a moving clock loses time relative to a stationary clock; the faster the clock moves, the more time it loses. Since human metabolic processes are in a sense clocks, a moving twin should age less than his stationary brother.

Until recently nobody had found a way to test this "clock paradox" outside a laboratory. But physicist Joseph C. Hafele hit on the idea of flying atomic clocks around the world in opposite directions, checking them at the trip's end against identical clocks left behind in the U.S. Naval Observatory in Washington. The clocks in Washington, although seemingly stationary, would be traveling at the speed of the earth's rotation. The clocks flying eastward, in the direction the earth turns, would be moving at the speed of the plane plus the speed of the earth and, because they were going faster, should—if Einstein was correct—record less time than the Washington clocks. The clocks flown westward, on the other hand, would move at the speed of the airplane subtracted from the speed of the rotation of the earth; because they were traveling slower than the Washington clocks, they should gain time relative to the clocks in Washington.

Hafele and an associate, astronomer Richard Keating of the U.S. Naval Observatory, announced their findings in July: the clocks that had flown east, and traveled faster, were approximately 59 billionths of a second behind the Washington clocks; the clocks that had flown west, and traveled slower, were 273 billionths of a second ahead.

NATURE'S NUCLEAR FISSION

A nuclear chain reaction, the energy that fuels power plants throughout the world, is neither a new nor a man-made phenomenon. So said French physicist Francis Perrin, who in September reported indications that a nuclear reaction occurred spontaneously more than a billion years ago in an African uranium deposit.

The evidence came to light when technicians at a French uranium-enrichment plant found that ore from the Oklo mine in Gabon is markedly deficient in U-235, the relatively rare type of uranium. Perrin theorized that the deficiency was caused by a natural chain reaction that had "burned out" some of its U-235.

The splitting of uranium atoms occurs in any uranium deposit, but it is ordinarily a random process that involves only the isotope U-238, not the U-235 with which it coexists. In Oklo, the whole deposit reacted, much as if a tree ignited by lightning had set a forest ablaze. Perrin believes that the African deposit is ancient. Billions of years ago, before natural radioactive decay could eliminate many U-235 atoms, their concentration was higher than it is in modern deposits. As the U-235 atoms decayed and split, the neutron particles released encountered hydrogen atoms from ground water. Hydrogen slows neutrons to a speed that makes them more likely to cause other U-235 atoms to split—and there was plenty of U-235 nearby. The concentration of U-235 atoms in the presence of neutron-slowing water set up a self-sustaining chain reaction, just as this combination does in a man-made power reactor. Eventually heat from the chain reaction turned the water to steam, which does not slow neutrons as much as liquid water; the neutrons speeded up, causing the chain reaction to halt. After the uranium cooled, the steam condensed into seeping water, and the chain reaction began again. Perrin speculates that the process could have gone on for more than a billion years, until the U-235 was largely depleted.

SPACE

In man's continuing reconnaissance of space, the Soviet Union finally achieved a satisfactory landing on the enigmatic planet Venus as the United States dispatched its sixth team of astronauts in a trouble-bedeviled but ultimately successful revisit to the moon. And evidence from instruments set up on the moon led to a reappraisal of the origin of the earth's life-sustaining oxygen.

ALL ENDS WELL FOR APOLLO 16

For the American television audience it started out as another ho-hum run to the moon, a rerun of a trip they had watched five times before. Then things began to go awry, and the Apollo 16 mission seemed jinxed. But the misadventures —some funny, some worrisome—turned out to be only the build-up for a mission productive of solid scientific data.

Apollo 16's troubles began soon after launch on April 16. The paint began to peel away from the lunar landing craft. Lieutenant Colonel Charles M. Duke Jr. inadvertently punched his orange juice dispenser button and got a juice-fogged helmet and a juice shampoo. Lieutenant Commander Thomas K. Mattingly, opening a can of peaches, was slapped in the face by free-floating fruit.

More serious than these Marx Brothers touches, the engine in the command module began wobbling sideways, and engineers pondered whether the mission should be called off. But luckily the wobble was judged to be too slight to affect the guidance system.

The lunar module, touching down on April 20, deposited astronauts Duke and Captain John W. Young for what was to be man's longest sojourn on the moon: 71 hours. The two men, scooting around in the moon car at about 11 miles an hour, collected 214 pounds of rock and soil and practically shattered a favorite theory about the formation of the lunar highlands: instead of being the product of volcanic activity, the moon mountains were apparently formed by meteoric activity. The terrain of the highlands was littered with breccias—rocks that have been torn into fragments, presumably by meteorite barrage, and subsequently cemented together again.

A miniature observatory, including an ultraviolet spectrograph camera *(below)*, was erected on the lunar soil; among the first tasks will be to provide useful information on how the earth and our solar system were formed. The trio of astronauts splashed down in the Pacific on April 27 as plans were being readied for the United States' final manned lunar exploration, Apollo 17, scheduled for a nighttime blast-off on December 6.

WHERE OUR OXYGEN COMES FROM

Green plants have been getting too much of the credit as the major source of life-sustaining oxygen in the earth's atmosphere. According to a report published in July by the U.S. Naval Research Laboratory, many scientists are convinced that most of the earth's free oxygen is generated by the direct action of the sun on the earth's upper atmosphere, rather than by plants as the end product of the process of photosynthesis.

The finding came from spectrum studies made by an instrument that accompanied Apollo 16 to the moon in April 1972 *(above)*. It recorded data on, among other things, the earth's "geocorona"—the outermost point of the earth's atmosphere, a layer of almost pure hydrogen. The evidence indicates that the geocorona is formed by the action of the sun on water vapor in the atmosphere, causing the water's hydrogen and oxygen to separate. The lighter hydrogen rises into the top of the atmosphere and eventually escapes the earth's gravity, while the heavier oxygen sinks toward the earth into the air we breathe.

RUSSIA REPORTS ON VENUS

After six failures and one partial success, the Russians put a spacecraft on Venus in July; the eighth try survived for almost an hour. The six earlier washouts either disintegrated in Venus' atmosphere or crash-landed, while the seventh craft landed safely, in December 1970, only to buckle after 23 minutes under the atmosphere's crushing weight. Number eight, in its brief hour of life, beamed back to Earth a range of useful data verifying what astronomers had learned with radio telescopes. Among the characteristics reported from the Venus 8 landing zone were these:

- The Venusian ground is covered with material much like earthly granite.
- Despite a dense pea-soup cloud cover, sunlight does penetrate to the surface.
- The temperature during the day (which lasts four months) reaches 880° F.
- Ninety-seven per cent of its atmosphere is composed of carbon dioxide.

TECHNOLOGY

The supersonic transport may have a second chance. A NASA engineer came up with a new design that he claims will avoid sonic boom and stratospheric pollution—problems that caused the first SST to be scrapped. Closer to earth, a new porous asphalt was developed to prevent flooding during heavy rains. And a sharper-turning rudder was sea-tested.

A QUIET, NONPOLLUTING SST

A PIVOTING WING MAY CUT OUT SONIC BOOM.

It would be one of the strangest-looking craft ever to take to the air, but a proposed new supersonic transport (SST) would answer the major criticisms of the previous U.S. model that was vetoed by Congress in 1971. It would create no glass-shattering sonic boom, would not generate a possibly permanent layer of pollution to prevent sunlight from penetrating the stratosphere and could take off from existing runways with only 25 per cent of the power required by existing SSTs, the Anglo-French Concorde and the Russian TU-144.

Such advantages stem from the odd design dreamed up by Robert T. Jones of NASA's Ames Research Center in California. In flight, the plane would resemble a pair of partly open scissors. On the ground and in takeoffs and landings, the elliptical wing would sit, conventionally, at right angles to the fuselage. But as relatively quiet turbofan jet engines pushed the airplane toward supersonic speed, the wing would pivot to a 45° angle, so that one tip is ahead of the other. This arrangement greatly reduces drag, lowering fuel consumption and, Jones claims, permitting economical operation at about 800 miles per hour. At this speed sonic boom would be inaudible on the ground. And the lowered drag also makes possible a cruising altitude of only 40,000 feet, where exhaust would stay out of the stratosphere and be harmlessly dissipated by winds.

A POROUS PAVEMENT

Development of a new asphalt paving material—so porous that 70 inches of water per hour can flow through a two-and-one-half-inch layer—promised to reduce flooding in heavy rains, prevent overloading of storm sewers and replenish underground water reservoirs.

The material, produced at the Franklin Institute Research Laboratories in Philadelphia, is made porous by the use of coarse particles of asphalt, concrete and rocks rather than the fine particles usually employed. Among the advantages claimed for it are durability equal to that of conventional paving, and lower cost.

TIGHT TURNS FOR BIG SHIPS

If a new rudder design that was tested by British government researchers in August proves seaworthy, big vessels, such as oil tankers, will be turning more sharply than has ever been thought possible before. With a regular rudder there is a limit to how far out the rudder can be turned. Beyond 35°, the water behind the trailing side of the rudder becomes turbulent *(top drawing, right)* so that the rudder loses the "grip" on the water necessary for turning. The turning force, like the lift generated by an airplane wing, is dependent on a smooth flow of fluid. When turbulence occurs, the rudder stalls in a manner comparable to the stalling of an airplane.

In the new British design, a rotating cylinder is attached to the leading edge of the rudder. When the rudder is swung out for a turn, the cylinder is spun by a motor in the direction the blade is being turned, driving water smoothly around the trailing edge of the blade. In this way turbulence is avoided even if the rudder turns the ship at an angle as sharp as 90°. Thus a quarter-million-ton ship equipped with the rudder should be able to make a complete circle in 600 yards.

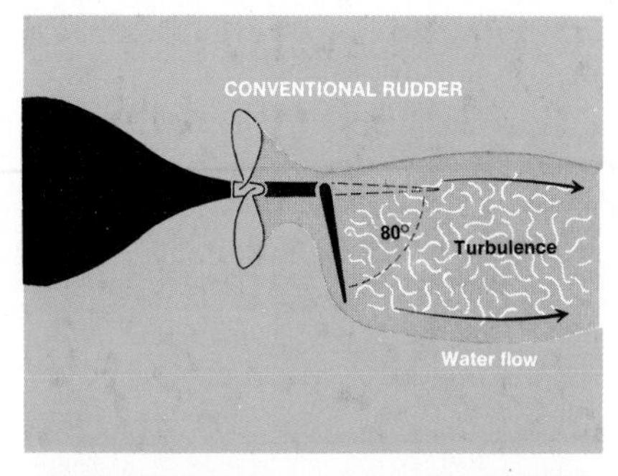

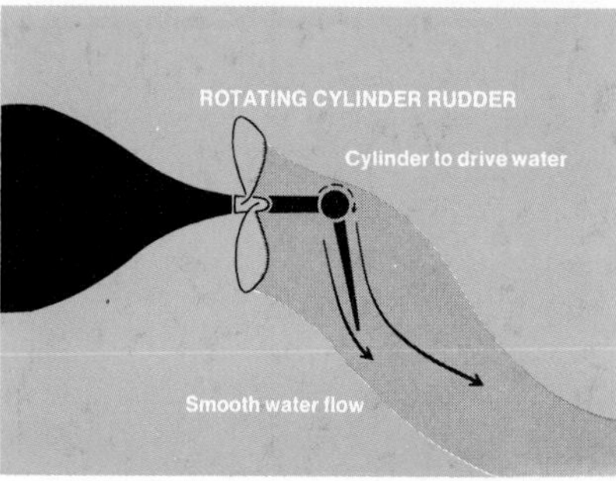

NEW RUDDER ALLOWS TIGHTER TURNS.

ZOOLOGY

The Navy enlisted the assistance of sea lions and whales in rescuing sunken missiles; an ichthyologist found a fish that routinely changed its sex from female to male; and crustaceologists learned to accelerate the growth of lobsters by putting them in warm water. On land, a psychologist figured out why birds bathe in dust, and a zookeeper helped to curb a population explosion in lion cages by putting his lionesses on the Pill.

LOVE SONG OF THE FISH

Ichthyologists have long known that certain "electric fish" emit as much as one or two volts of electricity. Now a behavioral scientist has discovered one of the uses some fish put it to: love songs. Electronically eavesdropping in a stream in Guyana, South America, Carl Hopkins of The Rockefeller University placed wires in the waters of the Moco-moco Creek, where a number of related species of electric fish thrive, and hooked the wires to a loudspeaker. Each species produced its own distinctive sound, apparently to identify itself; but in *Sternopygus macrurus* the usual monotonous, low-register note of the mature male suddenly became an electronic chant whenever a mature female approached.

A FISHY SEX STORY

A switch in sex—female to male—that depends on aggressiveness has turned up among the wrasse, a fish of Australia's Great Barrier Reef. In September D. R. Robertson, a zoologist from the University of Queensland, reported that ordinarily the male wrasse lives in a harem system in which one male dominates three to six females. The male directly bullies the principal female, while she in turn pushes around the second-ranking female, and so on down to the frailest. But when the male dies, the top-ranking female takes on the male behavior pattern at once. Within 14 to 18 days she can release sperm, and becomes the male master of the harem.

Robertson suggests that the female wrasse needs to be dominated by a male in order to suppress her natural propensity to change sex. "Probably all the females are capable of changing sex," he says, unless they have a male wrasse around to keep them feminine.

WHY BIRDS BATHE IN DUST

A bird tromping about in a patch of dust is a common sight. But only now has a psychologist at Michigan State University come up with a reason for this behavior.

In a doctoral thesis published by the American Ornithologists' Union in August, Peter L. Borchelt claimed that the birds cavort in the dust to rid themselves of excess oil. Birds secrete oil from a gland—the uropygial—above their tails.

The oil keeps them warm and gives their feathers greater lifting power in flight. But when Borchelt prevented test birds from dust-bathing, he found they soon became oil-heavy.

Getting just the right film of oil distributed through the feathers is a major chore for birds, it seems. Bobwhites were observed spending an hour preening oil over their feathers. Then they would spend another hour dust-dancing. "This at least suggests that a regulatory mechanism exists in birds, with one behavior to get oil into the feathers and another to get it off," Borchelt said.

SPEEDING LOBSTER GROWTH

Lobster fanciers could look forward to more plentiful supplies and perhaps lower price tags thanks to a discovery by researchers at the Massachusetts Lobster Hatchery on Martha's Vineyard. They reported a way to grow eating-size lobsters in only two years instead of the five and a half years now required. The trick lies in keeping the lobsters warm.

Ordinarily, New England lobsters live in waters that range in temperature from just above freezing in winter to a scant 70° F. in summer. Since their metabolism —the chemical processes by which any organism makes and uses the energy it needs to grow—depends on the temperature of their environment, lobsters grow slowly in the cold New England waters. But when the water in the hatchery's tanks was warmed to a year-round 72° to 75°, the lobsters' metabolism speeded up. As their bodies processed their food faster, they needed more of it. And the more they ate, the faster they grew.

NEW SPECIES OF FROGMEN

The Navy may someday use sea lions and pilot whales as frogmen. The marine mammals were successfully trained to locate and retrieve objects from the sea floor in two separate projects known as Quick Find (sea lions) and Deep Op (whales), announced the U.S. Naval Undersea Research and Development Center in September. The animals found dummy missiles and torpedoes by homing in on the acoustical "pings" emanating from the targets, then retrieved them by positioning giant slings or collars around them so that the targets could be lifted to the surface. Although sea lions were able to retrieve only from a depth no greater than 500 feet, the 1,200-pound pilot whale managed to lift objects from 1,654 feet.

PLANNED PARENTHOOD FOR LIONS

Every proper zoo must have a lion and a lioness—if not a pride—and therein lies the problem: for a lion's extraordinary ability to consume 12 or 13 pounds of raw meat every day is matched only by the male's almost insatiable appetite for the opposite sex when she is in heat. Witness a lion named Frazier, an elderly patriarch who died in July 1972 after fathering 35 cubs in his last 18 months. Frazier's reputation earned him a nomination for 1972's Father of the Year, and his keepers at California's Lion Country Safari received countless discreet inquiries on the details of his diet from self-described senior citizens.

In the jungle the lion population remains stable because, among other reasons, the young are the last to share the kill, with the result that half the lion cubs starve to death in their first year. But in the zoo where the meals are handouts (with the resultant staggering bills), the youngsters thrive and go on to create a geometric progression of problems.

Since few zoos can handle this population boom, some keepers quietly "put the cubs to sleep." Other, more innovative, keepers are employing their own form of Planned Parenthood, by slipping the Pill into their lionesses' diets. This solution is still in the experimental stages and, while no side effects have been observed, the results—or lack of them—have been satisfactory. Meanwhile it is estimated it will be at least four years before the Animal Pill is available for controlling the dog and cat population.

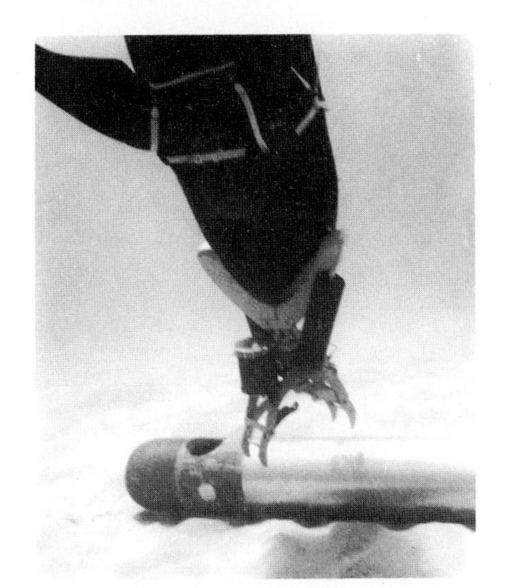

NAVY-TRAINED WHALE FINDS A TORPEDO.

PROWESS OF LIONS LIKE FRAZIER, SIRE OF MANY CUBS, LEADS ZOOKEEPERS TO USE THE PILL.

Nobel Prize Winners

All but one of the eight Nobel science laureates of 1972 were Americans. For one of them it was an unprecedented second prize. A trio of United States physicists won the prize in physics for a theory that explains a kind of perpetual-motion current flow; three United States biochemists shared the chemistry honors for shedding light on a genetic process; and the seventh American prize-winner, also a biochemist, split the award in medicine with a Briton for work on the body's defenses against disease.

CHEMISTRY

For "unscrewing the inscrutable" the Nobel Prize in chemistry went to three Americans: Christian B. Anfinsen, Stanford Moore and William H. Stein. The inscrutable, in Moore's phrase, was the structure of a key body chemical, ribonuclease, which breaks up RNA, the body's genetic "messenger." Once the structure of ribonuclease was known, Moore and Stein were able to figure out how it accomplishes its function—a function that is vital in the chain of events that transmits genetic information to newly forming cells.

Working at the National Institutes of Health at Bethesda, Maryland, Anfinsen discovered how the ribonuclease molecule acquires its unique, three-dimensional ball shape. He established that when the ball was unfolded, it would recombine and fold itself up again according to a pattern coded into the chemical groups—known as amino acids—of which it was formed.

At New York's Rockefeller University, Moore and Stein proceeded to analyze the ribonuclease's chemical structure and figure out the actual arrangement of the amino acids. They observed that a ribonuclease molecule was shaped in such a way that certain of its amino acids fell into very close proximity, and that these close neighbors were very active. These so-called active sites proved to be the places where the amino acids came together, giving the molecule its distinctive shape.

In honoring the three scientists, the Nobel citation pointed out that unraveling the operation of ribonuclease—one of a broad category of chemical activators called enzymes—is basic to the understanding of the life process, and that the research on ribonuclease is speeding up other research on the multitude of substances that make up about half of the human body.

MEDICINE OR PHYSIOLOGY

Two immunologists who attacked the same questions with different methods on different sides of the Atlantic shared the year's Nobel Prize in medicine. Gerald M. Edelman, a biologist-physician at The Rockefeller University, and Rodney R. Porter, an Oxford biochemist, were honored for their pioneering work on the chemistry of antibodies, the blood proteins that defend the body against infection and disease.

Since 1959 both men have been pursuing independent research on the structure of the molecular chains that combat viruses and bacteria but also frustrate organ transplants. "The fundamental problem of immunology," Dr. Edelman explained, "is to determine how the body can recognize foreign molecules from its own. Referring to the work of his co-laureate, Dr. Porter, he continued, "We both shared the same point of view: the only way to understand how the antibody molecule could recognize foreign substances was to determine something about its chemical structure."

To analyze antibody structures, both scientists set out to disassemble the molecules. Porter assumed

CHRISTIAN B. ANFINSEN

STANFORD MOORE

WILLIAM H. STEIN

GERALD M. EDELMAN

RODNEY R. PORTER

JOHN BARDEEN

LEON N. COOPER

J. ROBERT SCHRIEFFER

that at least some antibody molecules were single chains of amino acids, the substances basic to all forms of life. To break the links of the molecular chain, Porter used natural enzymes—substances produced by living cells that hasten chemical reactions (including one derived from the tropical fruit papaw). Meanwhile Dr. Edelman was breaking up antibody molecules with chemicals such as urea.

Both methods worked, though not in the same way. The picture that emerged from their scrutiny of fragments of antibodies was complex: An antibody molecule was a double pair of atomic chains of differing weights and characteristics. The dissimilar chains were joined by cross-links of sulfur atoms in such a way as to give the whole structure the shape of the letter Y.

The combined research of Edelman and Porter, which has inspired something of a worldwide boom in the study of immunology, was cited by the Nobel judges for dispelling a century of misconceptions and ignorance about body immunities.

PHYSICS

For the first time since founder Alfred Nobel's original bequest, a Nobel Prize was given twice to the same man for work in the same field. Physicist John Bardeen, honored in 1956 for his part in the invention of the transistor, shared his second award in 1972 with Leon N. Cooper and J. Robert Schrieffer for their explanation of the odd phenomenon of superconductivity—the abrupt disappearance of all resistance to the flow of electricity in certain metals that are chilled to near the absolute minimum of temperature, −459.7° F. (Two previous two-time Nobel winners, Linus Pauling and Marie Curie, got their prizes for their contributions in different fields: Pauling in chemistry and the cause of peace, Curie in physics and chemistry.)

This year's physics prize was also the second to be awarded for work on superconductivity; 59 years ago, in 1913, the Dutch physicist Heike Kamerlingh Onnes won his Nobel award for discovering the phenomenon. But its causes remained one of the strangest mysteries of matter until Bardeen, Cooper and Schrieffer, collaborating at the University of Illinois, propounded in 1957 the explanation known, after their surname initials, as the BCS theory.

The puzzle surrounding superconductivity was not caused by the fact that electrical resistance lessened with cold—resistance results from atomic vibrations, which diminish as temperature drops. What was most inexplicable was the fact that all resistance disappeared completely when the temperature stood slightly above absolute zero and atomic vibration persisted. The BCS theory showed how the retarding effect of this residual vibration is overcome at superconducting temperatures.

An electric current is a stream of negatively charged particles, called electrons, flowing through the atoms of a metallic conductor. In materials that are good conductors the atoms are arranged in a regular geometric structure, and this nearly rigid structure interacts with the flowing electrons. As an electron passes through, it displaces an atom from the normal position, distorting the structure and creating a slight positive charge. This charge attracts the following electron in the stream, so keeping the stream moving. Thus pairs of electrons in the current work together to cancel out all resistance to their flow (Nature/Science Annual, 1970 Edition). Exploiting this basic research, laboratories are already developing superconducting cables to transmit huge currents at low cost, and governments and industries are testing superconducting magnets to operate 300-mph wheelless trains *(page 121)*.

Acknowledgments

The editors of this book wish to thank the following persons and institutions for their assistance.

Ray Batson, Branch of Astrogeologic Studies, U.S. Geological Survey, Flagstaff, Arizona; William A. Baum, Lowell Observatory, Flagstaff, Arizona; Dwight M. Baumann, Professor of Mechanical Engineering, Carnegie-Mellon University, Pittsburgh, Pennsylvania; Glenn Brown, Liquid Crystal Institute, Kent State University, Kent, Ohio; Thomas H. Budzynski, University of Colorado Medical Center, Denver; Donald S. Burnett, Associate Professor of Nuclear Geochemistry, California Institute of Technology, Pasadena; Dr. Calvin H. Chen, Assistant Medical Superintendent, Northville State Hospital, Northville, Michigan; Frank Chilton, Senior Physicist, Stanford Research Institute, Menlo Park, California; Howard T. Coffey, Manager of Cryogenic Applications Group, Stanford Research Institute, Menlo Park, California; Larry Collins, National Zoological Park, Washington, D.C.; John T. Crissey, Pasadena, California; W. Kenneth Crowder, President, Linear Air Motors Inc., Pontiac, Michigan; Paul E. Damon, Professor of Geosciences, University of Arizona, Tucson; Thomas Davison, Kent State University, Kent, Ohio; Carl H. Dry, Executive Assistant, Space Shuttle Program, NASA, Washington, D.C.; Barry Dworkin, Research Associate, Laboratory of Physiological Psychology, The Rockefeller University, New York City; Marce Eleccion, I.E.E.E.-Spectrum, New York City; Bernard T. Engel, Gerontology Research Center, National Institute of Child Health and Baltimore City Hospitals, Baltimore, Maryland; Keith Ewing, Kent State University, Kent, Ohio; Patricia Farnsworth, Barnard College, New York City; James L. Fergason, International Liquid Xtal Company, Cleveland, Ohio; C. W. Ferguson, Associate Professor of Dendrochronology, Laboratory of Tree-Ring Research, University of Arizona, Tucson; Thomas H. Floyd Jr., Vice President, DGA International, Inc., Washington, D.C.; Dr. John W. C. Fox, Assistant Professor of Anesthesiology, State University of New York, Downstate Medical Center, Brooklyn; Henry L. Giclas, Lowell Observatory, Flagstaff, Arizona; Raymond M. Gilmore, La Jolla, California; Marija Gimbutas, Professor of European Archeology, University of California, Los Angeles; Peter E. Glaser, Vice President, Arthur D. Little Inc., Cambridge, Massachusetts; Joel Goldmacher, President, Optel, Princeton, New Jersey; M. M. Graff, Friends of Central Park, New York City; Elmer E. Green, The Menninger Foundation, Topeka, Kansas; William D. Green, Technical Assistant, Skylab Program Development, NASA, Washington, D.C.; Romaine Habert, New York City; John S. Hall, Director, Lowell Observatory, Flagstaff, Arizona; R. J. Hanold, Los Alamos Scientific Laboratory, Los Alamos, New Mexico; Lowell T. Harmison, Medical Devices Branch, National Heart and Lung Institute, Bethesda, Maryland; Carl Hubbs, Scripps Institution of Oceanography, La Jolla, California; Fred Huffman, Thermo Electron Corporation, Waltham, Massachusetts; Arthur Kantrowitz, Vice President, Avco Everett Research Laboratory, Everett, Massachusetts; Roland H. King, Carnegie-Mellon University, Pittsburgh, Pennsylvania; Robert Kraehe, Bay Area Rapid Transit District, Oakland, California; Austin Long, Associate Professor of Geosciences, University of Arizona, Tucson; George V. Lukianoff, IBM Components Division, East Fishkill, New York; John F. McCauley, Chief, Branch of Astrogeologic Studies, U.S. Geological Survey, Flagstaff, Arizona; Walter McClenny, The Goodyear Tire & Rubber Company, Akron, Ohio; L. R. McCreight, General Electric Company, Philadelphia, Pennsylvania; Robert M. Makla, Friends of Central Park, New York City; Dr. Pang L. Man, Director of Research, Northville State Hospital, Northville, Michigan; Spyridon Marinatos, Inspector General of Antiquities, Government of Greece, Athens; A. E. Marshall, Dual-Mode Vehicle Program Manager, Ford Motor Company, Dearborn, Michigan; Neal E. Miller, Laboratory of Physiological Psychology, The Rockefeller University, New York City; Ken Moritz, Marketing Communications, TRW Systems Group, Redondo Beach, California; J. W. Neudecker, Los Alamos Scientific Laboratory, Los Alamos, New Mexico; Peter Pick, Director, Diagnostics Division, Hoffmann-La Roche Inc., Nutley, New Jersey; Cyril Ponnamperuma, Professor of Chemistry, University of Maryland, College Park; Anand Prakash, Center for Space Research, Massachusetts Institute of Technology, Cambridge; Froelich Rainey, Director, Museum Applied Science Center for Archaeology, University of Pennsylvania, Philadelphia; Elizabeth K. Ralph, Associate Director, Museum Applied Science Center for Archaeology, University of Pennsylvania, Philadelphia; Colin Renfrew, Professor-Elect of Archaeology, University of Southampton, England; Dr. Samuel Rosen, Clinical Professor of Otology (Emeritus), Mount Sinai School of Medicine, New York City; James C. Rudosky, National Oceanic and Atmospheric Administration, Environmental Research Laboratories, Boulder, Colorado; Robert M. Salter Jr., The Rand Corporation, Santa Monica, California; David L. Sanson, Rohr Industries, Chula Vista, California; Ronald Senechal, Lamont-Doherty Geological Observatory, Palisades, New York; Edward Sharpless, Liquid Crystal Industries, Inc., Turtle Creek, Pennsylvania; Alan T. Spiher Jr., Chief, GRAS Review Branch, Bureau of Foods, U.S. Food and Drug Administration; Hal Stephens, Branch of Astrogeologic Studies, U.S. Geological Survey, Flagstaff, Arizona; Dr. Maurice B. Sterman, Veterans Administration Hospital, Sepulveda, California; Hans E. Suess, Professor of Chemistry, University of California, San Diego; Martin Tanzer, Diagnostics Division, Hoffmann-La Roche Inc., Nutley, New Jersey; Ting Ching-yuen, New York City; Leonard Trauberman, Managing Editor, *Food Engineering,* Bala Cynwyd, Pennsylvania; Marcel Vogel, IBM Advanced Systems Development Division, Los Gatos, California; George Wald, Professor of Biology, Harvard University, Cambridge, Massachusetts; Dr. Frank Z. Warren, Postgraduate Center for Mental Health, New York City; Virgil O. Wodicka, Director, Bureau of Foods, U.S. Food and Drug Administration.

Credits

The sources for the illustrations in this book are shown below. Credits from left to right are separated by semicolons, from top to bottom by dashes.

Cover—Brian Brake from Rapho-Guillumette. 6—Brian Brake from Rapho-Guillumette. 10,11—Andrée Abecassis. 12,13—Drawings by David Palladini. 14—Stephan Palos, *The Chinese Art of Healing* © 1971 Herder and Herder. 17—Drawing by Nicholas Fasciano. 19—Dr. Calvin Chen, Dr. Pang L. Man and Dr. Frank Z. Warren. 21—Ken Kay. 22—Marcel Vogel. 23—Models by Nicholas Fasciano. 24—George Lukianoff, IBM Laboratories; J. R. Eyerman. 25—Gruen Industries, Inc.—Lloyd's Electronics, Inc. 26—K. L. Ewing, T. W. Davison and J. L. Fergason—Hoffmann-La Roche Inc. 27—K. L. Ewing, T. W. Davison, J. L. Fergason. 28—Lennart Nilsson for LIFE; Dr. Patricia Farnsworth. 29—Lennart Nilsson for LIFE. 30,31,32—Paintings by Robert T. McCall. 34 through 37—Drawings by Nicholas Fasciano. 39—NASA. 42,43—Stan Wayman, courtesy LIFE. 44,45—© J. Allan Cash; Eddy van der Veen, courtesy Muséum d'Histoire Naturelle, Paris—map by Edward Frank. 46—Tierbilder Okapia, Frankfurt; drawing by Edward Frank—Michael Lyster, © Zoological Society of London. 47—© Zoological Society of London. 48—Eastfoto. 49—Terence Spencer for LIFE. 50—Edward Frank. 55—Drawings by Jerome Kühl. 56—Arthur Shay for FORTUNE. 61—John Bryson for FORTUNE. 63—Lowell Observatory. 64,65—U.S. Geological Survey, Branch of Astrogeologic Studies—airbrushed map, U.S. Geological Survey, Branch of Astrogeologic Studies, courtesy Ray Batson. 66,67—U.S. Geological Survey, Branch of Astrogeologic Studies; NASA, courtesy Jet Propulsion Laboratory, California Institute of Technology. 68,69—NASA, courtesy Jet Propulsion Laboratory, California Institute of Technology; NASA. 71—U.S. Geological Survey, Branch of Astrogeologic Studies. 72—David Muench. 75—Hirmer Fotoarchiv, Munich—Archives Photographiques, Paris. 76—Curtis Phillips. 77—Chart courtesy Laboratory of Tree-Ring Research, The University of Arizona. 78,79—Adapted from "Carbon 14 and the Prehistory of Europe" by Colin Renfrew, © 1971 by

Scientific American, Inc., All Rights Reserved. 81—Chart by Edward Frank. 84—© Derek Bayes. 85—Map by Edward Frank. 86,87—Weston Kemp from Photo Trends. 89—Background Gretchen Wessels. 90,91—Map courtesy the University of Massachusetts Press—Edwin Hawbecker, U.S. Coast and Geodetic Survey. 92,93—Esther Bubley; P. L. Sperr Collection from Frederic Lewis—Brown Brothers. 94,95—Brown Brothers, except left top and bottom Esther Bubley. 96—Bullaty-Lomeo from Rapho-Guillumette, except left top and bottom Photoworld. 97—Esther Bubley—courtesy Museum of the City of New York. 98,99—Left Esther Bubley; no credit—Sidney Bahrt; Sonja Bullaty. 100, 101—Courtesy Mr. and Mrs. Leonard Ances; Evelyn Hofer; *Seventh Annual Report of the Board of Commissioners of the Central Park*—Charles E. Beveridge. 102—Dan Bernstein. 105—The Rockefeller University. 106—Courtesy The Menninger Foundation. 110—Heinz Kluetmeier for LIFE. 111—Richard R. Hewitt from Globe Photos. 113—Bay Area Rapid Transit District. 114,115—Baron Wolman, except left top and bottom Bay Area Rapid Transit District. 116—The Goodyear Tire & Rubber Co., Akron, Ohio. 117—Stan Wayman; David Alan Harvey. 118—Stan Wayman, except right courtesy Carnegie-Mellon University. 120,121—Krauss-Maffei, Munich—Peter Britton; drawings by Nicholas Fasciano. 122,123—John Dominis for LIFE, except left Los Alamos Scientific Laboratory. 124—Philippe Cousteau. 127—Geo-Physical Globe © Rand McNally & Company, information for whale migration routes, courtesy Raymond M. Gilmore. 128—Copied by Frank Lerner from the book *The Marine Mammals of the Northwestern Coast of North America* by Charles M. Scammon courtesy Special Collections, Columbia University Libraries. 132,133—Stan Wayman for LIFE—David Roderick; Joyce MacFall Roderick. 138,139—Alfred L. Pentis. 141 Dmitri Kessel © 1972 Smithsonian Institution. 142—Dimitri Harissiadis. 143—Maps by Edward Frank. 144,145—Spyridon Marinatos except top Otis Imboden, © 1972 National Geographic Society. 146—Eric Schaal for TIME. 147—Dmitri Kessel © 1972 Smithsonian Institution—Eric Schaal for TIME; Sypridon Marinatos. 148,149—Drawing by Edward Frank—Eric Schaal for TIME; Dmitri Kessel © 1972 Smithsonian Institution. 150—Eric Schaal for TIME—Dmitri Kessel © 1972 Smithsonian Institution. 151—Spyros Meletzis. 152,153—Dmitri Kessel © 1972 Smithsonian Institution. 154—Courtesy National Heart and Lung Institute. 156—Courtesy Lowell T. Harmison. 160,161—Drawings by George V. Kelvin. 166—Copyrighted by the National Geographic Society; Nicos Kontos. 168—NASA. 169—Gerard Cappa, Institut Français de Spéléologie. 171—No credit. 175—David Lees for LIFE. 176—Charles Moore from Black Star for LIFE. 178—Jose Mercadó, *Stanford M.D.* 180—Westinghouse. 181—Nelson Wadsworth for TIME. 183—Painting by Robert T. McCall © 1972 Popular Science Publishing Co. 184—Time diagrams by J. Donovan adapted by Edward Frank. 185—Naval Undersea Center, San Diego, California; Ralph Crane for LIFE. 186—Edward A. Hubbard, National Institutes of Health, U.S. Department of Health, Education and Welfare—The Rockefeller University (2)—Wide World. 187—© 1972 *The Times*, London—University of Illinois at Urbana-Champaign—Hugh Smyser, Brown University—Frank Ross, University of Pennsylvania.

Index

Numerals in italics indicate an illustration of the subject mentioned.

PRINTED IN U.S.A.